STATISTICAL

ANALYSIS IN

EDUCATIONAL

RESEARCH

E. F. LINDQUIST
Professor of Education
THE STATE UNIVERSITY OF IOWA

HOUGHTON MIFFLIN COMPANY
BOSTON · NEW YORK · CHICAGO · DALLAS
ATLANTA · SAN FRANCISCO
The Riverside Press Cambridge

The Riverside Press
CAMBRIDGE · MASSACHUSETTS
PRINTED IN THE U.S.A.

PREFACE

THE past twenty years or more have been a period of extremely rapid and significant development in statistical theory and practice. Yet, while many of the recent contributions — particularly those of R. A. Fisher and his students — appear to have almost revolutionary significance for educational research, research workers in this field have in general failed to recognize their amazing possibilities, or at any rate have not widely realized these possibilities in practice.

A part of this neglect has been due to the mistaken notion that it is seldom necessary to use "small" samples in educational research — that most of our samples consist of large numbers of pupils or of individual observations — and that, hence, "small sample" theory can be of relatively little practical interest or value to research students in education. In taking this attitude, we have overlooked the very significant fact that most of our samples, however large in terms of numbers of individual observations, are not simple random samples, but consist of relatively homogeneous and intact subgroups, such as the pupils in a single school or under a single teacher. The number of these subgroups, furthermore, is usually indeed small, and it is only through the use of small sample theory that we can accurately evaluate the results obtained.

Perhaps a more telling reason, however, for this continued neglect is that the only expositions of these techniques that have thus far been readily available, particularly Fisher's *Statistical Methods for Research Workers* and *The Design of Experiments*, have proved inordinately difficult for students in education to comprehend. This fact is due in part to the unfamiliar statistical notation and terminology employed; in part to the frequent and wide gaps in the sequence of logic which are left to the reader to fill but which can be readily supplied only by a reader with advanced mathematical training; and perhaps most of all to the fact that all illustrations given are in the field of agricultural experimentation and are concerned with "plots," "blocks," "yields," "treatments," etc., rather than with "schools," "classes," "scores," "methods," "pupils," etc.

The writer's primary purpose in this book, accordingly, has been to translate Fisher's expositions into a language and notation familiar to the student of education; to clarify the exposition further by presenting all steps in the logic, in a manner such that they may be followed by students with little mathematical training; and to point out specifically and illustrate concretely what seem to be the most promising applications of Fisher's methods in educational research. Particular emphasis has been placed upon the importance of more careful *design* in educational research. Many of the difficulties that have been met by educational research workers in the analysis of their results have arisen from their tendency to plan their experiments and investigations with little direct regard to the methods of analysis that are later to be employed, or even to postpone any very careful consideration of analytical procedures until the investigation itself has been actually concluded. One of the most valuable features of the methods of analysis of variance is that they recognize that the problem of design is inseparable from that of analysis, and that their use makes it difficult to ignore the maxim that no investigation should be actually initiated until the analytical procedures have been thought through to the last detail.

This book, however, has not been restricted to techniques which are directly attributable to R. A. Fisher. Its purpose, more generally stated, has been to make more readily available and comprehensible to students in education any of the more recent developments in statistical theory and practice which seem likely to prove of value in educational research but which thus far have received little or no attention in the standard introductory texts in educational statistics. In particular, an effort has been made to bring the student up to date on the logic of statistical inference and to make him more keenly conscious of the constant need for very critical consideration of the *assumptions* underlying any statistical technique he may employ.

The writer is convinced that the development of a genuine understanding of the nature of statistical inference and a thorough training in the use of the methods of analysis of variance should be considered an absolute essential in the general preparation of research students in education. It is hoped, therefore, that this book will prove usable as a textbook in advanced courses in educational statistics or in the second half of a required full year introductory course. If so used, it will require considerable supplementation by other references, since (with a few minor exceptions) no attempt has been made in this book to discuss any problems that have already been adequately treated in the standard texts. It has been the writer's experience, however, that adequate consideration of the problems here treated will require a considerable share of a typical three-hour course.

It may be noted that the omission of a set of exercises for the student has not been accidental. The methods here considered have been so little used in educational research as to make impossible, for the present, the collection of a set of exercises or examples based on actual data in the field of education. Rather than attempt to prepare a set of exclusively artificial examples, the writer has preferred to postpone the publication of exercise material until a later date. He does, however, intend to prepare and publish as soon as possible an exercise book for the student somewhat along the lines of the *Study Manual* accompanying his *A First Course in Statistics*. Such an exercise book will also provide a means of supplementing this book with discussions of later contributions, and of drawing attention to any changes in emphasis or content in the present volume that later experience may prove desirable but which may not justify a new edition of this book. The omission of lists of references or supplementary readings at the end of each chapter is also deliberate. Most of the general references which could be given would be of doubtful value to the students to whom this book is addressed, for the reasons already indicated in the case of Fisher's books. Furthermore, many of the original papers which have been consulted in the preparation of this volume have appeared in journals which are not readily accessible to students in education. (The more important of these, however, have been cited in footnote references.)

The writer has been extremely fortunate in obtaining an unusual amount of assistance in the preparation of this book. He is grateful, first of all, to the students in his own classes who used the book in its preliminary mimeographed edition and who directed attention to many typographical errors and to instances in which the lucidity could be improved. Various parts of the preliminary manuscript were read by Dr. C. H. McCloy of the State University of Iowa, Dr. Marian Wilder of the University of Minnesota, Dr. John C. Flanagan of the Co-operative Test Service, New York City, Dr. Edward E. Cureton of the Alabama Polytechnic Institute, and Dr. Jack Dunlap of the University of Rochester, all of whom offered many valuable suggestions. The entire manuscript was carefully read by Professor Allen T. Craig of the Department of Mathematics of the State University of Iowa. Special acknowledgments are due Professor G. W. Snedecor of Iowa State College, who gave very generously of his time in consultations with the writer in the earlier stages of the book and whose *Mathematical Statistics* contributed greatly to the writer's own understanding of the possibilities in Fisher's methods.

The major acknowledgment is due Dr. W. G. Cochran, formerly of the Rothamsted Experimental Station, Harpenden, England, and now of the Statistical Laboratory of Iowa State College. Dr. Cochran read the entire manuscript most painstakingly and offered a very large number of concrete and constructive suggestions, all of which the writer found it desirable to observe in the final revision of the manuscript.

Grateful acknowledgment is made to Professor R. A. Fisher, and to his publishers, Oliver and Boyd, for permission to reproduce the tables of t and of χ^2, and the normal probability table from *Statistical Methods for Research Workers*, as well as a part of the table of random numbers from *Statistical Tables for Biological, Agricultural, and Medical Research* (Fisher and Yates).   Similar acknowledgment is due Professor G. W. Snedecor and the Collegiate Press for the use of the table for *F* from Snedecor's *Statistical Methods*.

E. F. LINDQUIST

CONTENTS

APPENDIX

LIST OF TABLES

CHAPTER I

FUNDAMENTAL CONCEPTS IN SAMPLING THEORY

I. INTRODUCTORY

NEARLY all experimental research in education, and most of that which is not experimental in character, involves the drawing of inferences about a population from what is known of a sample taken to represent that population. Accordingly, one of the most important of the technical problems faced by the research worker is that of determining just how much may confidently be said about a population from what is known of a sample, or of ascertaining the degree of confidence which may be placed in the inferences drawn. Closely related to this is the equally important problem of how to select a sample, or how to plan an experiment, so that it may yield the most dependable or precise information about the population involved, and so that it will permit an objective and valid estimate of the degree of precision attained.

In recognition of their extreme importance in the training of the research worker in education, a major share of this text will be devoted to a detailed consideration of these problems. Particular attention will be given to the *design of experiments*, to *small sample theory*, and to the *testing of statistical hypotheses*. While the contributions to statistical theory which have recently been made in these areas appear to be of revolutionary significance in educational research, they have thus far been available to the research worker in education for the most part only in the literature of agricultural research and mathematical statistics. The language and the setting in which they have there been presented have proved inordinately difficult for the student of education to comprehend, and have perhaps seriously retarded their much needed introduction into educational research practices. It is accordingly one of the major purposes of this text to interpret these contributions in a language and notation familiar to the student of education, and to discuss and illustrate their possibilities with specific reference to the types of problems and materials with which he will have to deal.

It will be assumed in these discussions that the student is already acquainted with those aspects of sampling theory which are usually presented in introductory texts in educational statistics. More specifically, it will be assumed that he is familiar with and able to interpret the basic standard error formulas designed for large random samples for which the errors of sampling are normally distributed. Rather than rest too heavily on this assumption, however, this first chapter will in part be devoted to a brief review of some of the concepts and techniques with which the student is presumably already acquainted. This review will then be supplemented by a discussion of the limitations of these techniques in actual practice, and by an introductory consideration of certain additional concepts which are fundamental in the later discussions.

2. DEFINITIONS OF IMPORTANT TERMS

A *population* may be defined as any identifiable group of individuals, or as any collection or aggregate of comparable measures. A *sample* is any number of the members of a population that have been selected to represent that population. In ordinary usage, populations are usually thought of as consisting of human beings; in the statistical sense, populations may consist of any kind of members whatever. For example, the assessed valuations of real property in the rural school districts of Iowa may constitute a population, as may the numbers of books in the school libraries, or the ages of the pupils, or the years of experience of the teachers.

Populations may be either *finite* or *infinite*, either *real* or *hypothetical*. A finite population is one all members of which may be counted; an infinite population is one of unlimited size. For example, all *possible* weights of eight-year-old children in this country would constitute an infinite population, while the actual weights of the eight-year-old children now living in this country would constitute a finite population. The derivations of nearly all sampling error formulas assume infinite populations, whereas the populations to which the formulas are applied are usually finite. This assumption offers little difficulty, however, since the populations actually involved are usually so large that they may be considered as practically infinite.

A real population is one that actually exists; a hypothetical population is one that exists only in the imagination. Many of the populations involved in educational research are hypothetical. For example, an experiment may be conducted to determine the relative effectiveness of two methods of instruction. For the purposes of the experiment, two groups of seventh-grade pupils are selected, one of which is taught by Method A, the other by Method B, and at the close of the experiment comparable measures of achievement are secured for all pupils. In interpreting the results, the pupils who studied under Method B, for example, are considered as a sample from a population of seventh-grade pupils, all of whom had been taught by this method. Since the pupils in the experiment may be the only ones who have ever been taught by this method, this population is of course hypothetical. It is nevertheless useful to recognize that the method might produce different results if used with other seventh-grade pupils, and that the experimental results must therefore be considered as only a fallible indication of the results that would be generally attained. In some instances, we may wish to select a sample from a real population, but find it impracticable to secure an unbiased sample from that population. In that case we may use the sample that is available to us, "construct" a hypothetical population from which the given sample *might* have been drawn at random, and restrict our generalizations to that hypothetical population.

A *random sample* is one selected in such a fashion that every member of the population has an equal chance to be selected. This means that each member must be selected independently of all others. It is useful also to think of a random sample as one so drawn that all other *possible combinations* of an equal number of members from the population had an equal chance to constitute the sample drawn.   Suppose, for example, that we are drawing a random sample of 300 cases from all high-school pupils in Indiana. There is, of course, an almost unlimited number of different combinations of 300 pupils in this population.   One of these combinations, for instance, might consist of 2 pupils from Terre Haute, 13 from Lafayette, 276 from Indianapolis, and 9 from Gary.   If our sampling is random, this particular combination must have the same chance of being selected as any other.   Emphasis is placed on this latter concept of random sampling, since it indicates quite clearly that the samples used in educational research are seldom simple random samples.   In practice, *accessibility* or *feasibility* are often determining factors in sampling.   If we were actually drawing a sample of 300 pupils from Indiana high schools, under the methods usually employed the particular combination described above would have *no* chance of being drawn.   The only feasible procedure would be to secure the co-operation of a few schools that together would provide the 300 cases needed; we could not expect to select each pupil independently from the whole population, and then use the pupils so selected regardless of how they were scattered throughout the state.   The extreme significance of such practical obstacles to random sampling in educational research will be made clear in a later section.   The procedure that may be followed to draw a random sample when no such obstacles exist is also to be explained later.

A *biased* sample is one so drawn that *in the long run* samples so selected will differ systematically from the population in the characteristic studied.   Otherwise stated, a sample is biased if, when more cases are added by the same method of sampling, a given group character (such as the mean) will become more stable, but will tend to approach a value differing from the corresponding characteristic of the population.   A sample may, of course, be biased with reference to one characteristic and unbiased with reference to another, if the two characteristics are entirely unrelated.   A sample of all university sophomores selected from those taking a sophomore course in psychology, for example, might be biased with reference to vocational interests, but their mean age might be an unbiased estimate of the mean age of all sophomores in the university. Freedom from bias is one of the most important characteristics of a sample, and random sampling is one of the surest ways of obtaining it.

A *stratified* sample is one which may be subdivided into groups, each of which may be considered a sample from the corresponding subdivision of the entire population. For example, we might subdivide the entire population of adult males in the United States into various income groups and select a random sample (of any size) from each income group. The total sample thus secured would be considered a stratified sample. Again, in selecting a sample of schools in a given state, we might classify all schools according to enrollment, and select any desired number of schools from each enrollment classification. The numbers constituting the subgroups in a stratified sample are arbitrarily determined, and need not be proportional to the numbers in the corresponding subdivisions of the population. Stratified sampling has much the same advantages as controlled sampling, which are discussed in the following paragraphs. Methods of estimating the standard error of the mean of a stratified sample will be presented later (pages 157 ff.).

A *controlled* sample is one in which the selection is not left to chance, or not entirely to chance, but in which the distribution of some selected characteristic is *made* to conform to some predetermined proportion. It is a stratified sample in which the subgroup numbers are proportional to the corresponding numbers in the population. For example, we may wish to study (in a given population of school children) some trait, such as weight, that is known to be related to sex, and may wish to insure that our sample does not by chance contain an undue proportion of either sex. Assuming that there are equal numbers of boys and girls in the entire population, we might then select a certain number of boys at random from all boys and the same number of girls at random from all girls. In other words, we would *make* our sample representative with respect to sex.   All samples so drawn would then contain the same predetermined proportion of boys and girls, and hence would not be simple random samples, since in random samples this proportion would fluctuate from sample to sample due to chance selection.   Samples of this type are also frequently known as *representative* samples, although this term has no standard meaning.

The exercise of control in sampling is worth while to the degree that the characteristic whose distribution is controlled is related to the characteristic being studied.   For example, there would be little point in "controlling" sex in a study concerned with the mean intelligence of a population of school children, since it is known that boys and girls do not differ appreciably in performance on general intelligence tests.   A control of the chronological age distribution, on the other hand, might markedly increase the reliability of obtained results in a study of this type.   The exercise of controls, however, always introduces the danger that the assumed or predetermined distribution of the control characteristic may differ from the true distribution, and hence result in bias.

A sample may be controlled with reference to more than one characteristic.   For example, we may select a sample so that it will not only contain a predetermined proportion of boys and girls, but so that it will also show a predetermined distribution of chronological ages and a predetermined proportion of children from families in the various income classes in the population.   It may be interesting to observe that samples in which such multiple controls have been exercised have been used to great advantage in conducting nation-wide polls of public opinion in this country. In such polls, relatively small but very carefully controlled samples have produced results much more reliable than could have been obtained from random or fortuitous samples many times as large.

Matched or *equated* samples represent the special case of controlled sampling in which two or more similarly controlled samples are drawn from the same population.   For the purpose of an instructional experiment, for example, we might wish to select two samples of school children so that they will show the *same* distribution of intelligence. To do this, we might divide the available pupils into "levels" of intelligence, each level consisting of pupils with the same intelligence test score, or with intelligence test scores in the same relatively narrow interval along the scale. We might then assign the pupils in each level to our two samples at random, half to each sample. The pupils would then be randomized *within* each level, but the samples would not be random samples from any population (although the two samples might be considered as a randomly selected pair from an infinite number of samples all of which show the same distribution of intelligence).

Controlled sampling may or may not involve random selection. For example, in selecting a sample of schools in a study of school cost-accounting practices in Iowa, one might decide in advance to select a certain number of schools from each enrollment classification within each of a number of geographical districts within the state. Within these restrictions the selection of schools might be fortuitous, or it might be from only those schools that are willing to co-operate — that is, the selection may not be strictly random at any point. If, however, there are any systematic differences in accounting practices of large and small schools, or of schools in different parts of the state, the controls may contribute appreciably to increased reliability of the results. Controlled sampling which does not involve random selection suffers from the very serious disadvantage that it does not permit any objective description of the reliability of the results obtained, but is nevertheless often worth while, particularly where random sampling is in any event impracticable.

The exercise of controls in sampling, particularly when the ultimate selection is random, is an extremely useful device in educational research, and its possibilities appear to have been seriously neglected. Considerable attention will therefore be given to this problem in this text (pages 157 ff.), particularly with reference to experimental research, in which the problem is essentially the same as that of how to *design* the experiment (Chapter IV).

A *parameter* is any measure based upon an entire population. Parameters are perhaps more widely known as "true" measures. For example, a true mean, which is a parameter, is the mean of all members of the population. A *statistic* is any measure derived from a sample, and is frequently referred to as an "obtained" measure, or as an "observed" measure. A parameter always has an exact constant value, although usually unknown; a statistic varies in value from sample to sample. Parameters are seldom determinable, since usually the entire population is not accessible; in most instances, the best we can do is to *estimate* the parameter by drawing a sample and calculating the corresponding statistic. For example, the best estimate of a true mean that may be derived from a random sample is the mean of that sample. The best estimate of a parameter, however, is not always the corresponding statistic from a random sample. For example, if our sample is small, the best estimate of the true standard deviation is *not* the standard deviation of the sample; we shall see later how a better estimate may be obtained (pages 48 ff.).

A *sampling error* is the difference between a parameter and an estimate of that parameter which is derived from a sample. *Errors in random sampling* are a special class of sampling errors, and are of course due only to the *random* selection of the members of the sample.

A *sampling distribution* (for an infinite population) is the theoretical distribution of a statistic for an infinite number of similar samples. The distribution of mean weights for an unlimited number of samples, each consisting of 50 individuals selected from a given population, would be the sampling distribution of the mean of a sample of 50 cases. This distribution might also be viewed as a distribution of the sampling errors in the observed means. The *standard error* of a statistic is the standard deviation of its sampling distribution. We can never, of course, actually construct a sampling distribution for an infinite population, since it is assumed to be infinite, but we can sometimes describe its form, and it is this fact that makes possible any quantitative description of the reliability of estimates based on samples. It is known, for example, that for most populations which will be encountered in practice the sampling distribution of the mean of a large random sample is a normal distribution, and hence if we can estimate the standard deviation of this sampling distribution we can also estimate the probability that an obtained mean will differ from the true mean by more than any given amount. Many students seem to have the notion that all sampling distributions are normal, particularly if the samples are simple random samples drawn from normal populations. This is a very serious misconception. For example, the sampling distribution of the standard deviation of a small random sample is markedly skewed positively; hence, even though we knew the standard error, we could not interpret it in terms of the normal probability integral table. It is sometimes possible to estimate the standard error of a statistic even though the form of its sampling distribution is unknown. For example, we have long had a standard error formula for the product-moment correlation coefficient, but it is now known that the sampling distribution of r is markedly skewed negatively when the true r is high. Many instances may be found in the literature of educational research of attempts to use the normal probability integral table in interpreting the standard errors of r's of large magnitude, and often with seriously misleading results. It is important to note, then, that a standard error formula is of little value unless the form of the sampling distribution is known to be approximately normal.

Sampling distributions are described in terms of mathematical equations, or in terms of probability integral tables derived from these equations. The student is already familiar with the normal probability integral table; he will later have occasion to use similar tables for other forms of distributions. The derivation of these formulae and tables is a problem for the mathematical statistician. The typical research worker in education, because of his lack of advanced mathematical training, must be content to accept these formulae and tables on faith, and no attempt will be made in this text to show how they are derived. It is important to note, however, that all of these derivations at some point involve the assumption of *random* selection. Most sampling distributions thus far determined are for simple random samples only, but some sampling distributions are known for controlled samples in which the last step in selection is random. Sampling distributions derived for randomly selected samples may be very misleading when applied to samples that are not truly random, even though they seem for all practical purposes to be equivalent to random samples. It is for this reason that so much emphasis is later placed in this text on the exercise of meticulous care in making random selections.

The *precision* or reliability of an estimate is dependent on the variability of its sampling distribution. It is significant that no estimate is of any value whatever unless something is known about its precision. This does not mean that we must always be able to compute the standard error of an estimate, but it does mean that unless we at least have an intuitive or subjective notion, based on observation or experience, of how precise an estimate is, we might as well not have an estimate at all. Obviously, it is much better if the precision can be quantitatively described on an objective basis. The advantage of objective description is so great that we might frequently use the less precise of two available estimates, because the exact *degree* of precision is known in one case but not in the other. It is for this reason that random selection is so important. since it is only for samples involving random selection that objective descriptions of the precision of estimates may be obtained.

3. TESTING STATISTICAL HYPOTHESES

It is generally believed that the ultimate purpose in drawing a sample is to obtain an estimate of some group characteristic of the population. This is of course true, but it might be more conducive to clear thinking to say that we draw a sample in order to determine which *hypotheses* about the population are *tenable* in light of what is learned from the sample. This way of viewing the situation has certain advantages: (1) it recognizes explicitly that our estimate is after all only an estimate; (2) it recognizes that it is just as important to know how precise or dependable the estimate is as to have an estimate at all; and (3) it suggests more directly the nature of the logic by which we describe the degree of precision attained.

Suppose, to take a very simple illustration, that we wish to estimate the mean weight in a certain population of ten-year-old girls. Suppose that we have drawn a random sample of 400 girls from this population, and have found the mean weight for this sample to be 65 pounds. Our "best estimate" of the population mean is therefore 65 pounds. This is but another way of saying that the *hypothesis* that the true mean is 65 is the best hypothesis we can make with the information at hand, or that it is the hypothesis which best accounts for the fact that our sample mean is 65 pounds. There are, however, many other hypotheses about the true mean that might readily be defended. It is possible, for instance, that the true mean is 66 pounds, and that our obtained mean of 65 represents a chance deviation of one unit from this true mean. How tenable this hypothesis is, or with what degree of confidence we may accept or reject it, depends upon the relative frequency with which the obtained means of random samples of this size would deviate one unit or more from the true mean. For example, if obtained means deviating as much as 1 unit from the true mean would very frequently occur by chance, we would have no good reason to reject the hypothesis that the true mean is 66 simply because a mean of 65 was found in one sample. However, if means deviating this much from the true mean would only very rarely be found, then the fact that the mean of our sample is 65 throws serious doubt on the hypothesis that the true mean is 66.

This relative frequency could be determined if we knew the sampling distribution of the mean of a sample of 400 cases, and in this instance sampling theory does provide us with a means of describing the sampling distribution. It is known that the sampling distribution of the mean of a large random sample is usually normal in form, and that its standard deviation is given by the

formula
$$\sigma_M = \frac{\sigma_{population}}{\sqrt{n}} \qquad (1)$$

in which n is the number of cases in the sample. The usefulness of this formula is limited by the fact that it involves a parameter, the σ of the population, which of course we cannot know. However, we can find the σ of our sample, and since our sample is quite large, we can derive a useful *estimate* of σ_M by substituting the σ of the sample for the σ_{pop} in the formula. Let us suppose that we have found the σ of the sample to be 8 pounds. Our estimated standard error of the mean is then

$$\text{est'd } \sigma_M = \frac{\sigma_{sample}}{\sqrt{n}} = \frac{8}{\sqrt{400}} = .4$$

We now have a complete description (subject, however, to whatever error is involved in the preceding estimate) of the sampling distribution under the hypothesis to be tested. We have assumed its true mean to be 66, have estimated its standard deviation to be .4, and know that it is a normal distribution. In this distribution, the value 65 deviates $1/.4 = 2.5$ standard deviations from the hypothetical true mean. According to the normal probability integral table (Appendix, Table 17) less than two per cent of the cases in a normal distribution deviate so far from the mean. Hence, if our hypothesis is true, something has happened in this one sample that would occur by chance in less than two per cent of such samples in the long run. Since it would be very unreasonable to suppose that so rare an event has actually "come off" in this one case, we conclude that the hypothesis itself must be false. Consider, on the other hand, the hypothesis that the true mean is 64.5. Under this hypothesis, means deviating as much from the true mean as does our obtained mean of 65 would be obtained in about 22 per cent of samples of this size. In this case, we obviously could not reject the hypothesis with any high degree of confidence.

The *degree* of confidence with which we may reject (or accept) any hypothesis would then depend upon the relative frequency with which results deviating as much from the hypothetical as those found in our sample would occur by chance if the hypothesis were true. Whether we would categorically reject or accept the hypothesis, that is, whether we adjudge it categorically as either "tenable" or "untenable," depends upon the degree of confidence which we have *arbitrarily* decided is essential. We might, for example, decide to consider any hypothesis "tenable" under which results as divergent as those obtained in our sample would be found in at least 5 per cent of such samples, or we might be more conservative and reject only those hypotheses under which chance would account for the divergence of our obtained result less than 1 per cent of the time. It will be useful to identify such arbitrarily defined levels of confidence in terms of per cents. For instance, we might term the first of the levels just defined as the "5 per cent level," and the second as the "1 per cent level." In general, to say that we reject an hypothesis at the "x per cent level of confidence" is to say that the absolute divergence of our observed result from the hypothetical true result would be exceeded in less than x per cent of such samples if the hypothesis were true. Whatever level of confidence we have decided to employ as a minimum, we may, by testing successive hypotheses, find what limiting values of the true mean constitute "tenable" hypotheses at that level. We could then say that we are confident (at the given level) that the true mean lies between these limits. For example, in the case of our illustration we may be confident at the 5 per cent level that the true mean does not lie outside 64.22 and 65.78, and at the 1 per cent level that it does not lie outside 63.97 and 66.03. (According to Table 17, page 261, 5 per cent of the cases in a normal distribution will deviate more than $1.960\,\sigma$ from the mean. Hence the limiting values of the true mean are $65 \pm 1.960 \times .4 = 65 \pm .784 = 64.22$ and 65.78.)

Since the preceding interpretation may differ somewhat from that to which the student is accustomed, it may be well to draw attention to some of the more important aspects of the logic involved.   Many students have learned to interpret results like those just given by constructing a normal distribution with a mean of 65 and a standard deviation of .4, finding the per cent of the distribution which lies between any two selected points in this distribution, and then stating that the "chances" are such and such that the true mean lies between these values.   He might then say, for instance, that "the chances are 95 in 100 that the true mean lies between 64.22 and 65.78," or that "the probability is less than 1 in 100 that the true mean lies outside of the values 63.97 and 66.03."   For most practical purposes, the end result is the same as if the "level of confidence" type of interpretation is employed, but the reasoning involved is based on a questionable assumption.   To draw a normal curve with a mean at 65 and to determine the "probability" that the true mean lies between any points along the curve is to reason as if there are many values of the *true* mean, and that these true means are normally distributed about the mean obtained for the sample.   Statements of probability may be made about an event only before it occurs, and then only if it is a *random* event.   *Knowing* that the true mean is 66 we can state the probability that a sample about to be drawn will have a mean below 65, but we cannot in strict logic invert that reasoning.   The true mean either is 66 or it is not — it does not have a number of different values any one of which may turn up at random.   However, knowing that the sample mean is 65, we can make the statement with a certain *degree of confidence* that the unknown true mean has a value below 66.

We may now summarize the general steps involved in testing a statistical hypothesis, given the facts for a single sample.   The first step is to state the hypothesis in *exact* terms, since to test an hypothesis we must be able to locate the sampling distribution exactly.   The second step is to deduce, from our hypothesis, what the sampling distribution would be under that hypothesis.   In practice, this has been done for the student, who has merely to refer to the appropriate probability integral tables.   The third step is to determine, from that distribution or from the tables, in what per cent of samples the obtained measures will deviate from the true measure as much as or more than the measure obtained in the sample at hand deviates from the hypothetical true measure. The fourth step is to reject the hypothesis, or not, depending upon the "level of confidence" which has been arbitrarily determined in advance.

4. TESTS OF SIGNIFICANCE: THE NULL HYPOTHESIS

In many sampling studies the interest is not so much in the limits within which a parameter may confidently be said to lie as in the single possibility that the parameter is zero. For example, we may ask, "Is there *any* correlation between these two traits?" or "Is there any difference in the effectiveness of these methods of instruction?" or "Are girls of a given age *equal* in intelligence to boys of the same age?" In such cases we may wish to test the hypothesis that the true correlation is zero, or that the true difference is zero, but may not be particularly concerned with the degree of correlation or with the magnitude of the difference if any does exist. Such hypotheses — that the parameter is zero — are known as null hypotheses.[1] If a statistic is such that the null hypothesis may be rejected with confidence, we say that the statistic is *significant*, meaning that it signifies that the parameter value is not zero. For example, we may select two random samples of pupils, teach one by one method and one by another, and find at the close of the experiment that the difference in final mean achievement is larger than could reasonably be attributed to fluctuations in random sampling, i.e., too large to permit us to accept the null hypothesis. We may then say that the observed difference in mean achievement is significant. It is important to note, however, that to prove the difference significant does not establish the *cause* of the difference. In rejecting the null hypothesis we have only rejected *one* possible cause — chance fluctuation due to random

[1] The term "null hypothesis" is used by Fisher (*Design of Experiments*, p. 18) to denote *any* exact hypothesis that we may be interested in disproving, not merely the hypothesis that a certain parameter is zero.

selection. What really accounts for the difference — whether it is a real difference in effectiveness of the methods, or some extraneous factor which was not adequately controlled in the experiment — is quite another matter.

It is convenient to speak of *levels* of significance, just as we spoke of levels of confidence in the preceding section. When we say that a statistic is significant "at the 5 per cent level," we mean that the observed divergence from zero would be exceeded in less than 5 per cent of similar samples if the null hypothesis were true, or that we may be confident, at the 5 per cent level, that the null hypothesis is false. The levels of significance most frequently employed are the 5 per cent and 1 per cent levels, and some tables are constructed for these levels only. It has been customary in educational research to declare a statistic significant if it is three or more times as large as its standard error. This is not satisfactory as a general practice, since it is limited to the case where the sampling distribution is normal. It is also too rigid a test for most purposes, since to require the "significance ratio" to exceed 3 is equivalent to requiring that the statistic be significant at the 0.26 per cent level (assuming a normal sampling distribution). If the sampling distribution is normal, a statistic must be 2.576 times its standard error to be significant at the 1 per cent level, or 1.960 times its standard error to be significant at the 5 per cent level.

It should be noted that it is by no means desirable to insist on the same level of significance in all tests of significance. The choice of the level of significance to employ should be based on the relative consequences of the two types of error that are risked. On the one hand, we run the risk of accepting the null hypothesis when it is false, i.e., of characterizing a difference as *not* significant when a real difference does exist; and on the other hand we risk rejecting the null hypothesis when it is true, i.e., of claiming significance when the difference is really due to chance. The farther apart we set our limits of acceptable hypotheses, i.e., the higher the level of significance we employ, the greater is the danger that we will include a false hypothesis among the "acceptable" hypotheses.

The more we narrow the range of acceptable hypotheses, i.e., the lower the level of significance we employ, the greater is the danger of rejecting a true hypothesis, or of claiming a real difference when no real difference exists.   In general, the latter danger is the more serious in educational research.   If we find in a methods experiment that the difference is not significant, we have in effect declared the experiment inconclusive.   That is, we recognize that there is a possibility of a real difference, even though none has been proven, and in effect *invite* further experimentation, with more precise procedures, to show that the difference is there.   However, if we find a significant difference, the experiment is usually considered as conclusive.   That is, the effect is to discourage further experimentation for purposes of verification only, and any further experimentation in the same area is likely to be based on the premise which has presumably already been established, but which may be false.   If our tests are too exacting, we may needlessly delay experimentation along new lines while waiting further verification of our tentative conclusions; if our tests are not sufficiently exacting, we may follow too many false leads.   Generally, we prefer to take the former risk, and consequently demand that our differences be significant at a high level before attempting any generalizations.   However, we need not always employ the *same* high level.   For example, if we are about to recommend a new method of instruction for a school system, and if the recommended change will prove very expensive and involve serious administrative difficulties, we would want to be *very* sure that we are not recommending a method which is inferior or only equal to the old.   However, if the change could be very easily and cheaply made, we might be more concerned with the danger of rejecting a method which is superior to the old, and might make the recommendation for a change even though not highly confident that we are right.   It is important that the research worker recognize clearly what is involved in the choice of a critical level of significance, and that he weigh carefully the possible consequences of each type of error in making that choice.

5. LIMITATIONS OF STANDARD ERROR FORMULAS CONTAINING POPULATION PARAMETERS: NEED FOR A SPECIAL SMALL SAMPLE THEORY

It was noted on page 12 that the formula for the standard error of the mean is based on an independent population parameter — the σ of the population. Since this parameter is usually unknown, we are unable to compute the true σ_M, but are able to secure an estimate of it by substituting for the parameter in the formula the corresponding statistic for our sample. Many, if not most, of the standard error formulas already familiar to the student are of this type. To use any of them we are compelled to substitute for the parameter in the formula some estimate of a parameter, and usually the corresponding sample statistic is taken as that estimate. This practice is never wholly satisfactory, but when the sample is large the statistic so closely approximates the parameter that only a negligible error is introduced. When the sample is small, however, this procedure breaks down seriously.

It will be worth while to consider carefully the reasons for this breakdown, since the matter is of very considerable practical import in educational research. These reasons may perhaps best be explained in the case of the formula for the standard error of the mean, in which case it is also most important. We saw in the preceding section that in testing the hypothesis that the true mean had a given value, M_H, we first found the amount, $M_O - M_H$, by which the observed mean differed from the hypothetical value. We then divided this difference by the *estimated* standard error of the mean, and then entered the normal probability integral table with the number equal to this ratio. We then read from the table the per cent of cases in a normal distribution that deviate from the mean by more than this number of σ units. Upon reflection, the student will recognize that this procedure assumes that the ratio $\dfrac{M_O - M_T}{\text{est'd } \sigma_M}$ is normally distributed for samples of the given size, and that the standard deviation of this distribution is 1.00 (M_T representing the true mean). For large samples, in which the observed σ's closely pproximate the true σ, the ratios $\dfrac{M_O - M_T}{\text{est'd } \sigma_M}$ are very nearly equal

o the corresponding ratios $\dfrac{M_O - M_T}{\text{true } \sigma_M}$, and we know that the latter

atios are normally distributed with unit standard deviation. Hence, for large samples the aforementioned assumptions are very nearly satisfied. For small samples, however, the ratios $\dfrac{M_O - M_T}{\text{est'd } \sigma_M}$

are not normally distributed, nor is the standard deviation of their sampling distribution equal to unity. In any small sample the observed mean may be relatively large (or small) at the same time that the observed standard deviation is relatively small (or large) as the result of chance fluctuations. In such cases, of course, the estimated σ_M would be smaller (or larger) than the true σ_M. We would therefore more frequently find large (either positive or neg-

ative) values of $\dfrac{M_O - M_T}{\text{est'd } \sigma_M}$ than of $\dfrac{M_O - M_T}{\text{true } \sigma_M}$, and as a result the

standard deviation of the ratios $\dfrac{M_O - M_T}{\text{est'd } \sigma_M}$ would be larger than 1.00

— how much larger [1] depending on the size of the samples — and the distribution would be less peaked than the normal distribution. All of this means, of course, that the use of the normal probability integral table to interpret this ratio is not justified if the sample is very small, and if so used may lead to serious misinterpretations.

It may be noted finally that the standard deviation of a small sample is not only highly unstable, but also tends to be *systematically* smaller than the true standard deviation. We shall see later (page 48) that it is possible to make a better estimate of the true σ from a small sample, but even the best estimate is still highly unstable, and what was said in the preceding paragraph would still be true even if the best available estimate of the population σ were used.

[1] The standard deviation of the ratios is equal to $\sqrt{\dfrac{n}{n-2}}$.

We have seen that the objections to the use with small samples of the formula for the standard error of the mean arose from the fact that to test an hypothesis about one parameter (the true mean) we are compelled to estimate another parameter (the true standard deviation). In the illustration considered in the preceding section, we were in effect testing the hypothesis that the true mean was 66 on the *further* hypothesis that the true standard deviation was 8. If the sample had been very small, the latter hypothesis would have been very shaky indeed. Objections similar to those just noted apply with equal force to any other standard error formulas or tests of significance based upon a population parameter other than that with which the hypothesis to be tested is concerned. To deal satisfactorily with small samples, then, our test of significance must require a knowledge of nothing more than the statistic available from the sample itself. In other words, the only parameter needed to describe the required sampling distribution *exactly* must be that with which the hypothesis to be tested is directly concerned.

A great deal of effort has been devoted, during recent years, to the formulation of statistical tests of this latter type. As a result there are now available tests of this character adequate for most of the needs of educational research. A number of these tests will be presented later in this text — the purpose of the preceding discussion has only been to demonstrate the need for them. It is obvious, however, that the practical need for a special "small sample" theory in any field depends upon the frequency with which research workers in that field are compelled to work with small samples. What, then, is the need for small sample theory in educational research?

In the past, the attitude seems to have been that we seldom have to use small samples in educational research — that most of our samples consist of large numbers of pupils or observations. It is perhaps partly for this reason that we have so seriously neglected many of the important contributions that have recently been made to statistical theory. This attitude, however, is based on a misconception of the nature of our samples, as the following section will attempt to show.   Most of our samples — regardless of the number of pupils or observations involved — *are* "small" samples, and the techniques that we have generally employed in the past are definitely inappropriate and have often been very seriously misleading.

6. THE PROBLEM OF SAMPLING IN EDUCATIONAL RESEARCH

We have already noted that many of the populations with which we are concerned in educational research are such that it is highly impracticable to draw truly random samples from them.   Suppose, for example, that we wished to draw a sample of 500 pupils from all pupils in the eighth grades of Iowa public schools.   As was noted before in a similar illustration, if we were to select a *random* sample of pupils from this population we would have to give every eighth-grade pupil in every school an equal chance to be selected. If we were to do this, we might find that the 500 pupils finally selected would be widely scattered over the whole state in several hundred different schools, and would therefore, for all practical purposes, be *inaccessible* for measurement, observation, or experimentation.   What we would actually do, therefore, would be to secure the co-operation of, say, 10 schools, which together could provide 500 eighth-grade pupils.   We might be able to select the schools at random from all schools, but usually even this would be impracticable.   In general, the best we could do would be to prepare a list of schools which we know in advance might be willing to co-operate in our investigation, and then select 10 schools at random from this list.   If then we have no reason to suppose that the schools in our list differ systematically from the other schools in the state with reference to the characteristic(s) we are investigating, we might be justified in considering our sample of 10 schools as *equivalent* to a random selection from *all schools* in the state.   Even so, we could *not* consider our 500 pupils as equivalent to a random selection from all *pupils* in the state.

The reasons for this is that the pupils in different schools show large systematic differences in almost any trait that may be the subject of a research investigation. The pupils in one school may have had the advantage of a long succession of superior teachers in the preceding grades, while those in another may have had consistently incompetent teachers under poor supervision. The pupils in one school may come from a high-class residential section of the community, a section made up of professional and successful business men, while those in another may have come from an impoverished and underprivileged section made up largely of illiterate day laborers of recent foreign extraction. Large differences, particularly in educational achievement, are frequently found even between schools that apparently have much the same external advantages. It is almost a commonplace, to those familiar with the results of wide-scale testing programs, that differences in mean achievement from school to school, regardless of the size of school, are of almost the same order of magnitude as differences in individual pupil achievement in a single school. The student is perhaps already familiar with much of the almost overwhelming mass of evidence on this point, but it might be worth while to consider here one representative bit of this evidence. The State University of Iowa annually conducts a state-wide end-of-the-year achievement testing program which involves the administration of objective tests of school achievement to over 50,000 pupils in several hundred high schools. In the 1935 program, an objective test of achievement in English correctness was administered to all ninth-grade pupils in 274 schools. For the 24 largest schools, each of which tested over 100 ninth-grade pupils, the total distribution of pupil scores is given in Table 1 at the left, while the distribution of mean scores in these schools is given at the right. Had the pupils in each school constituted a random sample from the pupils in all these schools, we should, according to sampling theory, expect the standard deviation of the distribution of *means* to be less than $31.54/\sqrt{100} = 3.15$, 31.54 being the standard deviation of the total pupil distribution, and 100 the minimum number of cases in any sample. Actually, however, we see that the stand-

TABLE I

DISTRIBUTIONS OF INDIVIDUAL AND MEAN SCORES OF NINTH-GRADE
PUPILS ON THE 1935 IOWA EVERY-PUPIL TEST IN ENGLISH COR-
RECTNESS FOR 24 SCHOOLS

(Each school tested over 100 ninth-grade pupils)

Pupil Scores		School Means	
Scores	Frequency	Means	Frequency
170–180	3	91.0–94.49	1
160–169	10	87.5–90.99	
150–159	15	84.0–87.49	
140–149	30	80.5–83.99	
130–139	43	77.0–80.49	
120–129	67	73.5–76.99	1
110–119	84	70.0–73.49	1
100–109	112	66.5–69.99	
90– 99	146	63.0–66.49	3
80– 89	188	59.5–62.99	2
70– 79	266	56.0–59.49	2
60– 69	335	52.5–55.99	2
50– 59	394	49.0–52.49	1
40– 49	553	45.5–48.99	4
30– 39	554	42.0–45.49	5
20– 29	508	38.5–41.99	1
10– 19	263	35.0–38.49	
0– 9	75	31.5–34.99	
		28.0–31.49	1
N	3646	N	24
M	54.08	M	54.58
S.D.	31.54	S.D.	13.29

ard deviation of school means is 13.29, or more than 4 times as
large as would be expected on the hypothesis of random sampling.

In consideration of these much-larger-than-chance differences
between schools, let us consider further our illustrative sample of
500 pupils of Iowa eighth-grade pupils. It is very obvious that
had all of these pupils come from a *single* school, the sample would
represent a very poor basis for generalization about the population, particularly in contrast to a truly random sample of equal
size. In the random sample, hundreds of different schools would
be represented, in the sample just considered only one is represented — and that might be one of the schools in which the level of
achievement is very high, or it might be one in which the level is
very low. It should be equally evident that a sample in which
only 10 schools are represented is neither as good as nor equivalent

to a random sample of 500 cases from the population at large. With so few schools involved, the danger is appreciable that we might by chance have selected 10 good schools, or 10 poor ones, or that most of the schools used are good schools or poor ones. If then, we were to use the standard-error-of-the-mean formula with this sample, substituting 500 for n, we would very seriously exaggerate the reliability of the mean. In spite of the fact that it contains 500 pupils, this sample must be considered as a very "small" sample — a sample of only *ten* schools — and in order to evaluate any estimate derived from it we must have a sampling theory appropriate for small samples.

In general, then, many of the samples employed in educational research consist of a small number of intact groups (such as *classes* in the same or different schools, groups of pupils in separate buildings in the same system, or groups of pupils from different communities or geographical regions), or of a small number of subsamples selected from different "strata" in the population (in the case of controlled samples). In all such cases, the "size" of the sample is dependent, not upon the number of individual observations, but upon the number of intact groups or subsamples of which the total sample is constituted. In other words, the *unit* of sampling in educational research is often the class, the school, or the community, rather than the pupil. It is for this reason that the need is so great in educational research for a special small sample theory, and that this text is in so large part devoted to an exposition of this theory.

7. THE TECHNIQUE OF RANDOM SELECTION

It is a fact of extreme practical significance that all mathematical sampling theory is based finally on the assumption of *random selection*, and that any application of this theory is valid only to the degree that the samples employed have been so selected. We may note at once, however, that random selection does not always mean simple random sampling. We have seen, for instance, that controlled samples or matched samples are not simple random samples, but that they may involve random selection, and that it is therefore sometimes possible to deduce the sampling distributions for estimates obtained from such samples. Simple random sampling is often impracticable in educational research, but it is nearly always possible to plan our investigations and experiments so as to provide for random selection, and thus to utilize sampling theory in interpreting our results. Since those interpretations will be valid only to the degree that the selection was actually random, it is obviously important that the student be provided with a technique that will *insure* random selection, in so far as that is possible.

In many of the instances in which random selection is necessary in educational research, the selection is made from a relatively small number of cases. This is particularly true in experimental work. For example, in each of the schools involved in a methods experiment, we may wish to divide the seventh-grade pupils at random into two or more equal groups to be taught by different methods, or we may wish to assign the *classes* (as already organized) at random to the different methods. Again, we may divide the available pupils into levels of intelligence, and *within* each level assign the pupils at random to the experimental treatments.

One method of making random selections in situations of this kind may be described as the "lottery" method. For example, if we wished to split a group of 30 pupils at random into 3 groups of 10 each, we could prepare 30 cards or slips of paper on each of which is written the name of one pupil, shuffle or mix these cards very thoroughly, and then "deal" or draw blindly 3 sets of 10 cards each. This is a troublesome procedure, however, and introduces the danger of bias through improper mixing or drawing of the cards.

A more certain and more convenient procedure is to make use of a table of "random numbers." For the convenience of the student, a part of one such table is reproduced in the Appendix (Table 18). The manner in which the original table was constructed is described on page 18 of *Statistical Tables for Biological, Agricultural and Medical Research*, by R. A. Fisher and F. Yates

(Oliver & Boyd, London, 1938).   It is sufficient to say here that
the digits in this table were so selected that any digit from o to
9 had an equal chance to appear in any given position in the table.
The manner in which this table may be used should be made clear
by the following illustrations.

Illustration No. 1: *To assign 5 classes at random one to each of 5 experimental treatments.*

Number the classes and the treatments separately from 1 to 5
in any order whatever.   Select any point at haphazard in the table
of random numbers.   Reading in any direction from this point
(right to left, bottom to top, diagonally, etc.) read the first five
unlike two digit numbers (skipping any that may previously have
been read) from the table.   Assign the first of these numbers to
class 1, the second to class 2, etc.   The class with the highest random number will then be assigned to treatment 1, that with the
second highest to treatment 2, etc.

Suppose, for example, that the first number selected haphaz-
ardly is that in the 14th row and the 4th double column on the first
page of Table 18.   Reading to the right from this point, the
first five unlike two-digit numbers are 19, 95, 50, 92 and 26.   The
second class would therefore be assigned to treatment 1, the fourth
to treatment 2, the third to treatment 3, etc.

The "starting point" in the table should be determined before
looking at any number in the table.   In the preceding case, for instance, the decision to begin with "the 14th row in the 4th column on the first page of the table" should be made before looking
in the table.   Otherwise one might, without being fully conscious
of the fact, begin with a large number, and thus in effect *deliberately* insure that class 1 will receive treatment 1, or otherwise bias
the selection.   Furthermore, once having selected the starting-
point and direction, no peculiarity in the numbers read should be
permitted to cause one to discard the results and start anew at
another point.

Illustration No. 2: *To select 20 pupils at random from 62 available pupils.*

Number the pupils from 00 to 61 in any order whatever. Turn to the table, and from any point and in any direction read the first 20 two-digit numbers that are less than 62, skipping any number previously read. For example, beginning in the 11th row of the 5th column on the first page of Table 18 and reading downward, the first 20 unlike numbers below 62 are 46, 12, 13, 35, 43, 53, 61, 24, 59, 06, 20, 38, 47, 14, 11, 00, 60, 23, 19, and 53. The pupils who had previously been assigned these numbers would then be the 20 required. If these numbers are checked off in the original list of numbered pupils as they are read from the table, there will be no difficulty in avoiding duplications.

If the selection is made from more than 99 cases, we must read three- or four-digit numbers from the table, as the case may be. These may be secured by combining columns in the table. Suppose, for instance, we wish to select 15 schools at random from the 418 high schools in a given state. We would first number all schools from 000 to 417 in any order whatever. We would then combine, say, the 7th double column (on the first page of Table 18) with the first half of the next column to the right, to secure a "column" of three-digit numbers. Reading upwards from the bottom of this "column," the first 15 unlike numbers less than 418 are 044, 416, 377, 358, 061, 057, 389, 325, 091, 373, 299, 278, 271, 332, and 395. The schools previously assigned these numbers would then constitute our sample of 15. If the total number from which the selection is to be made is a number like 160, for example, considerable "hunting" would be required in the table to find three-digit numbers less than this value. A more convenient procedure in such cases is explained by the following example.

Suppose that we wished to select 5 cases at random from 120 available cases, numbered from 0 to 119 in any order whatever. We would first observe that 120 is contained in 999 eight times, or that $8 \times 120 = 960$ is the largest multiple of 120 which is contained in 999. We would then select random numbers less than

960 from a three-digit column of the table, and divide each by 8, dropping any remainder. The first five unlike *quotients* would then be the numbers of the cases selected. Suppose, for instance, that we begin at a point in the table in which the following three-digit numbers appear in the order given below.

Random Numbers	Quotients
562	70
815	101
982	
322	40
057	7
815	101
723	90

The cases numbered 70, 101, 40, 7, and 90 would then constitute our random sample of 5.

Illustration No. 3: *To Split a Group at Random into a Number of Equal Groups*

The problem of splitting a group at random into a number of equal groups would simply involve an extension of the procedure just described. Suppose we wish to select 3 random groups of 20 each from 62 available pupils. We would first draw one sample of 20 in the manner already illustrated. We would then continue reading from the table until we had 20 more numbers (not previously read) that are less than 62. The pupils with these numbers would constitute the second group. We would then continue as before to get *two* more numbers (not previously read) less than 62. The pupils with these numbers would be discarded, the remaining 20 pupils would constitute the third group. If, again, the numbers in the original list were checked off as read, there would be no difficulty in avoiding duplications.

Other methods of employing tables of random numbers may be found described in the directions accompanying those tables.[1] The

---

[1] See the aforementioned tables by Fisher and Yates, or *Tracts for Computers, No. 15, Random Sampling Numbers*, by L. H. C. Tippett.

methods here described, however, will be adequate for most situations met in educational research.

It may be worth while to point out here the possible defects in a certain method of sampling (of pupils) that has been frequently employed in educational research — the practice of making the selection schematically from a list in which the pupils' names have been arranged in alphabetical order.   For example, we might take every 6th name in an alphabetical list of 95 names to secure a sample of 15, or if we wished to split the group into two equal groups, we might do so by selecting alternate names from the list.   A selection of this kind should be free from bias (unless the selection is made from only part of the list), so far as measures of central tendency are concerned, but it may nevertheless not be the equivalent of a random selection.   This is because of the possibility that alphabetized lists may be "stratified," since pupils with the same last name (or names beginning with the same letter) may be related, or of the same nationality, or otherwise more nearly alike than pupils selected at random.   In general, particularly since it involves so little trouble, there is no excuse for failing to use the "random numbers" type of selection in situations of the type described.

CHAPTER II

THE USE OF THE X^2 DISTRIBUTION IN TESTING HYPOTHESES

1. INTRODUCTORY

IN SITUATIONS in which the members of a random sample may be classified into mutually exclusive categories, we may sometimes wish to know whether the observed frequencies in these categories are consistent with some hypothesis concerning the relative frequencies in these categories in the entire population. To take a simple illustration, suppose we have asked each pupil in a random sample of 90 to indicate which of three school subjects he likes best, and that we find that 27 prefer subject A, 35 prefer B, and 28 prefer C. This seems to indicate that subject "B" is liked better than the others. However, the suggestion might be made that this is just the sort of distribution of responses we might readily get from a random sample of this size even though all subjects were equally well liked in the population at large. We might therefore set up the hypothesis that the distribution in the population is uniform, and ask how frequently we would expect the observed distribution for samples of 90 to "diverge" farther from a uniform distribution than did the one sample at hand.

The manner in which this hypothesis may be tested has already been suggested in the preceding chapter. We must first devise some statistic which measures the "divergence" of fact from hypothesis in the sample at hand. We must then find what the sampling distribution of this statistic would be if the hypothesis were true. We must then determine, from this distribution, in what per cent of random samples of the given size the observed value of this statistic would be exceeded if the hypothesis were true. If this percentage is very small, we can then say with a correspondingly high degree of confidence that the hypothesis must be false, since the only alternatives are that a very improbable event has occurred or that our sampling was faulty, neither of which may be acceptable.

The statistic, X^2, needed to test this and a wide variety of similar hypotheses will be defined in the next section. Its sampling distribution is generally considered one of the most important in all statistical theory. While its practical usefulness may not be as great in educational as in biological and other fields of research, it will nevertheless be worth our while to devote considerable attention to it.

2. THE MEANING OF X^2

The statistic X^2 (chi-square) may be defined as

$$X^2 = \Sigma \frac{(f_o - f_t)^2}{f_t} \tag{2}$$

in which f_o represents the observed frequency in a single category, f_t the corresponding theoretical or hypothetical frequency, and in which the Σ indicates that the terms $(f_o - f_t)^2/f_t$ are to be summed for all categories. The manner in which X^2 is computed may be illustrated with the example already given. The observed frequencies (f_o) in the preference categories A, B, and C are 27, 35, and 28 respectively. The corresponding theoretical frequencies (f_t) are those that would have been found had the facts for our sample corresponded exactly with our hypothesis of uniform distribution in the population. Hence the theoretical frequencies are 30, 30, and 30. The following tabular arrangement indicates the steps in the computation of X^2.

Preference Category	f_o	f_t	$(f_o - f_t)$	$(f_o - t)^2$	$\frac{(f_o - f_t)^2}{f_t}$
A	27	30	-3	9	.300
B	35	30	5	25	.833
C	28	30	-2	4	.133
					$266 = X^2$

It should be immediately apparent that X^2 is an index of the divergence of fact from hypothesis. If each of the observed frequencies agreed exactly with the corresponding theoretical frequency, X^2 would be zero. The greater the divergence of the individual observed frequencies from the theoretical, the greater the value of X^2. It should be noted, however, that X^2, being based on the squares of the deviations $(f_o - f_t)$, does not take the *direction* of the deviations into account. This is a limitation of X^2 which we shall consider later.

It should also be apparent that X^2 may be used as a measure of divergence from any other hypothesis that we may wish to set up. For example, we may set up the hypothesis that in the whole population the ratio of preferences for A, B, and C is as 8:5:5. Under this hypothesis, the theoretical frequencies would be 40, 25, and 25, and we could compute X^2 with reference to these theoretical frequencies just as we did with reference to the frequencies 30, 30, and 30 which were consistent with our first hypothesis. We may then use this procedure to measure the divergence in our sample from any set of theoretical frequencies that we may wish to write down, noting, however, that in this example these theoretical frequencies must add up to 90. This means that, in setting up an hypothesis in this instance, we may assign any values we please to *two* of the theoretical frequencies, but the third will of course be completely fixed by the first two selected. For example, if we assign the values 10 and 52 (selected at will) to two of the frequencies, the third must be 28 if their sum is to be 90. We therefore say that there are only two *degrees of freedom* in this table — this concept, however, will be more adequately defined later.

Let us now consider further our first hypothesis — that of a uniform distribution. It should be obvious that even though this hypothesis were true, we could hardly expect the observed frequencies in any random sample to agree exactly with the theoretical frequencies. Due to chance fluctuations in the observed frequencies, nearly all random samples would show a value of X^2 other than zero; in some samples the value of X^2 would be relatively large, in others relatively small. To evaluate our data, then, we must know how X^2 is distributed for random samples with the given number of degrees of freedom. Before considering this sampling distribution, however, it will be well to consider more fully the meaning of the concept of degrees of freedom.

3. DEGREES OF FREEDOM

The number of degrees of freedom in a table of frequencies is the number of those frequencies to which we may assign arbitrary values and still satisfy the external requirements imposed on the table. If we think of each frequency as occupying a *cell* in the table, the degrees of freedom is the number of cells that may be filled at will. When the only restriction imposed is that the frequencies add up to a given total, the number of degrees of freedom is one less than the number of cells, as we have already seen in the illustration used in the preceding section. In some instances, however, additional restrictions are imposed, and the number of degrees of freedom correspondingly lessened.

For example, we might have a four-celled table, like the following

11	59	70
9	38	47
20	97	

on which we impose the restriction that the cell frequencies in *each* row and column must add up to a fixed total for that row or column. There are many combinations of cell frequencies, other than the one given, which will satisfy this requirement, as, for instance, those on page 34. However, we note that in writing in these frequencies, we could select only *one* frequency at will in each table. Having decided to write 15 in the upper left-hand cell in the first example, we had no choice but to write 55 in the upper

15	55	70
5	42	47
20	97	

1	69	70
19	28	47
20	97	

right-hand cell, 5 in the lower left-hand, and 42 in the one remaining cell. In this table, then, because of the restrictions imposed, we have only one degree of freedom. To illustrate further, suppose that we have a table with 3 rows and 7 columns. If we impose only the restriction that the 21 cell frequencies must add up to a single fixed total, we have 20 degrees of freedom in filling the cells. If we specify that the *column* totals must equal certain fixed values, we have 14 degrees of freedom, 2 in each column. If we impose the further restriction that the row totals must also equal fixed values, so that both row and column totals are fixed, we have only 12 degrees of freedom.

Illustrations of the use of χ^2 with tables like those just described will be presented later in this chapter. There are many other types of restrictions that might be imposed on a table besides those concerned only with totals. Illustrations of some of these types of restrictions will also be presented later. The foregoing, however, will be sufficient for immediate purposes to indicate what is meant by degrees of freedom.

4. THE SAMPLING DISTRIBUTION OF χ^2

The importance of the concept of degrees of freedom in the present discussion lies in the fact that the form of the sampling distribution of χ^2 depends only upon the number of degrees of freedom in the table from which it is computed. In other words, χ^2 shows the same distribution for all random samples in which the number of degrees of freedom is the same, regardless of the size of the sample (so long as it is fairly large, say 50 or more, and no theoretical frequency is very small, say 10 or less). Due to Karl

Pearson, it is known that for any given number of degrees of freedom (*d.f.*), the sampling distribution of X^2 is given by

$$y = y_0 e^{-\frac{1}{2}x^2}(X^2)^{\frac{df-1}{2}}$$

This equation will of course mean very little to the student not trained in mathematics, and no attempt will be made here to show how it was derived. However, from this equation it has been possible to construct a table showing, for each of a number of degrees of freedom, what value of X^2 is exceeded in each of a number of percentages of random samples. This table is presented on page 36 (Table 2). This table may be read as follows: For one degree of freedom (first row of table) we note that in 99 per cent of all random samples the value of X^2 would exceed .000157. In 98 per cent it would exceed .000628, in 5 per cent it would exceed 3.841, in 2 per cent 5.412, and in 1 per cent 6.635. For 6 degrees of freedom, X^2 would exceed 12.592 in 5 per cent of all random samples, etc. The manner in which the table may be used will be made clear by the illustrations in the following sections.

In general, as may be noted by examining the values in the middle column (50 per cent) of Table 2, the median value of X^2 under a true hypothesis is very nearly the same as the number of degrees of freedom. Hence if a value of X^2 *less* than the number of degrees of freedom is obtained, we may conclude at once that the hypothesis is tenable without bothering to refer to Table 2.

When the number of degrees of freedom exceeds 30, the probability of exceeding any given value of X^2 may be read from the normal probability integral table by finding the normal deviate equivalent of X^2. For example, suppose X^2 is 48.52 for 40 degrees of freedom. The normal deviate equivalent of X^2 is then

$$x = \sqrt{2 X^2} - \sqrt{2\,df - 1} = \sqrt{2 \times 48.52} - \sqrt{2 \times 40 - 1} =$$
$$\sqrt{97.04} - \sqrt{79} = 9.85 - 8.89 = .96.$$

The probability of exceeding the given value of X^2 is then the same as the probability that a measure selected at random from a normal distribution will lie to the right of a point $+ .96\,\sigma$ from the mean. (If x happened to be negative, the same interpretation ap-

TABLE 2 — TABLE OF χ^2

d.f.	99%	98%	95%	90%	80%	70%	50%	30%	20%	10%	5%	2%	1%
1	.000157	.000628	.00393	.0158	.0642	.148	.455	1.074	1.642	2.706	3.841	5.412	6.635
2	.0201	.0404	.103	.211	.446	.713	1.386	2.408	3.219	4.605	5.991	7.824	9.210
3	.115	.185	.352	.584	1.005	1.424	2.366	3.665	4.642	6.251	7.815	9.837	11.341
4	.297	.429	.711	1.064	1.649	2.195	3.357	4.878	5.989	7.779	9.488	11.668	13.277
5	.554	.752	1.145	1.610	2.343	3.000	4.351	6.064	7.289	9.236	11.070	13.388	15.086
6	.872	1.134	1.635	2.204	3.070	3.828	5.348	7.231	8.558	10.645	12.592	15.033	16.812
7	1.239	1.564	2.167	2.833	3.822	4.671	6.346	8.383	9.803	12.017	14.067	16.622	18.475
8	1.646	2.032	2.733	3.490	4.594	5.527	7.344	9.524	11.030	13.362	15.507	18.168	20.090
9	2.088	2.532	3.325	4.168	5.380	6.393	8.343	10.656	12.242	14.684	16.919	19.679	21.666
10	2.558	3.059	3.940	4.865	6.179	7.267	9.342	11.781	13.442	15.987	18.307	21.161	23.209
11	3.053	3.609	4.575	5.578	6.989	8.148	10.341	12.899	14.631	17.275	19.675	22.618	24.725
12	3.571	4.178	5.226	6.304	7.807	9.034	11.340	14.011	15.812	18.549	21.026	24.054	26.217
13	4.107	4.765	5.892	7.042	8.634	9.926	12.340	15.119	16.985	19.812	22.362	25.472	27.688
14	4.660	5.368	6.571	7.790	9.467	10.821	13.339	16.222	18.151	21.064	23.685	26.873	29.141
15	5.229	5.985	7.261	8.547	10.307	11.721	14.339	17.322	19.311	22.307	24.996	28.259	30.578
16	5.812	6.614	7.962	9.312	11.152	12.624	15.338	18.418	20.465	23.542	26.296	30.633	32.000
17	6.408	7.255	8.672	10.085	12.002	13.531	16.338	19.511	21.615	24.769	27.587	30.995	33.409
18	7.015	7.906	9.390	10.865	12.857	14.440	17.338	20.601	22.760	25.989	28.869	32.346	34.805
19	7.633	8.567	10.117	11.651	13.716	15.352	18.338	21.689	23.900	27.204	30.144	33.687	36.191
20	8.260	9.237	10.851	12.443	14.578	16.266	19.337	22.775	25.038	28.412	31.410	35.020	37.566
21	8.897	9.915	11.591	13.240	15.445	17.182	20.337	23.858	26.171	29.615	32.671	36.343	38.932
22	9.542	10.600	12.338	14.041	16.314	18.101	21.337	24.939	27.301	30.813	33.924	37.659	40.289
23	10.196	11.293	13.091	14.848	17.187	19.021	22.337	26.018	28.429	32.007	35.172	38.968	41.638
24	10.856	11.992	13.848	15.659	18.062	19.943	23.337	27.096	29.553	33.196	36.415	40.270	42.980
25	11.524	12.697	14.611	16.473	18.940	20.867	24.337	28.172	30.675	34.382	37.652	41.566	44.314
26	12.198	13.409	15.379	17.292	19.820	21.792	25.336	29.246	31.795	35.563	38.885	42.856	45.642
27	12.879	14.125	16.151	18.114	20.703	22.719	26.336	30.319	32.912	36.741	40.113	44.140	46.963
28	13.565	14.847	16.928	18.939	21.588	23.647	27.336	31.391	34.027	37.916	41.337	45.419	48.278
29	14.256	15.574	17.708	19.768	22.475	24.577	28.336	32.461	35.139	39.087	42.557	46.693	49.588
30	14.953	16.306	18.493	20.599	23.364	25.508	29.336	33.530	36.250	40.256	43.773	47.962	50.892

For larger values of d.f., the expression $x = \sqrt{2\chi^2} - \sqrt{2\,d.f. - 1}$ may be used as a normal deviate with unit standard error.

This table is taken by consent from *Statistical Methods for Research Workers*, by R. A. Fisher, published at 15/ by Oliver and Boyd, Edinburgh. Attention is drawn to the larger collection in *Statistical Tables* by R. A. Fisher and F. Yates, published at 12/6 by Oliver and Boyd, Edinburgh.

ɔlies.   For example, if $x = -.62$, the probability of exceeding the corresponding value of χ^2 is the same as the probability that a measure selected at random from a normal distribution will lie to the right of a point $-.62\,\sigma$ from the mean.   The probability in this case would be about .732.)

5. TESTS OF GOODNESS OF FIT

One important class of tests in which χ^2 is employed consists of tests of *goodness of fit,* meaning that they are tests of whether or not a table of observed frequencies "fits" or is consistent with a corresponding set of theoretical frequencies conforming to a given hypothesis.   The illustration on page 31 is of this type.   In that example, the observed value of χ^2 was 1.266, and the number of degrees of freedom involved was 2.   According to Table 2, for 2 *d.f.,* χ^2's as large as 1.266 would be exceeded in between 70 per cent and 50 per cent of all random samples if our hypothesis were true.   In other words, the observed value of 1.266 is just about what we would generally expect if the hypothesis were true. This of course does not establish that our hypothesis *is* true, but it certainly leaves us with no grounds for rejecting it as an hypothesis.

Suppose, however, that for the same sample we test the hypothesis for which the theoretical frequencies are 40, 25, and 25.   In this case we would have

Preference Category	f_o	f_t	$(f_o - f_t)$	$(f_o - f_t)^2$	$\dfrac{(f_o - f_t)^2}{f_t}$
A	27	40	-13	169	4.225
B	35	25	10	100	4.000
C	28	25	3	9	.360
					$8.585 = \chi^2$

From Table 2 we see that, for 2 *d.f.,* values of χ^2 as large as 8.585 would in the long run be found in less than 2 per cent of all random samples.   In other words, if our hypothesis were true, we could expect only once or twice in a hundred to find a sample which diverged as far from expectation as the sample we have. Hence, we must conclude, either that the hypothesis is true and that a very improbable event has occurred, or that the hypothesis is false (assuming that our sample is truly random). Unless we were being very conservative, then, we would probably feel justified in rejecting this hypothesis.

A procedure similar to that already described may be used to test the hypothesis that the frequency distribution of some continuous variable has a given form of distribution for a given population. Suppose, for example, that we wish to test the hypothesis that the scores on a certain psychological examination are normally distributed for a certain population of school children. Suppose we have taken a random sample of 332 cases from this population, and find that the scores are distributed as follows:

Scores	Frequency
150–159	1
140–149	2
130–139	6
120–129	10
110–119	20
100–109	30
90–99	23
80–89	35
70–79	51
60–69	40
50–59	45
40–49	35
30–39	21
20–29	7
10–19	5
0–9	1

$$N = 332$$
$$M = 73.54$$
$$S.D. = 28.07$$

Since we are interested in the *form* of distribution only, and not in the exact value of the true mean or true standard deviation, we will set up our theoretical frequencies so that they conform to the mean and $S.D.$ of the sample. In other words, our theoretical distribution must be normal, and have a mean of 73.54 and an $S.D.$ of 28.07. How these theoretical frequencies may be obtained may be illustrated in the case of the interval 100–109. The upper limit of this interval is 109.5, which is 1.281 $S.D.$ from the mean; the lower limit (99.5) is .925 $S.D.$ from the mean. Hence, according to the normal probability integral table,[1] we would expect, in a normal distribution, to find $39.99 - 32.25 = 7.74$ per cent of the cases in this interval. Since the total number of cases is 332, the theoretical frequency for the interval is $332 \times .0774 = 25.70$. The theoretical frequencies for each of the intervals is given in the table below. It will be noted that the three original upper intervals have been combined into one, as well as the three original lower intervals. This is because the χ^2 test should not be applied to a table in which any frequency is very small, and we combined these intervals to avoid such small frequencies. The steps in the computation of χ^2 are indicated in the table below.

Scores	f_o	f_t		$\dfrac{(f_o - f_t)^2}{f_t}$
130 and above	9	7.67	(+)	.2306
120–129	10	9.20	(+)	.0696
110–119	20	16.37	(+)	.8049
100–109	30	25.70	(+)	.7195
90–99	23	35.56	(−)	4.4363
80–89	35	43.62	(−)	1.7034
70–79	51	46.91	(+)	.3566
60–69	40	44.55	(−)	.4647
50–59	45	37.35	(+)	1.5669
40–49	35	27.72	(+)	1.9119
30–39	21	17.99	(+)	.5036
29 and below	13	19.36	(−)	2.0893
				$14.8573 = \chi^2$

[1] A table appropriate to this purpose may be found in any introductory text in statistics. The table (Table 17) given in the Appendix to this book is not designed for this purpose, since it is to be entered with the probability to find the corresponding deviation, and also because the probability is derived from the *sum* of the areas in corresponding segments of *both* tails of the distribution.

Now, before we may evaluate the observed X^2, we must determine the number of degrees of freedom. If the theoretical frequencies had been determined independently of the observed frequencies, subject only to the restriction that their sum be 332, we would have 11 degrees of freedom — one less than the number of intervals. In this case, however, we have imposed the additional restrictions that the mean of the theoretical distribution be 73.54 and that its *S.D.* be 28.07. In such instances, we follow the rule that *the number of degrees of freedom is reduced by one for each constant that has been derived from the observed frequencies.* Since two constants (the *M* and *S.D.*) have been derived in this case, the number of degrees of freedom is 11–2 or 9.

In Table 2, we see that for 9 degrees of freedom, X^2 exceeds 14.86 just slightly less than 10 per cent of the time. We hardly have an adequate basis, therefore, for rejecting the hypothesis of normality, although the results certainly do not give us added confidence in that hypothesis.

It has been previously noted that one limitation of X^2 as an index of divergence is that it does not take into consideration the *signs* of the individual deviations. This limitation is particularly serious in a test of the type just illustrated. In the preceding table, the signs in parentheses following the theoretical frequencies indicate the direction of the differences between the observed and theoretical frequencies. We note that there is a strong tendency for the outlying deviations to be positive and for those near the middle to be negative. In other words, the observed distribution shows a marked tendency to be "flatter" or less peaked than a normal distribution. This pattern of signs, which is ignored in the X^2 test, constitutes strong evidence that the sample was not drawn from a normal population, and it is probable that if we had applied some more efficient test [1] of goodness of fit that takes these signs into consideration, we could quite confidently have rejected the hypothesis of normality. (Several actual instances in which the

[1] See R. A. Fisher, *Statistical Methods*, Chapter III, Section 14.

x^2 test proved unsatisfactory for this reason are presented in Table 10, page 138.)

6. TESTS OF INDEPENDENCE

Another important class of tests involving x^2 consists of *tests of independence*, meaning that they are tests of the hypothesis that two variables or attributes are *unrelated*. The simplest case is that in which each classification is dichotomous, or in which there are only two categories for each variable. For example, we might wish to know if there is any significant difference in the performance of boys and girls on certain items in a general science examination. Suppose that, in a random sample of 150 pupils, consisting of 80 boys and 70 girls, 56 of the boys respond correctly to a given item, while only 34 of the girls respond correctly. These facts may be arranged in a table, as follows (the numbers in parentheses will be explained later):

	Right	Wrong	
Boys	56 (48)	24 (32)	80
Girls	34 (42)	36 (28)	70
	90	60	150

The hypothesis we wish to test is that there is no relationship between sex and performance on this item, or that in the population at large equal proportions of boys and girls would respond correctly to the item. Since we are not interested in the true proportions, but only in whether or not they are independent, we must make our theoretical frequencies conform to the observed marginal totals. We note that $\frac{90}{150}$ of the total sample made the correct response, hence the observed frequencies would have agreed exactly with our hypothesis if $\frac{90}{150}$ of both the boys and girls had made the correct response, that is, if $\frac{90}{150} \times 80 = 48$ boys and $\frac{90}{150} \times 70 = 42$ girls had responded correctly. This would leave 32 boys and 28 girls in the column of incorrect responses. These theoretical frequencies are given in parentheses in the table above. It may be noted that the theoretical frequency in each cell is equal to the product of the corresponding marginal totals divided by the grand total. Only one need be thus computed, however, since the others may be obtained by subtraction from the marginal totals. It may be noted also that the difference $(f_o - f_t)$ between observed and theoretical frequencies is the same (8) for each cell. The value of X^2 is then

$$\frac{8^2}{48} + \frac{8^2}{32} + \frac{8^2}{42} + \frac{8^2}{28} = 7.14$$

We have already noted that there is only one degree of freedom in a 2×2 table when the restriction is imposed that the cell frequencies in each row and column add up to fixed totals. In Table 2, for 1 $d.f.$, we note that X^2 will exceed 7.14 less than 1 per cent of the time. Hence, in this case we can reject the hypothesis of independence with a very high degree of confidence.

It should be clearly understood that while this test may reveal that there is some relationship between the traits involved, it does not indicate the *degree* of relationship. That is, a larger X^2 in another table (or a correspondingly lower probability that it is due to chance) would not necessaily mean a higher relationship, but only that we may more confidently assert that *some* relationship exists.

Tests of independence may similarly be applied to any contingency table, regardless of the numbers of rows and columns. In any case, the theoretical frequency in each cell is equal to the product of the corresponding row and column totals divided by the grand total, and the number of degrees of freedom is the product of one less than the number of rows and one less than the number of columns. It might be well to consider one illustration of this type. Suppose we wish to know if there is any relationship between the letter grades given pupils in high-school physics and the number of courses in high-school mathematics previously taken by the pupils. Suppose we classify the pupils into 3 groups as to numbers of courses: those having had one course or less, those having had two courses, and those who have had three or more. For a sample of 1645, the contingency table for "grades" and "courses" might then be as follows:

Courses	Grades					
	A	B	C	D	Fd	
3 or more	36 (27.23)	76 (66.17)	171 (158.94)	55 (75.96)	12 (21.70)	350
2	73 (67.85)	165 (164.86)	377 (395.98)	206 (189.24)	51 (54.07)	872
1 or less	19 (32.91)	70 (79.97)	199 (192.09)	96 (91.80)	39 (26.23)	423
	128	311	747	357	102	1645

The theoretical frequency in the upper left-hand cell, for example, is $350 \times 128/1645 = 27.23$, and the remaining theoretical frequencies are similarly computed. The value of χ^2 is therefore
$$(36 - 27.23)^2/27.23 + (76 - 66.17)^2/66.17 + \ldots$$
$$+ (73 - 67.85)^2/67.85 + \ldots + (19 - 32.91)^2/32.91 + \ldots$$
$$+ (39 - 26.23)^2/26.23 = 32.0589$$
For 8 $d.f.$, this value of χ^2 is exceeded much less than 1 per cent of the time under a true hypothesis. Hence, we may confidently reject the hypothesis that there is no relation between the number of mathematics courses taken by high-school students and their subsequent grades in high-school physics.

7. TESTS OF HOMOGENEITY

Tests of independence may sometimes be considered, from another point of view, as tests of *homogeneity*. The example on page

41, for instance, might be considered as involving a test of the hypothesis that the two sexes are *homogeneous* (that is, *alike*) in their responses to the given test item. The following example may be more representative of tests of homogeneity in educational research. In a study of the difficulty of the items in an algebra examination, it was found that the per cent of correct responses for certain items varied considerably from school to school. The question then arose of whether these variations were larger than could be attributed to chance, or were indicative of real differences in the difficulty of the items from school to school. In other words, were the schools fundamentally homogeneous with reference to pupil performance on these items? For one of the items, the numbers of correct and incorrect responses in 10 schools are presented in the table below.

School Number	Number Correct (R)	Number Wrong (W)	Total (T)	R^2/T
1	5	15	20	1.2500
2	20	23	43	9.3023
3	32	62	94	10.8936
4	23	13	36	14.6944
5	18	41	59	5.4915
6	45	62	107	18.9252
7	9	19	28	2.8929
8	34	42	76	15.2105
9	11	31	42	2.8810
10	16	65	81	3.1605
Totals	213	373	586	84.7019

$$p = \frac{213}{586} = .36348; \quad q = .63652; \quad pq = .23136$$

$$x^2 = \frac{1}{.23136}(84.7019 - 213 \times .36348) = 31.47$$

The method of computing X^2 which has been employed in this table is the exact algebraic equivalent of the method described in the preceding section, but takes less time. For data that have been arranged in 2 columns (in this case the R and W columns) the steps in this method of computation are as follows (the results for the example are given in brackets under each step):

(1) For each row separately, square the first frequency and divide by the sum of the two frequencies.

[For first row: $5^2/(5 + 15) = R^2/T = 1.2500$]

(2) Add these quotients for all rows.

[84.7019]

(3) Divide the first column total by the grand total.   Call this result p.

[$p = 213/586 = .36348$]

(4) Find $q = 1 - p$, and compute pq.

[$q = 1 - .36348 = .63652$; $pq = .23136$]

(5) Multiply the first column total by p, and subtract this product from the sum obtained in step (2).

[$84.7019 - 213 \times .36348 = 7.2805$]

(6) Divide the result of step (5) by pq to get X^2.

[$X^2 = 7.2805/.23136 = 31.47$]

If desired, the computations may be based on the second column rather than the first, that is, "second" may be substituted for "first" in steps (1), (3), and (5). It will be apparent from step (1) that the computation will be more convenient if based on the column containing the smaller frequencies. It is desirable, when using this method, to carry the results of step (1) to at least three decimal places, and those of steps (3) to (5) to at least five. This method of computation may of course be applied only when one of the classifications contains only two classes. In tests of homogeneity involving several classes in each classification, the method of computation described in the preceding section must be applied.

As in any test of independence, the number of degrees of freedom in the contingency table is one less than the number of rows times one less than the number of columns. In this case, there are $9 \times 1 = 9$ d.f. In Table 2 we see that, for 9 d.f., the observed value of X^2 goes far beyond the 1 per cent point (21.666). Hence we may be practically certain that these schools are not homogeneous in responses to this item, or that there are real differences in the difficulty of the item from school to school.

Incidentally, the data just considered are fairly representative of those that would be found for most items in most school examinations intended for widespread use.   It may be worth while, therefore, to draw attention to certain important implications of these facts.   We may note, in the example, that the per cent of correct responses in the entire sample was 36.35.   Since these schools are not homogeneous, it follows that we may not consider the pupils involved as a random sample of pupils from any population, and may therefore not apply the formula for the standard error of a percentage $\left(\sigma_{x\%} = \sqrt{\dfrac{x(100 - x)}{N}} \right)$ to describe the reliability of this percentage.   It means also that, in preliminary try-outs for difficulty of items intended for use in standardized tests, the important consideration is not the number of pupils involved in the try-out, but the number of *schools* represented.

8. COMBINING PROBABILITIES FROM INDEPENDENT
TESTS OF SIGNIFICANCE

Suppose that three investigators have each conducted an independent experiment to determine the relative effectiveness of the same two methods of instruction, and that each has drawn his samples at random from the same population.   Suppose that each has used a different criterion test, and that it is therefore impossible to throw all results for each method into a single distribution for the purpose of a single combined comparison.   The first investigator finds that, under the null hypothesis, the chances are only 8.2 in 100 of getting a chance difference as large as that he obtained; i.e. the probability is .082.   The corresponding probabilities for the second and third investigators are .115 and .060 respectively.   None has found a "significant" difference, but all observed differences favor the same method.   Are the collective results significant of a real difference in favor of this method?

This problem may be solved by thinking of each of these probabilities as corresponding to a given value of X^2.   It is known that the sum of a number of independent values of X^2 is itself distributed as X^2, with a number of degrees of freedom equal to the sum of those for the separate χ^2's. It also happens that, for 2 $d.f.$, the value of χ^2 which is exceeded in any given proportion (p) of cases is equal to $- 2 \log_e p$. Hence we may think of any probability as corresponding to a χ^2 whose value is $- 2 \log_e p$ (for 2 $d.f.$). We can thus compute a χ^2 for each probability, add these χ^2's to secure a composite χ^2, and then evaluate this composite χ^2 in the ordinary manner, its $d.f.$ being twice the number of probabilities combined.

The rules for combining a number of probabilities are therefore as follows (these rules are for use with the more accessible tables of common logarithms):

(1) Find the common logarithm of each probability.
(2) Add these logarithms and change the sign of the result.
(3) Multiply this result by 4.60517 (= 2 × 2.302585) to get the composite χ^2. (The number 2.302585 is the "modulus constant" which transforms a common logarithm to a natural logarithm).
(4) The number of $d.f.$ for the composite χ^2 is twice the number of probabilities involved.

For the example already given, the computation is as follows:

p	$\log_{10} p$
.082	8.91381–10
.115	9.06070–10
.060	8.77815–10
	26.75266–30 = − 3.24734

$$\chi^2 = 4.60517 \times 3.24734 = 14.95$$

For 6 $d.f.$, this value of χ^2 is exceeded between 5 per cent and 2 per cent of the time. Hence the collective results are significant at the 5 per cent level, whereas no individual probability reached that level of significance.

CHAPTER III

SMALL SAMPLE ERROR THEORY

1. AN IMPROVED ESTIMATE OF THE TRUE STANDARD DEVIATION

WE HAVE noted earlier (page 19) that the standard deviations of small random samples tend to be smaller than the standard deviation of the population, and that this is one of the reasons why it is invalid to use the observed standard deviation of a small sample in the formula for the standard error of the mean. We shall now consider the proof of this statement, and at the same time derive a formula for securing an unbiased estimate of the true standard deviation from the data for a single random sample.

It will be convenient in this discussion to deal with the square of the standard deviation, rather than with the standard deviation itself. The square of the standard deviation of any distribution is known as the *variance* of the distribution. Accordingly, if d represents the deviation of an individual measure from the mean of a sample, and n represents the number of measures, the variance of the sample is given by

$$\sigma^2 = \frac{\Sigma\, d^2}{n}. \tag{3}$$

Now suppose that we take r random samples of n cases each from a population whose true mean is M. We shall call the first sample drawn sample 1, and let M_1 represent its mean. We shall also let d_1' represent the deviation from M_1 of any measure in sample 1, and let d_1 represent the deviation of the same measure from the population mean M. It then follows that

$$d_1' = d_1 + (M - M_1).$$

Squaring both sides of this equality, we have

$$d_1'^2 = d_1^2 + 2\, d_1(M - M_1) + (M - M_1)^2.$$

If we now sum such expressions for all of the n measures in sample 1, we get

$$\Sigma\, d_1'^2 = \Sigma\, d_1^2 + 2(M - M_1)\Sigma\, d_1 + n(M - M_1)^2,$$

which, since $\Sigma\, d_{\scriptscriptstyle \mathrm{I}} = \mathrm{o}$, reduces, after transposition of terms and change of signs, to

$$\Sigma\, d_{\scriptscriptstyle \mathrm{I}}^2 = \Sigma\, d_{\scriptscriptstyle \mathrm{I}}'^2 - n(M - M_{\scriptscriptstyle \mathrm{I}})^2.$$

We may of course write a similar expression for each of our r samples. These expressions may be arranged in column order for convenience in summing, as follows:

$$\Sigma\, d_{\scriptscriptstyle \mathrm{I}}^2 = \Sigma\, d_{\scriptscriptstyle \mathrm{I}}'^2 - n(M - M_{\scriptscriptstyle \mathrm{I}})^2$$

$$\Sigma\, d_{2}^2 = \Sigma\, d_{2}'^2 - n(M - M_{2})^2$$

$$\Sigma\, d_{3}^2 = \Sigma\, d_{3}'^2 - n(M - M_{3})^2 \qquad (4)$$

$$\cdot \qquad \cdot \qquad \cdot$$
$$\cdot \qquad \cdot \qquad \cdot$$
$$\cdot \qquad \cdot \qquad \cdot$$

$$\Sigma\, d_{r}^2 = \Sigma\, d_{r}'^2 - n(M - M_{r})^2$$

The sum of the left-hand terms in (4) may be written as $\Sigma\,(\Sigma\, d^2)$, meaning the sum of the sums of squared deviations from the sample means. The sum of the first of the right-hand terms would be the grand total of the squared deviations from the population mean for all of the $nr = N$ measures in all of the samples. This grand total may be written simply as $\Sigma\, d'^2$, with the understanding that the summation is over all samples. The sum of the last terms in (4) may similarly be written as $n\,\Sigma(M - M_p)^2$, in which the subscript p is a general term referring to any sample, and in which the summation is for all values of p from I to r. Under this notation, we may write the sum of the expressions in (4) as

$$\Sigma(\Sigma\, d^2) = \Sigma\, d'^2 - n\,\Sigma(M - M_p)^2, \qquad (5)$$

which, upon dividing through by $N = nr$, leads to

$$\frac{\Sigma(\Sigma\, d^2)}{rn} = \frac{\Sigma\, d'^2}{N} - \frac{n\,\Sigma(M - M_p)^2}{nr},$$

or to

$$\frac{\mathrm{I}}{r}\Sigma\!\left(\frac{\Sigma\, d^2}{n}\right) = \frac{\Sigma\, d'^2}{N} - \frac{\Sigma(M - M_p)^2}{r}. \qquad (6)$$

We may now note that the left-hand term of (6) is the mean value of $\left(\dfrac{\Sigma d^2}{n}\right)$ for all r samples. Let us now let r (and hence N as well) become infinitely large. The left-hand term is still the mean value of $\overline{\left(\dfrac{\Sigma d^2}{n}\right)}$ for all samples, but the first right-hand term becomes the true variance of the population, or σ^2_{pop}. The second right-hand term becomes the variance of the sampling distribution of observed means, i.e., the square of the standard error of an observed mean, or σ^2_M. But we know that

$$\sigma^2_M = \frac{\sigma^2_{pop}}{n}.$$

Hence, (6) may be written as

$$\text{Mean value of } \left(\frac{\Sigma d^2}{n}\right) = \sigma^2_{pop} - \frac{1}{n}\sigma^2_{pop} = \frac{n-1}{n}\sigma^2_{pop}.$$

It is now apparent from this equation that the mean value of $\left(\dfrac{\Sigma d^2}{n}\right)$, that is, the mean of the sample variances, is less than the population variance, since $(n-1)/n$ is of course less than unity. This is but another way of saying that the variance of a sample tends to be less than the variance of the population, which is what we set out to prove. Furthermore, by multiplying through in this equation by $n/(n-1)$, we get

$$\text{Mean value of } \left(\frac{\Sigma d^2}{n-1}\right) = \sigma^2_{pop}.$$

This means that for a single random sample $\dfrac{\Sigma d^2}{n-1}$ is an *unbiased* estimate of the population variance, since in the long run its mean value is exactly equal to the true variance. It is on this basis, then, that we are able to write the formula

$$\text{est'd } \sigma^2_{pop} = \frac{\Sigma d^2}{n-1}. \tag{7}$$

2. THE SAMPLING DISTRIBUTION OF "*t*"

We have observed (p. 19) that the ratio $\dfrac{M_0 - M_T}{\text{est'd } \sigma_M}$, is not normally distributed for small samples, and that therefore we may not use the normal probability integral table to evaluate the significance of this ratio when the sample is small. This is true even though we get an improved estimate of σ_M by substituting $\sqrt{\dfrac{\Sigma d^2}{n-1}}$, rather than $\sqrt{\dfrac{\Sigma d^2}{n}}$, for the σ_{pop} in the formula for the standard error, as follows:

$$\text{est'd } \sigma_M = \frac{\sqrt{\dfrac{\Sigma d^2}{n-1}}}{\sqrt{n}} = \sqrt{\frac{\Sigma d^2}{n(n-1)}} \tag{8}$$

If, then, we are to use the ratio $\dfrac{M_0 - M_H}{\text{est'd } \sigma_M}$ in testing the hypothesis that the true mean has a value M_H, we must know the exact sampling distribution of this ratio. This ratio, using the improved estimate of σ_M, is known as the "*t*" statistic. That is,

$$t = \frac{M_0 - M_H}{\sqrt{\dfrac{\Sigma d^2}{n(n-1)}}} \tag{9}$$

An English statistician, writing under the pen name of "Student," has shown that for random samples drawn from normal populations, the sampling distribution of *t* is given by

$$y = \frac{y_0}{\left(1 + \dfrac{t^2}{n-1}\right)^{\frac{n}{2}}}$$

in which *n* is the number of cases in the sample. We may note that the denominator of this expression has its minimum value when $t = 0$, and that therefore the curve has its maximum ordinate at this point. We note also that the ordinate *y* is the same for a given value of t whether t is positive or negative and that the distribution is therefore symmetrical.   Finally, as t increases the ordinate y decreases, and the curve is asymptotic to the base line.   The curve is much like the normal curve except that it is less peaked for small values of n, as we have noted previously.   For large values of n, the distribution approaches the form of the normal distribution.

A different distribution of t, of course, will be found for each value of n, or for each number of degrees of freedom.   The number of degrees of freedom for any value of t is one less than the number of cases involved, that is, $d.f. = n - 1$.   Fisher has prepared a table [1] showing, for each value of $d.f.$ from 1 to 30, what absolute value of t would be exceeded in 1 per cent of all samples, as well as in 2 per cent, 5 per cent, ... 90 per cent of all such samples. This table is reproduced on page 53.

The table for t may be read in the same manner as the table for χ^2.   (The statistic t is a measure of the divergence of fact from hypothesis, just as is χ^2, although a different type of hypothesis is involved.)   For example, for 3 $d.f.$ (that is, for samples of 4 cases each), t exceeds the value .137 in 90 per cent of all random samples of this size if the hypothesis is true.   For the same size sample, t exceeds .277 in 80 per cent of such samples, or exceeds 4.541 in 2 per cent, etc.   It should be remembered that the table tells what *absolute* value of t (either positive or negative) is exceeded in a given per cent of random samples.   Thus, while for a true hypothesis t has an absolute value greater than 1.729 in 10 per cent of all samples of 20 ($d.f. = 19$), its value will exceed $+ 1.729$ just 5 per cent of the time, or lie below $- 1.729$ just 5 per cent of the time for samples of this size.

It will be noted, in the last column of Table 3, that the value of t demanded for a given level of significance (the 1 per cent level)

[1] A somewhat different form of the table is given in Yule and Kendall, Appendix, Table 5, showing in what proportion of all samples of a given size (from $\nu = 1$ to $\nu = 20$) the value of t will be *less* than a given positive value (in tenths from 0 to 6). The symbol (nu) used in this table represents the degrees of freedom.   In the table on page 166 of Fisher, *Statistical Methods for Research Workers*, a small n is used for $d.f.$

TABLE 3 — TABLE OF t

d.f.	90%	80%	70%	60%	50%	40%	30%	20%	10%	5%	2%	1%
1	.158	.325	.510	.727	1.000	1.376	1.963	3.078	6.314	12.706	31.821	63.657
2	.142	.289	.445	.617	.816	1.061	1.386	1.886	2.920	4.303	6.965	9.925
3	.137	.277	.424	.584	.765	.978	1.250	1.638	2.353	3.182	4.541	5.841
4	.134	.271	.414	.569	.741	.941	1.190	1.533	2.132	2.776	3.747	4.604
5	.132	.267	.408	.559	.727	.920	1.156	1.476	2.015	2.571	3.365	4.032
6	.131	.265	.404	.553	.718	.906	1.134	1.440	1.943	2.447	3.143	3.707
7	.130	.263	.402	.549	.711	.896	1.119	1.415	1.895	2.365	2.998	3.499
8	.130	.262	.399	.546	.706	.889	1.110	1.397	1.860	2.306	2.896	3.355
9	.129	.261	.398	.543	.703	.883	1.100	1.383	1.833	2.262	2.821	3.250
10	.129	.260	.397	.542	.700	.879	1.093	1.372	1.812	2.228	2.764	3.169
11	.129	.260	.396	.540	.697	.876	1.088	1.363	1.796	2.201	2.718	3.106
12	.128	.259	.395	.539	.695	.873	1.083	1.356	1.782	2.179	2.681	3.055
13	.128	.259	.394	.538	.694	.870	1.079	1.350	1.771	2.160	2.650	3.012
14	.128	.258	.393	.537	.692	.868	1.076	1.345	1.761	2.145	2.624	2.977
15	.128	.258	.393	.536	.691	.866	1.074	1.341	1.753	2.131	2.602	2.947
16	.128	.258	.392	.535	.690	.865	1.071	1.337	1.746	2.120	2.583	2.921
17	.128	.257	.392	.534	.689	.863	1.069	1.333	1.740	2.110	2.567	2.898
18	.127	.257	.392	.534	.688	.862	1.067	1.330	1.734	2.101	2.552	2.878
19	.127	.257	.391	.533	.688	.861	1.066	1.328	1.729	2.093	2.539	2.861
20	.127	.257	.391	.533	.687	.860	1.064	1.325	1.725	2.086	2.528	2.845
21	.127	.257	.391	.532	.686	.859	1.063	1.323	1.721	2.080	2.518	2.831
22	.127	.256	.390	.532	.686	.858	1.061	1.321	1.717	2.074	2.508	2.819
23	.127	.256	.390	.532	.685	.858	1.060	1.319	1.714	2.069	2.500	2.807
24	.127	.256	.390	.531	.685	.857	1.059	1.318	1.711	2.064	2.492	2.797
25	.127	.256	.390	.531	.684	.856	1.058	1.316	1.708	2.060	2.485	2.787
26	.127	.256	.390	.531	.684	.856	1.058	1.315	1.706	2.056	2.479	2.779
27	.127	.256	.389	.531	.684	.855	1.057	1.314	1.703	2.052	2.473	2.771
28	.127	.256	.389	.530	.683	.855	1.056	1.313	1.701	2.048	2.467	2.763
29	.127	.256	.389	.530	.683	.854	1.055	1.311	1.699	2.045	2.462	2.756
30	.127	.256	.389	.530	.683	.854	1.055	1.310	1.697	2.042	2.457	2.750
∞	.12566	.25335	.38532	.52440	.67449	.84162	1.03643	1.28155	1.64485	1.95996	2.32634	2.57582

This table is taken by consent from *Statistical Methods for Research Workers*, by R. A. Fisher, published at 15/ by Oliver and Boyd, Edinburgh. Attention is drawn to the larger collection in *Statistical Tables* by R. A. Fisher and F. Yates, published at 12/6 by Oliver and Boyd, Edinburgh.

becomes larger as the sample becomes smaller. In samples of 31 cases ($d.f.$ = 30), for example, t must exceed 2.750 to be significant at the 1 per cent level, but for a sample of 6 cases t must exceed 4.032 to be equally significant. This is consistent with the fact that as the sample becomes smaller, the estimated σ_M in the denominator of t, and hence t itself, will become more variable. This does not mean that the sampling distribution of t is inexact for small samples. On the contrary, the sampling distribution of t is described exactly in terms of t itself, and does not require any estimate of a population parameter. While the denominator in t may be considered as an estimate of the standard error of the mean, t itself must be considered as a *statistic* computed entirely from the data given by the sample.

3. THE SIGNIFICANCE OF THE MEAN OF A SMALL SAMPLE

We may now consider a concrete illustration of the use of the t-test. Suppose we have selected a random sample of 10 girls from a certain population of elementary school girls, and have found their weights to be 60, 68, 54, 59, 67, 62, 52, 59, 56, and 63 pounds. The mean of these weights is 60. Now suppose we have some exact hypothesis concerning the value of the true mean, such that the true mean is 56 pounds. With reference to this value of M_H, the value of t is

$$t = \frac{M_0 - M_H}{\sqrt{\dfrac{\Sigma d^2}{n(n-1)}}} = \frac{60 - 56}{\sqrt{\dfrac{244}{10(10-1)}}} = \frac{4}{1.65} = 2.4$$

Turning now to Table 3 we see that, if our hypothesis is true, an absolute value of t greater than 2.4 would be found in between 5 per cent and 2 per cent of random samples of this size ($d.f.$ = 9). Hence we must conclude, either that our hypothesis is true and that something has happened in our one sample that happens less than once in 20 times, or that our hypothesis is false. Whether or not we reject the hypothesis, then, depends upon the level of significance that we have arbitrarily decided to require. This t is significant at the 5 per cent level, but not at the 2 per cent level.

It may be well to emphasize certain features of the logic involved in this *t*-test.   In the preceding example, we found that if the true mean were 56, the chances would be less than 5 in 100 of getting a *t* as large as 2.4 (in absolute value) in a random sample of this size.   If our assumptions of random sampling and a normal population are satisfied, this is an *exact* statement, involving no estimates or approximations whatever.   This, however, does not mean that if the true mean were 56 the chances would be less than 5 in 100 of getting an obtained mean as high as 60 or as low as 52. Depending upon the population σ, these chances might be either greater or less than 5 in 100.   Nevertheless, if *t* is significant at the 1 per cent level, we can be highly *confident* that our hypothesis concerning the true mean is false.

The *t*-test may of course be employed to test any other exact hypothesis as to the value of the true mean, and it will often be desirable to establish the limiting values outside of which any such hypothesis may be rejected with a given degree of confidence. Suppose, for example, that we wished to determine the highest and lowest hypothetical values of the true mean of the population of elementary school girls which would be admissible at the 1 per cent level.   To do this, we would find the value of *t*, in the last column of Table 3, for 9 *d.f.*   We would then substitute this value and our estimate of the standard error of the mean in the formula for *t*, and solve for $M_O - M_H$.

The computation in this case is as follows:

$$t = \frac{M_O - M_H}{\text{est'd } \sigma_M}; \qquad 3.250 = \frac{M_O - M_H}{1.65}$$

$$M_O - M_H = 1.65 \times 3.25 = 5.36$$

Hence the limiting values of the true mean are 60 $\pm$ 5.36, or 54.64 and 65.36.   We may then, at the 1 per cent level of confidence, reject any hypothesis that the true mean lies beyond these limits, or, otherwise stated, we may be "practically certain" that the true mean is within these limits.

4. THE SIGNIFICANCE OF A DIFFERENCE IN THE MEANS OF INDEPENDENT SMALL SAMPLES

The t-test of the significance of a difference between the means of two small samples is of much the same character as that just described. The hypothesis we really wish to test is that the two samples were drawn at random from populations whose means are equal, that is, we may not be interested in other characteristics of the population, such as the standard deviation. We cannot use the t-test to test an hypothesis concerned only with the difference in the population means, since if the samples are drawn from populations whose means are equal but whose variances differ, the t's computed from a series of pairs of samples like these would not be distributed exactly as is indicated by the t-table. However, we can use it to test the hypothesis that both samples were drawn at random from *identical* normal populations, i.e., from normal populations with the same mean and same standard deviation.[1] This, of course, is equivalent to saying that they were drawn from the *same* population, since populations with identical distributions may be considered as constituting a single population.

If this hypothesis be true, then, according to the reasoning of the preceding sections, the best estimate of σ_{pop} that we can make from the first sample alone is

$$\text{est'd } \sigma_{pop} = \sqrt{\frac{\Sigma d_1^2}{n_1 - 1}}$$

in which d_1 represents a deviation from the mean (M_1) of the first sample, and n_1 is the number of cases. A similar estimate may of course be made from the second sample. However, a still better estimate[2] of σ_{pop} may be secured by considering both samples together. This best estimate is

$$\text{est'd } \sigma_{pop} = \sqrt{\frac{\Sigma d_1^2 + \Sigma d_2^2}{n_1 + n_2 - 2}}$$

[1] It has been suggested that the t-test may also be considered as a test of the hypothesis that the true means are equal, on the *further* hypothesis that the true variances are equal. We may, if we wish, use the test later described in Section 6, page 60, to determine whether or not the latter hypothesis (of equal variances) is tenable.

[2] The proof of this, which is similar to that for (7), is left as an exercise for the student.

Using this estimate of σ_{pop}, our best estimate of the standard error of M_1 is

$$\text{est'd } \sigma_{M_1} = \frac{\text{est'd } \sigma_{pop}}{\sqrt{n_1}} = \sqrt{\frac{\Sigma d_1^2 + \Sigma d_2^2}{n_1 + n_2 - 2}} \cdot \sqrt{\frac{1}{n_1}}$$

The estimated standard error of M_2 would be similarly obtained. Now, since the standard error of a difference between two independent measures is the square root of the sum of the squares of their respective standard errors ($\sigma_{diff} = \sqrt{\sigma_1^2 + \sigma_2^2}$), it follows that our best estimate of the standard error of the difference between M_1 and M_2 is

$$\text{est'd } \sigma_{M_1 - M_2} = \sqrt{\left(\frac{\Sigma d_1^2 + \Sigma d_2^2}{n_1 + n_2 - 2}\right)\left(\frac{1}{n_1} + \frac{1}{n_2}\right)} \qquad (10)$$

Now t may be defined as

$$t = \frac{M_1 - M_2}{\text{est'd } \sigma_{M_1 - M_2}}$$

or

$$t = \frac{M_1 - M_2}{\sqrt{\left(\frac{\Sigma d_1^2 + \Sigma d_2^2}{n_1 + n_2 - 2}\right)\left(\frac{1}{n_1} + \frac{1}{n_2}\right)}} \qquad (11)$$

for which the number of degrees of freedom is $d.f. = n_1 + n_2 - 2$.

To illustrate the t-test as applied to a difference, suppose we have two random samples, each from a different population, and that the individual measures for these samples are as follows:

Sample 1: 43, 37, 50, 23, 32, 31   ($n_1 = 6$)

Sample 2: 30, 24, 15, 42, 28, 19, 35, 7   ($n_2 = 8$)

The mean of the first sample is 36, and of the second is 25. The value of t is accordingly

$$t = \frac{36 - 25}{\sqrt{\left(\frac{456 + 884}{6 + 8 - 2}\right)\left(\frac{1}{6} + \frac{1}{8}\right)}} = \frac{11}{5.71} = 1.93$$

Now from Table 3 we find (in the row for $d.f. = 6 + 8 - 2 = 12$) that in a large number of pairs of samples like this a value of t as large as 1.93 would be found between 10 per cent and 5 per cent of the time. This value of t, then, fails to be significant at the 5 per cent level. If we were using conservative standards, therefore, we would not feel justified in rejecting the null hypothesis in this case.

It is important to remember the exact nature of the hypothesis that we have tested. When the value of t exceeds that required for a given level of significance we may, with a corresponding degree of confidence, reject the hypothesis that the samples were drawn at random from the *same* or identical populations. While this is equivalent to saying that the samples came from *different* populations, it is not equivalent to saying that the *means* of these populations necessarily differ. It is possible, though improbable, that the samples came from populations whose means are the same but whose standard deviations differ. In most applications this possibility need not concern us greatly, and we may generally be quite confident that the means do differ if t is highly significant. However, in case there is any doubt, it might be well to make a separate test of the hypothesis that the true variance is the same for both samples. A method of testing this hypothesis will be presented in section 6 following.

5. THE SIGNIFICANCE OF A DIFFERENCE IN THE MEANS OF RELATED MEASURES

Quite frequently, when selecting two samples for the purpose of evaluating the effect of a variation in a given factor, we may select the cases in *pairs*, such that the members of a pair are more likely to be similar than two cases independently selected. One of our samples is then made up of the first members of the pairs; the second sample is made up of the second members. For example, in a methods experiment, we may select pairs of pupils who have made equal scores on an intelligence test, and hence may expect them to be more nearly alike in achievement than randomly paired pupils. Again, we might sometimes have two measures for each pupil, one secured before and the other after a given "treatment," and may wish to know if the "treatment" has affected the mean status of the pupils.

In such cases, if the paired measures are correlated, we may find the difference for each pair and then, for this distribution of *differences*, we may determine whether or not the mean of the distribution (the mean difference) differs significantly from zero. Suppose, for example, in a methods experiment in which the pupils had been originally "matched" for intelligence, the final measures of achievement were as follows:

	ACHIEVEMENT SCORES		
Pair	Sample 1	Sample 2	Differences
1	20	16	+ 4
2	34	35	− 1
3	24	22	+ 2
4	37	29	+ 8
5	23	24	− 1
6	35	30	+ 5
7	30	27	+ 3
8	29	25	+ 4
Means	29.00	26.00	+ 3.00

The mean of the differences is 3.00. Hence, for $M_H = 0$, the value of t for the distribution of differences is

$$ t = \frac{M_0 - M_H}{\sqrt{\dfrac{\Sigma d^2}{n(n - 1)}}} = \frac{3.0 - 0}{\sqrt{\dfrac{64}{8(8 - 1)}}} = \frac{3.0}{1.07} = 2.80 $$

If our hypothesis were true, an absolute value of t this large would be found less than 5 per cent of the time ($d.f. = 7$). Hence, we may be reasonably confident that the observed difference is not due entirely to chance.

It is worth noting that had we considered the measures in this example as independent measures, and had applied the t-test described in the preceding section, we would have found a t of 1.01 (with 14 degrees of freedom), which would have made the difference seem far from significant.

6. THE SIGNIFICANCE OF A DIFFERENCE IN VARIABILITY FOR SMALL SAMPLES: THE "F" TEST

The significance of a difference in the standard deviations of two large samples is usually tested by comparing the observed difference with its standard error, computed as

$$\sigma_{\sigma_1 - \sigma_2} = \sqrt{\sigma_{\sigma_1}^2 + \sigma_{\sigma_2}^2}$$

in which the standard errors of the standard deviations are estimated as

$$\sigma_{\sigma_1} = \frac{\sigma_1}{\sqrt{2\,n_1}}, \text{ and } \sigma_{\sigma_2} = \frac{\sigma_2}{\sqrt{2\,n_2}}$$

This procedure breaks down for small samples, primarily because the standard deviations of small samples are not normally distributed. However, the significance of a difference in the standard deviations of two small samples may be tested in a manner similar to that employed with means. The hypothesis we wish to test is that the samples were drawn from equally variable populations. Rather than deal directly with the *difference* between the observed σ's, we will deal with the *ratio* between the corresponding estimates of the true *variances*. This "variance ratio" may be defined as

$$F = \frac{\sigma_1'^2}{\sigma_2'^2}$$

in which $\sigma_1'^2 = \dfrac{\Sigma\, d_1^2}{n_1 - 1}$ and $\sigma_2'^2 = \dfrac{\Sigma\, d_2^2}{n_2 - 1}$, or in which σ_1' and σ_2' are the *estimated* σ's of the populations sampled.

The ratio F is always taken so that the larger variance is in the numerator. The number of degrees of freedom for each variance is one less than the n on which it is based.

The test of significance which is based on this ratio is due to R. A. Fisher, who showed how the function z, defined as

$$z = \frac{1}{2} \log_e \frac{\sigma_1'^2}{\sigma_2'^2}$$

is distributed for pairs of random samples of various size combinations all drawn from the same population. Fisher prepared tables [1] showing, for various combinations of degrees of freedom, how large a value of z is exceeded in 5 per cent, 1 per cent, and 0.1 per cent of an infinite number of pairs of samples of the given size combination. These tables, however, are relatively inconvenient to use; to use them, we must find the logarithm of the variance ratio. To avoid this inconvenience, G. W. Snedecor computed the value of F corresponding to the value of z for each combination of degrees of freedom within a useful range, and prepared tables [2] for F similar to Fisher's tables for z.

Snedecor's table for F is reproduced on the following pages (Table 4). The columns in this table correspond to the number of degrees of freedom for the larger variance, the rows to that for the smaller variance. Within each cell of the table two values of F are given. The upper number in each pair is the value of F that would be exceeded in 5 per cent of an infinite number of pairs of random samples (with the given numbers of degrees of freedom) all drawn from the same population. The lower number in each pair is the value of F that would be exceeded 1 per cent of the time. The 5 per cent and 1 per cent points for combinations of degrees of freedom not given in the table may be secured by interpolation between those for the nearest combinations given.

To illustrate the use of this table, suppose that for a sample of 9 cases $\sigma_1'^2 = \dfrac{\Sigma d^2}{8} = 42.1$ and for a sample of 5 cases $\sigma_2'^2 = \dfrac{\Sigma d^2}{4} = 6.3$.

The value of F would then be $\dfrac{42.1}{6.3} = 6.68$.

In Table 4 we find, for $d.f._1 = 8$ and $d.f._2 = 4$, that an F of 6.04 would be exceeded in 5 per cent of all pairs of samples of this size

[1] R. A. Fisher, *Statistical Methods for Research Workers*, Sixth Edition, Table VI, pages 248–253, or *Statistical Tables*, by Fisher and Yates, pages 28–35. (The latter reference also contains tables for the variance ratio (F), and gives the 20 per cent and 0.1 per cent points, as well as the 5 per cent and 1 per cent.)

[2] G. W. Snedecor, *Statistical Methods*, Table 10.2, pp. 174–177.

TABLE 4 — TABLE I FOR F

(Upper numbers in the pairs are the 5 per cent points, lower or boldface numbers the 1 per cent points.)

Degrees of freedom for larger variance (d.f.1)

Degrees of freedom for smaller variance (d.f.2) — rows; n_2 at right.

d.f.2	1	2	3	4	5	6	7	8	9	10	11	12	14	16	20	24	30	40	50	75	100	200	500	∞
1	161 / 4,052	200 / 4,999	216 / 5,403	225 / 5,625	230 / 5,764	234 / 5,859	237 / 5,928	239 / 5,981	241 / 6,022	242 / 6,056	243 / 6,082	244 / 6,106	245 / 6,142	246 / 6,169	248 / 6,208	249 / 6,234	250 / 6,258	251 / 6,286	252 / 6,302	253 / 6,323	253 / 6,334	254 / 6,352	254 / 6,361	254 / 6,366
2	18.51 / 98.49	19.00 / 99.01	19.16 / 99.17	19.25 / 99.25	19.30 / 99.30	19.33 / 99.33	19.36 / 99.34	19.37 / 99.36	19.38 / 99.38	19.39 / 99.40	19.40 / 99.41	19.41 / 99.42	19.42 / 99.43	19.43 / 99.44	19.44 / 99.45	19.45 / 99.46	19.46 / 99.47	19.47 / 99.48	19.47 / 99.48	19.48 / 99.49	19.49 / 99.49	19.49 / 99.49	19.50 / 99.50	19.50 / 99.50
3	10.13 / 34.12	9.55 / 30.81	9.28 / 29.46	9.12 / 28.71	9.01 / 28.24	8.94 / 27.91	8.88 / 27.67	8.84 / 27.49	8.81 / 27.34	8.78 / 27.23	8.76 / 27.13	8.74 / 27.05	8.71 / 26.92	8.69 / 26.83	8.66 / 26.69	8.64 / 26.60	8.62 / 26.50	8.60 / 26.41	8.58 / 26.35	8.57 / 26.27	8.56 / 26.23	8.54 / 26.18	8.54 / 26.14	8.53 / 26.12
4	7.71 / 21.20	6.94 / 18.00	6.59 / 16.69	6.39 / 15.98	6.26 / 15.52	6.16 / 15.21	6.09 / 14.98	6.04 / 14.80	6.00 / 14.66	5.96 / 14.54	5.93 / 14.45	5.91 / 14.37	5.87 / 14.24	5.84 / 14.15	5.80 / 14.02	5.77 / 13.93	5.74 / 13.83	5.71 / 13.74	5.70 / 13.69	5.68 / 13.61	5.66 / 13.57	5.65 / 13.52	5.64 / 13.48	5.63 / 13.46
5	6.61 / 16.26	5.79 / 13.27	5.41 / 12.06	5.19 / 11.39	5.05 / 10.97	4.95 / 10.67	4.88 / 10.45	4.82 / 10.27	4.78 / 10.15	4.74 / 10.05	4.70 / 9.96	4.68 / 9.89	4.64 / 9.77	4.60 / 9.68	4.56 / 9.55	4.53 / 9.47	4.50 / 9.38	4.46 / 9.29	4.44 / 9.24	4.42 / 9.17	4.40 / 9.13	4.38 / 9.07	4.37 / 9.04	4.36 / 9.02
6	5.99 / 13.74	5.14 / 10.92	4.76 / 9.78	4.53 / 9.15	4.39 / 8.75	4.28 / 8.47	4.21 / 8.26	4.15 / 8.10	4.10 / 7.98	4.06 / 7.87	4.03 / 7.79	4.00 / 7.72	3.96 / 7.60	3.92 / 7.52	3.87 / 7.39	3.84 / 7.31	3.81 / 7.23	3.77 / 7.14	3.75 / 7.09	3.72 / 7.02	3.71 / 6.99	3.69 / 6.94	3.68 / 6.90	3.67 / 6.88
7	5.59 / 12.25	4.74 / 9.55	4.35 / 8.45	4.12 / 7.85	3.97 / 7.46	3.87 / 7.19	3.79 / 7.00	3.73 / 6.84	3.68 / 6.71	3.63 / 6.62	3.60 / 6.54	3.57 / 6.47	3.52 / 6.35	3.49 / 6.27	3.44 / 6.15	3.41 / 6.07	3.38 / 5.98	3.34 / 5.90	3.32 / 5.85	3.29 / 5.78	3.28 / 5.75	3.25 / 5.70	3.24 / 5.67	3.23 / 5.65
8	5.32 / 11.26	4.46 / 8.65	4.07 / 7.59	3.84 / 7.01	3.69 / 6.63	3.58 / 6.37	3.50 / 6.19	3.44 / 6.03	3.39 / 5.91	3.34 / 5.82	3.31 / 5.74	3.28 / 5.67	3.23 / 5.56	3.20 / 5.48	3.15 / 5.36	3.12 / 5.28	3.08 / 5.20	3.05 / 5.11	3.03 / 5.06	3.00 / 5.00	2.98 / 4.96	2.96 / 4.91	2.94 / 4.88	2.93 / 4.86
9	5.12 / 10.56	4.26 / 8.02	3.86 / 6.99	3.63 / 6.42	3.48 / 6.06	3.37 / 5.80	3.29 / 5.62	3.23 / 5.47	3.18 / 5.35	3.13 / 5.26	3.10 / 5.18	3.07 / 5.11	3.02 / 5.00	2.98 / 4.92	2.93 / 4.80	2.90 / 4.73	2.86 / 4.64	2.82 / 4.56	2.80 / 4.51	2.77 / 4.45	2.76 / 4.41	2.73 / 4.36	2.72 / 4.33	2.71 / 4.31
10	4.96 / 10.04	4.10 / 7.56	3.71 / 6.55	3.48 / 5.99	3.33 / 5.64	3.22 / 5.39	3.14 / 5.21	3.07 / 5.06	3.02 / 4.95	2.97 / 4.85	2.94 / 4.78	2.91 / 4.71	2.86 / 4.60	2.82 / 4.52	2.77 / 4.41	2.74 / 4.33	2.70 / 4.25	2.67 / 4.17	2.64 / 4.12	2.61 / 4.05	2.59 / 4.01	2.56 / 3.96	2.55 / 3.93	2.54 / 3.91
11	4.84 / 9.65	3.98 / 7.20	3.59 / 6.22	3.36 / 5.67	3.20 / 5.32	3.09 / 5.07	3.01 / 4.88	2.95 / 4.74	2.90 / 4.63	2.86 / 4.54	2.82 / 4.46	2.79 / 4.40	2.74 / 4.29	2.70 / 4.21	2.65 / 4.10	2.61 / 4.02	2.57 / 3.94	2.53 / 3.86	2.50 / 3.80	2.47 / 3.74	2.45 / 3.70	2.42 / 3.66	2.41 / 3.62	2.40 / 3.60
12	4.75 / 9.33	3.88 / 6.93	3.49 / 5.95	3.26 / 5.41	3.11 / 5.06	3.00 / 4.82	2.92 / 4.65	2.85 / 4.50	2.80 / 4.39	2.76 / 4.30	2.72 / 4.22	2.69 / 4.16	2.64 / 4.05	2.60 / 3.98	2.54 / 3.86	2.50 / 3.78	2.46 / 3.70	2.42 / 3.61	2.40 / 3.56	2.36 / 3.49	2.35 / 3.46	2.32 / 3.41	2.31 / 3.38	2.30 / 3.36
13	4.67 / 9.07	3.80 / 6.70	3.41 / 5.74	3.18 / 5.20	3.02 / 4.86	2.92 / 4.62	2.84 / 4.44	2.77 / 4.30	2.72 / 4.19	2.67 / 4.10	2.63 / 4.02	2.60 / 3.96	2.55 / 3.85	2.51 / 3.78	2.46 / 3.67	2.42 / 3.59	2.38 / 3.51	2.34 / 3.42	2.32 / 3.37	2.28 / 3.30	2.26 / 3.27	2.24 / 3.21	2.22 / 3.18	2.21 / 3.16

The function, $F = e$ with exponent $2z$, is computed in part from Fisher's Table VI (3). Additional entries are by interpolation, mostly graphical.

[1] Reproduced from *Statistical Methods*, by G. W. Snedecor, by his permission and that of the publishers, Collegiate Press, Inc., Ames, Iowa.

TABLE 4 (continued) — TABLE FOR F

(Upper numbers in the pairs are the 5 per cent points, lower or boldface numbers the 1 per cent points.)

Degrees of freedom for larger variance (d.f.₁)

n_2	∞	500	200	100	75	50	40	30	24	20	16	14	12	11	10	9	8	7	6	5	4	3	2	1
14	2.13 / **3.00**	2.14 / **3.02**	2.16 / **3.06**	2.19 / **3.11**	2.21 / **3.14**	2.24 / **3.21**	2.27 / **3.26**	2.31 / **3.34**	2.35 / **3.43**	2.39 / **3.51**	2.44 / **3.62**	2.48 / **3.70**	2.53 / **3.80**	2.56 / **3.86**	2.60 / **3.94**	2.65 / **4.03**	2.70 / **4.14**	2.77 / **4.28**	2.85 / **4.46**	2.96 / **4.69**	3.11 / **5.03**	3.34 / **5.56**	3.74 / **6.51**	4.60 / **8.86**
15	2.07 / **2.87**	2.08 / **2.89**	2.10 / **2.92**	2.12 / **2.97**	2.15 / **3.00**	2.18 / **3.07**	2.21 / **3.12**	2.25 / **3.20**	2.29 / **3.29**	2.33 / **3.36**	2.39 / **3.48**	2.43 / **3.56**	2.48 / **3.67**	2.51 / **3.73**	2.55 / **3.80**	2.59 / **3.89**	2.64 / **4.00**	2.70 / **4.14**	2.79 / **4.32**	2.90 / **4.56**	3.06 / **4.89**	3.29 / **5.42**	3.68 / **6.36**	4.54 / **8.68**
16	2.01 / **2.75**	2.02 / **2.77**	2.04 / **2.80**	2.07 / **2.86**	2.09 / **2.89**	2.13 / **2.96**	2.16 / **3.01**	2.20 / **3.10**	2.24 / **3.18**	2.28 / **3.25**	2.33 / **3.37**	2.37 / **3.45**	2.42 / **3.55**	2.45 / **3.61**	2.49 / **3.69**	2.54 / **3.78**	2.59 / **3.89**	2.66 / **4.03**	2.74 / **4.20**	2.85 / **4.44**	3.01 / **4.77**	3.24 / **5.29**	3.63 / **6.23**	4.49 / **8.53**
17	1.96 / **2.65**	1.97 / **2.67**	1.99 / **2.70**	2.02 / **2.76**	2.04 / **2.79**	2.08 / **2.86**	2.11 / **2.92**	2.15 / **3.00**	2.19 / **3.08**	2.23 / **3.16**	2.29 / **3.27**	2.33 / **3.35**	2.38 / **3.45**	2.41 / **3.52**	2.45 / **3.59**	2.50 / **3.68**	2.55 / **3.79**	2.62 / **3.93**	2.70 / **4.10**	2.81 / **4.34**	2.96 / **4.67**	3.20 / **5.18**	3.59 / **6.11**	4.45 / **8.40**
18	1.92 / **2.57**	1.93 / **2.59**	1.95 / **2.62**	1.98 / **2.68**	2.00 / **2.71**	2.04 / **2.78**	2.07 / **2.83**	2.11 / **2.91**	2.15 / **3.00**	2.19 / **3.07**	2.25 / **3.19**	2.29 / **3.27**	2.34 / **3.37**	2.37 / **3.44**	2.41 / **3.51**	2.46 / **3.60**	2.51 / **3.71**	2.58 / **3.85**	2.66 / **4.01**	2.77 / **4.25**	2.93 / **4.58**	3.16 / **5.09**	3.55 / **6.01**	4.41 / **8.28**
19	1.88 / **2.49**	1.90 / **2.51**	1.91 / **2.54**	1.94 / **2.60**	1.96 / **2.63**	2.00 / **2.70**	2.02 / **2.76**	2.07 / **2.84**	2.11 / **2.92**	2.15 / **3.00**	2.21 / **3.12**	2.26 / **3.19**	2.31 / **3.30**	2.34 / **3.36**	2.38 / **3.43**	2.43 / **3.52**	2.48 / **3.63**	2.55 / **3.77**	2.63 / **3.94**	2.74 / **4.17**	2.90 / **4.50**	3.13 / **5.01**	3.52 / **5.93**	4.38 / **8.18**
20	1.84 / **2.42**	1.85 / **2.44**	1.87 / **2.47**	1.90 / **2.53**	1.92 / **2.56**	1.96 / **2.63**	1.99 / **2.69**	2.04 / **2.77**	2.08 / **2.86**	2.12 / **2.94**	2.18 / **3.05**	2.23 / **3.13**	2.28 / **3.23**	2.31 / **3.30**	2.35 / **3.37**	2.40 / **3.45**	2.45 / **3.56**	2.52 / **3.71**	2.60 / **3.87**	2.71 / **4.10**	2.87 / **4.43**	3.10 / **4.94**	3.49 / **5.85**	4.35 / **8.10**
21	1.81 / **2.36**	1.82 / **2.38**	1.84 / **2.42**	1.87 / **2.47**	1.89 / **2.51**	1.93 / **2.58**	1.96 / **2.63**	2.00 / **2.72**	2.05 / **2.80**	2.09 / **2.88**	2.15 / **2.99**	2.20 / **3.07**	2.25 / **3.17**	2.28 / **3.24**	2.32 / **3.31**	2.37 / **3.40**	2.42 / **3.51**	2.49 / **3.65**	2.57 / **3.81**	2.68 / **4.04**	2.84 / **4.37**	3.07 / **4.87**	3.47 / **5.78**	4.32 / **8.02**
22	1.78 / **2.31**	1.80 / **2.33**	1.81 / **2.37**	1.84 / **2.42**	1.87 / **2.46**	1.91 / **2.53**	1.93 / **2.58**	1.98 / **2.67**	2.03 / **2.75**	2.07 / **2.83**	2.13 / **2.94**	2.18 / **3.02**	2.23 / **3.12**	2.26 / **3.18**	2.30 / **3.26**	2.35 / **3.35**	2.40 / **3.45**	2.47 / **3.59**	2.55 / **3.76**	2.66 / **3.99**	2.82 / **4.31**	3.05 / **4.82**	3.44 / **5.72**	4.30 / **7.94**
23	1.76 / **2.26**	1.77 / **2.28**	1.79 / **2.32**	1.82 / **2.37**	1.84 / **2.41**	1.88 / **2.48**	1.91 / **2.53**	1.96 / **2.62**	2.00 / **2.70**	2.04 / **2.78**	2.10 / **2.89**	2.14 / **2.97**	2.20 / **3.07**	2.24 / **3.14**	2.28 / **3.21**	2.32 / **3.30**	2.38 / **3.41**	2.45 / **3.54**	2.53 / **3.71**	2.64 / **3.94**	2.80 / **4.26**	3.03 / **4.76**	3.42 / **5.66**	4.28 / **7.88**
24	1.73 / **2.21**	1.74 / **2.23**	1.76 / **2.27**	1.80 / **2.33**	1.82 / **2.36**	1.86 / **2.44**	1.89 / **2.49**	1.94 / **2.58**	1.98 / **2.66**	2.02 / **2.74**	2.09 / **2.85**	2.13 / **2.93**	2.18 / **3.03**	2.22 / **3.09**	2.26 / **3.17**	2.30 / **3.25**	2.36 / **3.36**	2.43 / **3.50**	2.51 / **3.67**	2.62 / **3.90**	2.78 / **4.22**	3.01 / **4.72**	3.40 / **5.61**	4.26 / **7.82**
25	1.71 / **2.17**	1.72 / **2.19**	1.74 / **2.23**	1.77 / **2.29**	1.80 / **2.32**	1.84 / **2.40**	1.87 / **2.45**	1.92 / **2.54**	1.96 / **2.62**	2.00 / **2.70**	2.06 / **2.81**	2.11 / **2.89**	2.16 / **2.99**	2.20 / **3.05**	2.24 / **3.13**	2.28 / **3.21**	2.34 / **3.32**	2.41 / **3.46**	2.49 / **3.63**	2.60 / **3.86**	2.76 / **4.18**	2.99 / **4.68**	3.38 / **5.57**	4.24 / **7.77**
26	1.69 / **2.13**	1.70 / **2.15**	1.72 / **2.19**	1.76 / **2.25**	1.78 / **2.28**	1.82 / **2.36**	1.85 / **2.41**	1.90 / **2.50**	1.95 / **2.58**	1.99 / **2.66**	2.05 / **2.77**	2.10 / **2.86**	2.15 / **2.96**	2.18 / **3.02**	2.22 / **3.09**	2.27 / **3.17**	2.32 / **3.29**	2.39 / **3.42**	2.47 / **3.59**	2.59 / **3.82**	2.74 / **4.14**	2.98 / **4.64**	3.37 / **5.53**	4.22 / **7.72**

Degrees of freedom for smaller variance (d.f.₂)

The function, $F = e$ with exponent $2z$, is computed in part from Fisher's Table VI (3). Additional entries are by interpolation, mostly graphical.

TABLE 4 (*continued*) — TABLE FOR F

(Upper numbers in the pairs are the 5 per cent points, lower or boldface numbers the 1 per cent points.)

Degrees of freedom for larger variance (d.f.₁)

Degrees of freedom for smaller variance (d.f.₂)

d.f.₂	1	2	3	4	5	6	7	8	9	10	11	12	14	16	20	24	30	40	50	75	100	200	500	∞
27	4.21 / 7.68	3.35 / 5.49	2.96 / 4.60	2.73 / 4.11	2.57 / 3.79	2.46 / 3.56	2.37 / 3.39	2.30 / 3.26	2.25 / 3.14	2.20 / 3.06	2.16 / 2.98	2.13 / 2.93	2.08 / 2.83	2.03 / 2.74	1.97 / 2.63	1.93 / 2.55	1.88 / 2.47	1.84 / 2.38	1.80 / 2.33	1.76 / 2.25	1.74 / 2.21	1.71 / 2.16	1.68 / 2.12	1.67 / 2.10
28	4.20 / 7.64	3.34 / 5.45	2.95 / 4.57	2.71 / 4.07	2.56 / 3.76	2.44 / 3.53	2.36 / 3.36	2.29 / 3.23	2.24 / 3.11	2.19 / 3.03	2.15 / 2.95	2.12 / 2.90	2.06 / 2.80	2.02 / 2.71	1.96 / 2.60	1.91 / 2.52	1.87 / 2.44	1.81 / 2.35	1.78 / 2.30	1.75 / 2.22	1.72 / 2.18	1.69 / 2.13	1.67 / 2.09	1.65 / 2.06
29	4.18 / 7.60	3.33 / 5.42	2.93 / 4.54	2.70 / 4.04	2.54 / 3.73	2.43 / 3.50	2.35 / 3.33	2.28 / 3.20	2.22 / 3.08	2.18 / 3.00	2.14 / 2.92	2.10 / 2.87	2.05 / 2.77	2.00 / 2.68	1.94 / 2.57	1.90 / 2.49	1.85 / 2.41	1.80 / 2.32	1.77 / 2.27	1.73 / 2.19	1.71 / 2.15	1.68 / 2.10	1.65 / 2.06	1.64 / 2.03
30	4.17 / 7.56	3.32 / 5.39	2.92 / 4.51	2.69 / 4.02	2.53 / 3.70	2.42 / 3.47	2.34 / 3.30	2.27 / 3.17	2.21 / 3.06	2.16 / 2.98	2.12 / 2.90	2.09 / 2.84	2.04 / 2.74	1.99 / 2.66	1.93 / 2.55	1.89 / 2.47	1.84 / 2.38	1.79 / 2.29	1.76 / 2.24	1.72 / 2.16	1.69 / 2.13	1.66 / 2.07	1.64 / 2.03	1.62 / 2.01
32	4.15 / 7.50	3.30 / 5.34	2.90 / 4.46	2.67 / 3.97	2.51 / 3.66	2.40 / 3.42	2.32 / 3.25	2.25 / 3.12	2.19 / 3.01	2.14 / 2.94	2.10 / 2.86	2.07 / 2.80	2.02 / 2.70	1.97 / 2.62	1.91 / 2.51	1.86 / 2.42	1.82 / 2.34	1.76 / 2.25	1.74 / 2.20	1.69 / 2.12	1.67 / 2.08	1.64 / 2.02	1.61 / 1.98	1.59 / 1.96
34	4.13 / 7.44	3.28 / 5.29	2.88 / 4.42	2.65 / 3.93	2.49 / 3.61	2.38 / 3.38	2.30 / 3.21	2.23 / 3.08	2.17 / 2.97	2.12 / 2.89	2.08 / 2.82	2.05 / 2.76	2.00 / 2.66	1.95 / 2.58	1.89 / 2.47	1.84 / 2.38	1.80 / 2.30	1.74 / 2.21	1.71 / 2.15	1.67 / 2.08	1.64 / 2.04	1.61 / 1.98	1.59 / 1.94	1.57 / 1.91
36	4.11 / 7.39	3.26 / 5.25	2.86 / 4.38	2.63 / 3.89	2.48 / 3.58	2.36 / 3.35	2.28 / 3.18	2.21 / 3.04	2.15 / 2.94	2.10 / 2.86	2.06 / 2.78	2.03 / 2.72	1.98 / 2.62	1.93 / 2.54	1.87 / 2.43	1.82 / 2.35	1.78 / 2.26	1.72 / 2.17	1.69 / 2.12	1.65 / 2.04	1.62 / 2.00	1.59 / 1.94	1.56 / 1.90	1.55 / 1.87
38	4.10 / 7.35	3.25 / 5.21	2.85 / 4.34	2.62 / 3.86	2.46 / 3.54	2.35 / 3.32	2.26 / 3.15	2.19 / 3.02	2.14 / 2.91	2.09 / 2.82	2.05 / 2.75	2.02 / 2.69	1.96 / 2.59	1.92 / 2.51	1.85 / 2.40	1.80 / 2.32	1.76 / 2.22	1.71 / 2.14	1.67 / 2.08	1.63 / 2.00	1.60 / 1.97	1.57 / 1.90	1.54 / 1.86	1.53 / 1.84
40	4.08 / 7.31	3.23 / 5.18	2.84 / 4.31	2.61 / 3.83	2.45 / 3.51	2.34 / 3.29	2.25 / 3.12	2.18 / 2.99	2.12 / 2.88	2.07 / 2.80	2.04 / 2.73	2.00 / 2.66	1.95 / 2.56	1.90 / 2.49	1.84 / 2.37	1.79 / 2.29	1.74 / 2.20	1.69 / 2.11	1.66 / 2.05	1.61 / 1.97	1.59 / 1.94	1.55 / 1.88	1.53 / 1.84	1.51 / 1.81
42	4.07 / 7.27	3.22 / 5.15	2.83 / 4.29	2.59 / 3.80	2.44 / 3.49	2.32 / 3.26	2.24 / 3.10	2.17 / 2.96	2.11 / 2.86	2.06 / 2.77	2.02 / 2.70	1.99 / 2.64	1.94 / 2.54	1.89 / 2.46	1.82 / 2.35	1.78 / 2.26	1.73 / 2.17	1.68 / 2.08	1.64 / 2.02	1.60 / 1.94	1.57 / 1.91	1.54 / 1.85	1.51 / 1.80	1.49 / 1.78
44	4.06 / 7.24	3.21 / 5.12	2.82 / 4.26	2.58 / 3.78	2.43 / 3.46	2.31 / 3.24	2.23 / 3.07	2.16 / 2.94	2.10 / 2.84	2.05 / 2.75	2.01 / 2.68	1.98 / 2.62	1.92 / 2.52	1.88 / 2.44	1.81 / 2.32	1.76 / 2.24	1.72 / 2.15	1.66 / 2.06	1.63 / 2.00	1.58 / 1.92	1.56 / 1.88	1.52 / 1.82	1.50 / 1.78	1.48 / 1.75
46	4.05 / 7.21	3.20 / 5.10	2.81 / 4.24	2.57 / 3.76	2.42 / 3.44	2.30 / 3.22	2.22 / 3.05	2.14 / 2.92	2.09 / 2.82	2.04 / 2.73	2.00 / 2.66	1.97 / 2.60	1.91 / 2.50	1.87 / 2.42	1.80 / 2.30	1.75 / 2.22	1.71 / 2.13	1.65 / 2.04	1.62 / 1.98	1.57 / 1.90	1.54 / 1.86	1.51 / 1.80	1.48 / 1.76	1.46 / 1.72
48	4.04 / 7.19	3.19 / 5.08	2.80 / 4.22	2.56 / 3.74	2.41 / 3.42	2.30 / 3.20	2.21 / 3.04	2.14 / 2.90	2.08 / 2.80	2.03 / 2.71	1.99 / 2.64	1.96 / 2.58	1.90 / 2.48	1.86 / 2.40	1.79 / 2.28	1.74 / 2.20	1.70 / 2.11	1.64 / 2.02	1.61 / 1.96	1.56 / 1.88	1.53 / 1.84	1.50 / 1.78	1.47 / 1.73	1.45 / 1.70

The function, $F = e$ with exponent $2z$, is computed in part from Fisher's Table VI (3). Additional entries are by interpolation, mostly graphical.

TABLE 4 (continued) — TABLE FOR F

(Upper numbers in the pairs are the 5 per cent points, lower or boldface numbers the 1 per cent points.)

Degrees of freedom for larger variance ($d.f._1$)

Degrees of freedom for smaller variance ($d.f._2$)

n_2	1	2	3	4	5	6	7	8	9	10	11	12	14	16	20	24	30	40	50	75	100	200	500	∞
50	4.03 / **7.17**	3.18 / **5.06**	2.79 / **4.20**	2.56 / **3.72**	2.40 / **3.41**	2.29 / **3.18**	2.20 / **3.02**	2.13 / **2.88**	2.07 / **2.78**	2.02 / **2.70**	1.98 / **2.62**	1.95 / **2.56**	1.90 / **2.46**	1.85 / **2.39**	1.78 / **2.26**	1.74 / **2.18**	1.69 / **2.10**	1.63 / **2.00**	1.60 / **1.94**	1.55 / **1.86**	1.52 / **1.82**	1.48 / **1.76**	1.46 / **1.71**	1.44 / **1.68**
55	4.02 / **7.12**	3.17 / **5.01**	2.78 / **4.16**	2.54 / **3.68**	2.38 / **3.37**	2.27 / **3.15**	2.18 / **2.98**	2.11 / **2.85**	2.05 / **2.75**	2.00 / **2.66**	1.97 / **2.59**	1.93 / **2.53**	1.88 / **2.43**	1.83 / **2.35**	1.76 / **2.23**	1.72 / **2.15**	1.67 / **2.06**	1.61 / **1.96**	1.58 / **1.90**	1.52 / **1.82**	1.50 / **1.78**	1.46 / **1.71**	1.43 / **1.66**	1.41 / **1.64**
60	4.00 / **7.08**	3.15 / **4.98**	2.76 / **4.13**	2.52 / **3.65**	2.37 / **3.34**	2.25 / **3.12**	2.17 / **2.95**	2.10 / **2.82**	2.04 / **2.72**	1.99 / **2.63**	1.95 / **2.56**	1.92 / **2.50**	1.86 / **2.40**	1.81 / **2.32**	1.75 / **2.20**	1.70 / **2.12**	1.65 / **2.03**	1.59 / **1.93**	1.56 / **1.87**	1.50 / **1.79**	1.48 / **1.74**	1.44 / **1.68**	1.41 / **1.63**	1.39 / **1.60**
65	3.99 / **7.04**	3.14 / **4.95**	2.75 / **4.10**	2.51 / **3.62**	2.36 / **3.31**	2.24 / **3.09**	2.15 / **2.93**	2.08 / **2.79**	2.02 / **2.70**	1.98 / **2.61**	1.94 / **2.54**	1.90 / **2.47**	1.85 / **2.37**	1.80 / **2.30**	1.73 / **2.18**	1.68 / **2.09**	1.63 / **2.00**	1.57 / **1.90**	1.54 / **1.84**	1.49 / **1.76**	1.46 / **1.71**	1.42 / **1.64**	1.39 / **1.60**	1.37 / **1.56**
70	3.98 / **7.01**	3.13 / **4.92**	2.74 / **4.08**	2.50 / **3.60**	2.35 / **3.29**	2.23 / **3.07**	2.14 / **2.91**	2.07 / **2.77**	2.01 / **2.67**	1.97 / **2.59**	1.93 / **2.51**	1.89 / **2.45**	1.84 / **2.35**	1.79 / **2.28**	1.72 / **2.15**	1.67 / **2.07**	1.62 / **1.98**	1.56 / **1.88**	1.53 / **1.82**	1.47 / **1.74**	1.45 / **1.69**	1.40 / **1.62**	1.37 / **1.56**	1.35 / **1.53**
80	3.96 / **6.96**	3.11 / **4.88**	2.72 / **4.04**	2.48 / **3.56**	2.33 / **3.25**	2.21 / **3.04**	2.12 / **2.87**	2.05 / **2.74**	1.99 / **2.64**	1.95 / **2.55**	1.91 / **2.48**	1.88 / **2.41**	1.82 / **2.32**	1.77 / **2.24**	1.70 / **2.11**	1.65 / **2.03**	1.60 / **1.94**	1.54 / **1.84**	1.51 / **1.78**	1.45 / **1.70**	1.42 / **1.65**	1.38 / **1.57**	1.35 / **1.52**	1.32 / **1.49**
100	3.94 / **6.90**	3.09 / **4.82**	2.70 / **3.98**	2.46 / **3.51**	2.30 / **3.20**	2.19 / **2.99**	2.10 / **2.82**	2.03 / **2.69**	1.97 / **2.59**	1.92 / **2.51**	1.88 / **2.43**	1.85 / **2.36**	1.79 / **2.26**	1.75 / **2.19**	1.68 / **2.06**	1.63 / **1.98**	1.57 / **1.89**	1.51 / **1.79**	1.48 / **1.73**	1.42 / **1.64**	1.39 / **1.59**	1.34 / **1.51**	1.30 / **1.46**	1.28 / **1.43**
125	3.92 / **6.84**	3.07 / **4.78**	2.68 / **3.94**	2.44 / **3.47**	2.29 / **3.17**	2.17 / **2.95**	2.08 / **2.79**	2.01 / **2.65**	1.95 / **2.56**	1.90 / **2.47**	1.86 / **2.40**	1.83 / **2.33**	1.77 / **2.23**	1.72 / **2.15**	1.65 / **2.03**	1.60 / **1.94**	1.55 / **1.85**	1.49 / **1.75**	1.45 / **1.68**	1.39 / **1.59**	1.36 / **1.54**	1.31 / **1.46**	1.27 / **1.40**	1.25 / **1.37**
150	3.91 / **6.81**	3.06 / **4.75**	2.67 / **3.91**	2.43 / **3.44**	2.27 / **3.14**	2.16 / **2.92**	2.07 / **2.76**	2.00 / **2.62**	1.94 / **2.53**	1.89 / **2.44**	1.85 / **2.37**	1.82 / **2.30**	1.76 / **2.20**	1.71 / **2.12**	1.64 / **2.00**	1.59 / **1.91**	1.54 / **1.83**	1.47 / **1.72**	1.44 / **1.66**	1.37 / **1.56**	1.34 / **1.51**	1.29 / **1.43**	1.25 / **1.37**	1.22 / **1.33**
200	3.89 / **6.76**	3.04 / **4.71**	2.65 / **3.88**	2.41 / **3.41**	2.26 / **3.11**	2.14 / **2.90**	2.05 / **2.73**	1.98 / **2.60**	1.92 / **2.50**	1.87 / **2.41**	1.83 / **2.34**	1.80 / **2.28**	1.74 / **2.17**	1.69 / **2.09**	1.62 / **1.97**	1.57 / **1.88**	1.52 / **1.79**	1.45 / **1.69**	1.42 / **1.62**	1.35 / **1.53**	1.32 / **1.48**	1.26 / **1.39**	1.22 / **1.33**	1.19 / **1.28**
400	3.86 / **6.70**	3.02 / **4.66**	2.62 / **3.83**	2.39 / **3.36**	2.23 / **3.06**	2.12 / **2.85**	2.03 / **2.69**	1.96 / **2.55**	1.90 / **2.46**	1.85 / **2.37**	1.81 / **2.29**	1.78 / **2.23**	1.72 / **2.12**	1.67 / **2.04**	1.60 / **1.92**	1.54 / **1.84**	1.49 / **1.74**	1.42 / **1.64**	1.38 / **1.57**	1.32 / **1.47**	1.28 / **1.42**	1.22 / **1.32**	1.16 / **1.24**	1.13 / **1.19**
1000	3.85 / **6.66**	3.00 / **4.62**	2.61 / **3.80**	2.38 / **3.34**	2.22 / **3.04**	2.10 / **2.82**	2.02 / **2.66**	1.95 / **2.53**	1.89 / **2.43**	1.84 / **2.34**	1.80 / **2.26**	1.76 / **2.20**	1.70 / **2.09**	1.65 / **2.01**	1.58 / **1.89**	1.53 / **1.81**	1.47 / **1.71**	1.41 / **1.61**	1.36 / **1.54**	1.30 / **1.44**	1.26 / **1.38**	1.19 / **1.28**	1.13 / **1.19**	1.08 / **1.11**
∞	3.84 / **6.64**	2.99 / **4.60**	2.60 / **3.78**	2.37 / **3.32**	2.21 / **3.02**	2.09 / **2.80**	2.01 / **2.64**	1.94 / **2.51**	1.88 / **2.41**	1.83 / **2.32**	1.79 / **2.24**	1.75 / **2.18**	1.69 / **2.07**	1.64 / **1.99**	1.57 / **1.87**	1.52 / **1.79**	1.46 / **1.69**	1.40 / **1.59**	1.35 / **1.52**	1.28 / **1.41**	1.24 / **1.36**	1.17 / **1.25**	1.11 / **1.15**	1.00 / **1.00**

The function, $F = e$ with exponent $2z$, is computed in part from Fisher's Table VI (3). Additional entries are by interpolation, mostly graphical.

combination if the samples were drawn from equally variable populations, and that a value of 14.80 would be exceeded 1 per cent of the time. If our hypothesis were true, we would secure an F as large as 6.68 between 1 per cent and 5 per cent of the time just as a result of chance fluctuations from sample to sample. Whether or not we would describe the difference in variability of these samples as "significant" would then depend upon the "level of significance" which we chose arbitrarily to employ.

7. THE SIGNIFICANCE OF THE MEAN OF A SAMPLE CONSISTING OF RANDOMLY SELECTED INTACT GROUPS

We have noted in Chapter I that small sample error theory is of particular importance in educational research because so many of our samples consist of a small number of intact and relatively homogeneous subgroups. Usually each of these groups consists of the pupils in a single class, or under a single teacher, or in a single school or community. If these groups have been selected at random from all such groups in the population, it is possible to determine the significance of the obtained mean of the total sample by the procedure presented in the following illustration.

This illustration is based upon actual data obtained from the 1938 Iowa Every-Pupil Testing Program. Table 5 presents the distributions of scores on a certain achievement test in English Correctness for the ninth-grade pupils in 11 Iowa high schools. These schools were selected at random from all schools of 65 to 125 enrollment that participated in the 1938 program. We note that a total of 414 pupils was tested in these 11 schools, and that the mean and standard deviation of the combined distribution are 164.3 and 29.3 respectively. If we were to consider this as a random sample of 414 pupils, we would estimate the standard error of the mean as $\frac{29.3}{\sqrt{414}} = 1.44$, and hence we would say, at the 1 per cent level of confidence, that the true mean of the population lies between 160.48 and 168.12 (i.e., not more than 2.576 standard errors from the obtained mean).

This sample, however, is not a random sample of pupils, even though it is a random sample of schools.   It is almost self-evident that a sample of, say, 37 pupils all selected from school No. 1 would not be as good a basis for generalization as a sample of 37 cases selected at random from all pupils in the entire population.   In the random sample many different schools would be represented, and the mean would not be unduly influenced by the systematic supe-

TABLE 5

DISTRIBUTIONS OF SCORES ON THE 1938 IOWA EVERY-PUPIL TEST IN ENGLISH CORRECTNESS FOR THE NINTH-GRADE PUPILS IN 11 IOWA HIGH SCHOOLS

Scores	Schools											
	1	2	3	4	5	6	7	8	9	10	11	Total
230–239					3							3
220–229		1			1					1	1	4
210–219	1	8			2		5		3	2	1	22
200–209	4	5	2	1	4	1		2	4		1	24
190–199	5	9		1	4	3	5	2	2	1	4	36
180–189	6	6	3	3	5	1	4		7	4	2	41
170–179	5	4	1	2	5	3	3	7	4	4	4	42
160–169	5	1	5	10	9	5	7	4	7	1	7	61
150–159	5	2	8	2	3	3	6	6	7	8	6	56
140–149	4	1	4	3	4	3	5	6	2	6	1	39
130–139	1	1	5	5	1	6	1	3	1	5	1	30
120–129	1	1	3	6	2	3	2	4	1	6	3	32
110–119			4		1	6	2	1			1	15
100–109			1	1		1		1			1	5
90– 99											1	1
80– 89							2					2
70– 79							1					1
Sum of Scores	6416.5	7395.5	5382.0	5213.0	7768.0	5187.5	6963.5	5592.0	6621.0	5971.0	5533.0	68043.0
N	37	39	36	34	44	35	43	36	38	38	34	414
M	173.4	189.6	149.5	153.3	176.6	148.2	161.9	155.3	174.2	157.1	162.7	164.3
σ	22.0	22.0	24.6	23.5	29.4	27.2	34.5	24.1	22.5	26.5	29.8	29.3

Mean of School Means = 163.8; Mean of σ's = 26.0

riority or inferiority of any one school.   It should be equally evident that a sample of 414 pupils from 11 schools is not as good as a *random* sample of 414 cases from all schools in the whole population.

This sample, then, should be considered as consisting of 11 *schools* rather than of 414 *pupils*.   The mean of the sample should be considered as a weighted mean of 11 school means, rather than of 414 pupil scores.   The significance of this mean should be determined from the distribution of the 11 school means by means of the *t*-test as for a sample of 11 cases.

If the number of cases is the same or very nearly the same for all schools, it will be convenient to use as the mean of the sample the unweighted mean of the school means. The t-test may then be applied as in the following illustration, based on the data of Table 5.

	School Means	Deviations from Unweighted Mean	Deviations squared
	173.4	9.6	92.16
	189.6	25.8	665.64
	149.5	− 14.3	204.49
	153.3	− 10.5	110.25
	176.6	12.8	163.84
	148.2	− 15.6	243.36
	161.9	− 1.9	3.61
	155.3	− 8.5	72.25
	174.2	10.4	108.16
	157.1	− 6.7	44.89
	162.7	− 1.1	1.21
Total	1801.8	Sum of squared d's =	1709.86

Unweighted Mean   163.8

$$\text{est'd } \sigma_M = \sqrt{\frac{1709.86}{11 \times 10}} = 3.94$$

If, as usually happens, the number of cases varies considerably from school to school, it will be necessary to deal with the *weighted* mean, and also to *weight* each squared deviation (of school mean from this weighted mean) by the ratio between the number of cases in the corresponding school and the average number of cases in all schools. In this instance, for example, the average number of pupils per school is $414/11 = 37.65$. Hence, the number of cases in School No. 1 is $37/37.65 = .9827$ times as large as in the average school. For School No. 2 this ratio is $39/37.6 = 1.0358$, for School No. 5 it is $44/37.6 = 1.6866$, etc. The squared deviation of each school mean is then multiplied by the corresponding ratio, and these products are added to secure the sum of the weighted squared deviations. From this sum, the standard error of the mean is computed as before. These steps are illustrated below for the data of Table 5.

School Means	Deviations from Weighted Mean	Deviations Squared	Ratio	Weighted d^2's
173.4	9.1	82.81	.9827	81.38
189.6	25.3	640.09	1.0358	663.01
149.5	− 14.8	219.04	.9562	209.45
153.3	11.0	121.00	.9031	109.28
176.6	− 12.3	151.29	1.6866	255.17
148.2	− 16.1	259.21	.9296	240.96
161.9	− 2.4	5.76	1.1421	6.58
155.3	− 9.0	81.00	.9562	77.45
174.2	9.9	98.01	1.0093	98.92
157.1	− 7.2	51.84	1.0093	52.32
162.7	− 1.6	2.56	.9031	2.31

Sum of weighted squared d's = 1796.83

Weighted Mean 164.3

$$\text{est'd } \sigma_M = \sqrt{\frac{1796.83}{11 \times 10}} = 4.03$$

For $M_H = 168.12$, $t = \dfrac{168.12 - 164.3}{4.03} = .97$

For $M_H = 177$, $t = 3.15$

The method of computation that was used in the preceding example is not the easiest to employ, and was presented only to show the essential nature of the procedure. A more convenient method of computation is to multiply each school mean by the total of the scores on which it is based, to add these products, and to subtract from this sum the product of the mean of the total distribution and the sum of all scores. This result should then be divided by the product of the total number of pupils and the number of degrees of freedom (one less than the number of schools) to yield the square of the standard error of the mean.[1] The square root of this result

[1] This procedure may be expressed in terms of a formula, as

$$\text{est'd } \sigma_M^{\bullet} = \frac{\Sigma M_p T_p - GM \cdot GT}{N (r - 1)}$$

in which M_p represents the mean for any school, T_p the corresponding sum of pupil scores, $\Sigma M_p T_p$ the sum of the MT products for all schools, GM the general mean for all schools, GT the grand total of pupil scores, N the total number of pupils, and r the number of schools. The theoretical basis for this method of computation will be explained later in the discussion of analysis of variance, pages 87 to 92.

will then be the desired standard error. In this example, using the data from Table 5, we find the sum of all products of means and totals, as follows:

$$(6416.5)(173.4) + (7395.5)(189.6) + (5382.0)(149.5) + \cdots \text{etc.}$$
$$= 11{,}246{,}655.75$$

We then find the product of the total and mean for the combined distribution and subtract this product from the result just obtained, as follows:

$$11{,}246{,}655.75 - (68043.0)(164.3) = 67190.85$$

If this is done on a Monroe calculator, or a similar computing machine, this result can be obtained without any transcription. The procedure is to secure the first product, then leave it in the lower dial while the second product is secured, etc., until all products of totals and means for individual schools have been cumulated. The product of total and mean for the combined distribution may then be subtracted from the result already in the machine by "multiplying backward."

We now divide this result by $414 \times 10 = 4140$, to secure

$$\text{est'd } \sigma_M^2 = \frac{67190.85}{4140} = 16.2296$$

The square root of this result is the estimated standard error of the mean, in this case

$$\text{est'd } \sigma_M = \sqrt{16.2296} = 4.03,$$

which is the same result obtained before by the more laborious computational procedure.

We note that in the case of this illustrative problem the results secured from the unweighted data were approximately the same as those secured from the weighted data. This is because the number of cases was nearly constant for the schools used in the illustration. Ordinarily, of course, the latter computational procedure should be employed.

We may now see how invalid were the results secured (page 66) when the whole sample was considered as a random sample of 414 pupils. This false assumption led to an estimate of 1.44 as the standard error of the mean, whereas the more valid estimate is 4.03. On the basis of the assumption of random sampling, we reasoned that the true mean could hardly exceed 168.12. When we use the more valid estimate of the standard error and apply the t-test, we find that for an M_T even as large as 177 the value of t is only 3.15. For 10 degrees of freedom, this large a value of t just fails to be significant at the 1 per cent level. The mean of this sample, then, is not nearly as reliable as the mean of a sample of 414 pupils selected at random, and the application of the usual large sample techniques which assume random sampling would be seriously misleading.

It should be noted that an underlying assumption in the t-test is that the measures from which t is computed are a random sample from a normal population. In the case just considered, this implies that the 11 school means must be considered as a *random* sample of the means of all such schools in the state, and assumes that these means will be normally distributed. This latter assumption may be fairly well satisfied if the individual schools are of approximately the same size, but it is less likely to be if they differ widely in size. There is reason to believe, however, that the t-test is reasonably valid even though the form of distribution for the population sampled differs considerably from that of the normal curve.

This method also assumes that the variability within schools is fundamentally constant from school to school; that is, it assumes that the differences in variability from school to school are no larger than would be found in random samples of the same size. This will be given further consideration in the discussion of analysis of variance.

It should be noted also that if the number of schools is very small, there will be a considerable loss due to the small number of degrees of freedom upon which the t is based. (This will not be serious if the number of schools is 10 or larger, since, as we may note in the table for t, the critical value of t for any given level of significance does not decrease markedly for further increases in $d.f.$)

It may be worth observing that the foregoing considerations are of particular significance in the evaluation of a norm established for a standardized test.[1]   Many current norms, while based on large numbers of pupils, include pupils from only a very small number of schools.   A norm of this type, even though based on several thousand pupils, may be no more reliable than one based on a truly random sample of only 50 or 100 pupils.

8. THE SIGNIFICANCE OF A DIFFERENCE IN MEANS FOR SAMPLES EACH OF WHICH CONSISTS OF RELATIVELY HOMOGENEOUS SUBGROUPS

When each of two samples is of the character of that of Table 5, and when the subgroups in one sample are independent of those in the other, the difference in means for the two samples may be evaluated in a manner suggested in Section 4, pages 56–58.   For the first sample, we would find the sum of *weighted* squared deviations of the means of the subgroups from the weighted mean of that sample.   This would be done by (1) adding the products of totals and means for the subgroups, (2) subtracting the product of total and mean for the sample, (3) dividing the result by the total number of cases, and (4) multiplying this result by the number of subgroups.   (Note that this last multiplication was not necessary in the example with Table 5.)   The sum of the weighted squared deviations of subgroup means from the general mean would similarly be found for the second sample.   The sum of these two sums is then the same as $(\Sigma d_1^2 + \Sigma d_2^2)$ in formulas (10) and (11), and the rest of the procedure would be that suggested on page 57, n_1 representing the number of subgroups in the first sample, and n_2 the number of subgroups in the second.

To illustrate this procedure, suppose that for two samples like

---

[1] Lindquist, E. F., "Factors Determining the Reliability of Test Norms." *Journal of Educational Psychology*, 21:512–20 (October, 1928).

that of Table 5 the totals and means for the various schools are as follows:

TOTALS AND MEANS FOR SUBGROUPS IN TWO SAMPLES

	Sample 1				Sample 2		
School	N	Total	Mean	School	N	Total	Mean
1	30	678	22.6	1	18	488	27.1
2	26	840	32.3	2	31	682	22.0
3	52	1503	28.9	3	44	766	17.4
4	16	358	22.4	4	17	502	29.5
5	8	171	21.4	5	52	1170	22.5
				6	17	432	25.4
Totals	132	3550		7	25	892	35.7

Weighted Mean = 26.93   Totals   204   4932

Weighted Mean = 24.18

The sum of products of school totals and means, minus the product of the grand total and weighted general mean for Sample 1 is 1968.6. For Sample 2 the corresponding result is 6252.6. The sum of weighted squared deviations (Σd_1^2) for Sample 1 is then $\frac{5 \times 1968.6}{132} = 74.57$, and ($\Sigma d_2^2$) for Sample 2 is $\frac{7 \times 6252.6}{204} = 214.55$.
We may then substitute in Formula (11) as follows:

$$t = \frac{26.93 - 24.18}{\sqrt{\left(\frac{74.57 + 214.55}{5 + 7 - 2}\right)\left(\frac{1}{5} + \frac{1}{7}\right)}} = \frac{2.75}{\sqrt{9.91}} = .88$$

We note in Table 3, for 10 degrees of freedom, that this is almost exactly the value of t that would be exceeded 40 per cent of the time by chance alone. Clearly this difference is not significant.

If the subgroups in the two samples have been paired on some basis such that there is a significant correlation between the means of the paired subgroups, a different procedure must be followed. If the numbers in all subgroups are the same (or very nearly so), we may deal with the unweighted means, following the procedure suggested in Section 5, page 58. To illustrate, suppose we have the scores made on a test in world history in 6 high schools, that the numbers in each high school are very nearly the same, and that there is very nearly the same number of boys as of girls in each school. Suppose that the means are as given below,

MEAN SCORES OF BOYS AND GIRLS IN EACH SCHOOL SEPARATELY

	Means		Differences in Means
	Boys	Girls	
School 1	34.7	34.6	0.1
" 2	44.4	37.5	6.9
" 3	41.0	39.2	1.8
" 4	34.5	34.1	0.4
" 5	33.5	29.5	4.0
" 6	47.8	41.6	6.2
Totals	235.9	216.5	19.4
Means	39.31	36.08	3.23
$\sum d^2$	180.56	92.35	42.73

We note at once that there is some correlation between the means for boys and girls. The school (#6) whose mean for boys is highest is also that whose mean for girls is highest, and the lowest mean for boys (#5) is also associated with the lowest for girls. Accordingly, the estimated standard error of the mean of the differences (3.23) in school means for the sexes is

$$\text{est'd } \sigma_{M_1 - M_2} = \sqrt{\frac{42.73}{5 \times 6}} = 1.19$$

and hence $t = 3.23/1.19 = 2.71$.

For 5 degrees of freedom, an absolute value of t as large as 2.71 would be found less than 5 per cent of the time if the true difference were zero, or a positive value of t this large would be found less than 2.5 per cent of the time. We are therefore fairly well justified in asserting that boys in general are superior to girls in general in achievement in world history, although the evidence may not be as strong as we should like it to be.

It will be interesting to compare these results with those that would be obtained by the method of Section 4, pages 56–58. In this case, the estimated standard error of the difference is

$$\text{est'd } \sigma_{M_1 - M_2} = \sqrt{\frac{180.56 - 92.35}{6 + 6 - 2} \left(\frac{1}{6} + \frac{1}{6}\right)} = 3.0$$

This estimate is much larger than before (1.19) and t now becomes $3.23/3.00 = 1.08$.

For 10 degrees of freedom, this absolute value of t would be exceeded by chance alone at least 30 times in 100. Hence, this test would make the difference appear much less significant than it really is.

The first of these tests, then, takes advantage of the homogeneity of achievement in individual schools. It should be noted, however, that this procedure again deals with unweighted means and that there is considerable loss due to the small number of degrees of freedom involved. A still more adequate test which may sometimes be employed in situations like this — a test which takes differences in size of school into consideration — will be suggested later by the methods of analysis of variance (see pages 87 ff.)

CHAPTER IV

THE IMPORTANCE OF DESIGN IN EDUCATIONAL EXPERIMENTS

1. THE NEED FOR MEASURES OF PRECISION

THE fundamental purpose of most experimental research in education is to discover the effects upon the pupil of specific variations in his environment or training. The typical procedure in such experiments is (1) to select two or more groups of pupils, each of which is presumably representative of some defined population about which generalizations are to be established, (2) to subject each of these groups to one of a number of prescribed "treatments," (3) to secure criterion measures of the final status or change of status of each pupil with reference to the particular trait or traits which the treatments are intended to modify, and (4) to analyze and evaluate the results by means of statistical techniques.

The *precision* of any such experiment may be defined as the degree to which the observed differences in results from group to group are due only to the differences which have been deliberately introduced into the "treatments." The precision of the experiment will then depend upon the success with which all factors which might otherwise affect the results, other than the deliberate variations in "treatment," have been controlled or equalized (or corrections made) from group to group, and upon the extent to which the criterion measures really measure the things which they are intended to measure.

Absolute precision is, of course, impossible. The factors which may conceivably affect the results are ordinarily too numerous and complex even to permit the identification of all of them, to say nothing of their equalization or measurement, and the effects which it is desired to measure are often only vaguely defined, and may usually be measured only indirectly and with high fallibility. The results obtained from an experiment may therefore never be taken at their face value, but must always be considered as only approximate in character, or as likely to be in error by some indefinite amount. In other words, it is always possible that any observed difference in results is due, not to the treatment differences, but to uncontrolled and unmeasured variations in factors extraneous to the purposes of the experiment.

While it is obviously impossible to determine the magnitude and direction of these errors, it is sometimes possible to determine the *probability* that the error arising from *certain* sources will exceed a given magnitude, and thus to estimate the *maximum* error that it is reasonable to suppose might arise from those sources. Allowance may then be made for this maximum error in the evaluation of results and, if the other sources of error have been adequately controlled, the experiment may yet lead to sound and useful conclusions.

It is extremely significant that unless one has a fairly definite and dependable (even though subjectively derived) estimate of the maximum error which might be present in an obtained difference, one can draw no useful conclusion from that difference, no matter how precise it may be in reality. So long as the error may be of any magnitude, it is always conceivable that the difference is due to error alone. Given a dependable estimate of error, one can demonstrate that certain hypotheses are inconsistent with the results obtained; without any such estimate any hypothesis whatever is admissible, including of course the hypothesis that there are no real differences in treatments.

In a very real sense, then, it is more important to know the *degree* of precision of an experiment, whether high or low, than it is that the precision be in reality high. An observed difference in results may be of very low precision and yet reveal conclusively that there is a corresponding difference in treatments, if one can demonstrate objectively that the maximum error, however large, could not alone account for all of the observed difference. In other words, a difference may be statistically significant even though very unreliable. On the other hand, an investigator may so design and conduct an experiment that the degree of precision attained is in reality very high, but unless he *knows* and can convince others that this is the case, that is, unless he can set definite limits to the errors present, anyone may successfully contend that the observed differences, regardless of their magnitude, are in fact due to error alone.

In designing an experiment, then, it is just as important to provide for an objective and dependable estimate of error as it is to provide for high precision.   In fact, no efforts to increase the precision of an experiment will be of any avail unless one can also dependably describe the increased *degree* of precision attained.   On the contrary, if by some device one eliminates a certain source of error, and yet continues to employ an estimate of error that still makes allowance for errors from that source, the experiment may even appear *less* conclusive than otherwise.   This is because the observed differences may actually become smaller (since there is no longer any possibility of their being inflated by this particular source of error), but this fact will only make the available estimates of error appear *larger* in relation to the reduced differences. This is a mistake that has very frequently been made in educational research, as will be shown by illustrations later.

It should therefore be a maxim of experimental design that if a given source of error cannot be eliminated *both* from the experimental results and from the estimates of error, it had better not be eliminated at all.   In other words, it may sometimes be desirable to select an experimental design that will lead to lower precision than another, if the first design will permit a valid estimate of error and the second will not.

2. SOURCES OF ERROR IN EDUCATIONAL METHODS EXPERIMENTS

With reference to this problem of the estimation of error, we may distinguish between two major sources of error in experiments of the type considered.   The first of these is the possibility that the experimental groups are so unlike one another in their ability to profit by any treatment which may be administered that the observed differences in results are due entirely to differences in the groups themselves, rather than in the treatments received by them. The second is the possibility that, in spite of the precautions taken, other factors than those involved in the treatments may have been permitted to vary from group to group during the course of the experiment, and that these uncontrolled variations alone or in part account for the differences observed. The first type of error arises from individual differences among the *pupils* constituting the groups, the second from variations in outside factors affecting the groups as a whole. The first may be illustrated in an experimental comparison of two methods of instruction by differences in the intelligence or learning ability of the pupils within the experimental groups, or in the quality of their home environments, or in their established habits of study. The second may be illustrated in the same situation, by differences in the abilities of the two teachers selected to teach the experimental groups, or by differences in the circumstances attending the administration of the methods, such as the fact that one group was taught in a poorly ventilated and the other in a well-ventilated classroom.

In a *single* experiment, objective estimates may be derived only for errors of the first of these two types. This is because the only basis we have for the estimation of error is the mathematical theory of probability. In order to utilize this theory, it is *essential* that the "error" variables be distributed strictly at *random* with reference to the treatments compared. It is also essential that there be a number of observations for each treatment, since no statement of probability can be based on a single observation. In a properly designed experiment, therefore, all errors related to pupil-variables may be readily taken into consideration. The pupils may be assigned at random to the treatments, and since there is a number of pupils in each group, it is possible to compute a measure of the variability of results from pupil to pupil under each treatment, and this in turn will make possible an estimate of the variation in means (or other derived measures) that would be expected for other random groups of the same size and given the same treatment.   Errors arising from variations outside the groups, however, may not be so treated.   For example, in a methods experiment in which there is only one teacher for each method, no estimate may be made of the degree to which the results would vary for other teachers using the same method, that is, there would be no possibility of discriminating between the error in results due to the teachers and the real differences due to the methods.   In a single experiment then, the only recourse for the experimenter is to attempt to eliminate the second type of error entirely.

While errors of the second type may, with proper care, be markedly reduced, they obviously cannot be eliminated.   This has heretofore constituted one of the principal limitations of experimental methods in education, since the methods of statistical analysis usually employed do not take this second type of error into adequate account in the estimate of error.   To make matters worse, the methods of control over this source of error which have been employed have often rendered invalid the estimate of error due to pupil variables, and have sometimes reduced the magnitude of the observed differences without any reduction in the error estimate.

3. TYPES OF EXPERIMENTAL DESIGNS

To clarify the principles and observations which have thus far been presented in generalized form, it may be well to consider a number of concrete illustrations.   Let us suppose that an experiment is to be designed to determine the relative effectiveness of two methods of teaching spelling to fourth-grade pupils, and let us consider specifically the relative merits and limitations of several experimental designs representative of those that have frequently been employed in educational research.   We shall first describe briefly the essential feature of each design and then comment on its merits and limitations.   In all illustrations we shall assume that the experiment is of the same duration, say 12 weeks, that the criterion is a list-dictation type of spelling test based on a random sampling of the words taught, and that this test is in all cases administered under the same conditions at the close of the experiment. It will also be assumed that the crucial comparison in each case will be a comparison of the *mean* scores on the criterion test for the experimental groups. The two methods, which need not be described, will be referred to as Methods A and B.

Design I: Experiment conducted in a single school enrolling 48 fourth-grade pupils. These pupils assigned strictly at random to two specially constituted classes of 24 pupils each. One class taught by Method A, the other by Method B, but by different teachers.

Comments: This design will permit a perfectly valid estimate of the errors due to *pupil-variables*, such as differences in initial spelling ability or differences in learning ability, but *only* of such errors. The appropriate error estimate and test of significance for the difference in means in this case would be that described in Section 3 of Chapter III (pages 54–55). The precision of the experiment, even with reference only to errors of the first type, will be quite low. Pupils are so variable in ability to profit by instruction that random samples of this size are likely to differ widely in this respect and this difference in ability could alone account entirely for a difference in means much larger than is likely to be produced by any two methods. Uncontrolled variations outside the groups, such as teacher differences, are of course entirely ignored in the estimate of error.

Design II: Same as Design I, except that both groups are taught by same teacher.

Comments: This design is presented only to illustrate the possibility of reducing errors of the second type. Obviously, however, even in this case the teacher-variable is not eliminated since the teacher may strive harder to make one of the methods work, or may be prejudiced against one, or may be more familiar with one, etc. The error estimate (as in Design I) would be valid for total error only if all errors of the second type were completely eliminated.

Design III: Experiment conducted in 10 schools.   Five schools, selected at random, use Method A, the other five use Method B. Results are evaluated by pooling scores on criterion test in a single distribution for all pupils under each method; by computing the standard error of the mean of each distribution according to formula (1) (page 12), and from these computing the standard error of the difference in means.   Difference declared "significant" if three times its standard error.

Comments: This is a design which has actually been employed quite often in educational research.   The estimate of error is invalid, even with reference only to errors of the first type, since the samples are not random samples of pupils.   An important source of error which was not present in Designs I and II, is the large systematic difference in achievement and other factors from school to school.   This source of error may render this design less precise than either of the preceding, even though many more pupils are involved.   A more valid estimate of error could be derived, using the methods of Section 8, Chapter III, or others to be suggested later, but this of course would not increase the precision of the design.   The estimate which assumes random sampling of pupils seriously underestimates the error and the results may therefore appear "significant" even though really due to error.

Design IV: Experiment conducted in 10 schools.   Procedure in *each* school like that of Design II, but the results for all pupils under each method are pooled in a single distribution and the difference in means evaluated as in Design III.

Comment: This has been one of the most frequently used and generally approved designs in educational research.   The precision of this design may be very much greater than that of Design III, since school differences tend to be equalized by the device of using both methods in each school.   It would in fact be a very efficient procedure if a valid estimate of error were employed.   The estimate of error which is used assumes random sampling, but these samples are likely to be more like one another than would random samples of the same size, since the same schools are equally represented in each. In this case, therefore, the error estimate exaggerates the magnitude of errors of the first type, but very largely ignores errors of the second type. While the precision of this design is much greater than that of Design III, the results are less likely to appear "significant" as judged by the estimate of error, since the difference in means is likely to be smaller, but the estimate of error will be as large or larger than before (larger because the variability in scores of pupils from 10 schools is likely to be greater than of those from 5).

As will be shown later, this experiment should be considered as consisting of 10 parallel experiments of the nature of Design II, rather than as a single experiment. If so considered, and if certain other conditions are satisfied, a much more valid estimate of error may be derived for the combined experiments.

Design V: Conducted in one school. Pupils are given a preliminary test of spelling ability and two classes are organized such that they show as nearly as possible the same distribution of scores on this test. The standard error of the difference in means on the criterion test is then computed by the special formula for differences in means of matched samples, which takes into consideration the correlation between initial and final scores.

Comments: This is the familiar "matched" or "equated" groups type of experiment. Depending on the correlation between initial and final scores, this design will result in higher precision than Design I, and the estimate of error will be highly valid (recognizing the increased precision) but only so far as errors of the first type are concerned. A disadvantage of the design is that the initial test must be administered and scored before the groups can be organized, and then only with additional administrative difficulties. A procedure will later be suggested which will eliminate this limitation, but which will yield equal precision and equal validity of the error-estimate.

Design VI: Duplicates Design V in each of 10 schools. Results pooled in a single distribution for each method and results evaluated as in single school of Design V.

Comments: This is the most precise of the designs considered, but the estimate of error is decidedly invalid since it assumes that pupils with the *same* score on the initial test are assigned at *random* to the two methods. The estimate therefore exaggerates errors of the first type, and only indirectly and inadequately considers those of the second.

4. VALID METHODS OF ANALYSIS OF EXPERIMENTAL DATA

The foregoing illustrations should be sufficient to clarify the principles earlier suggested and to demonstrate the importance of selecting a design that will not only lead to high precision, but will also permit a valid estimate of error. It should be noted that one of the principal obstacles to the discovery of a satisfactory design was the existence of large systematic differences from school to school. Were it not for this factor, designs of the type of I, II, and V preceding could be extended to include enough pupils to secure any desired degree of reliability. For practical reasons, however, large samples for educational experiments can be secured only by combining a number of intact school groups or, otherwise stated, by duplicating the same experiment in a number of school situations. When this is done, the total group under any treatment may no longer be considered as a random sample and the familiar random sampling techniques applied to the pooled results will no longer provide a valid estimate of error. What is needed, then, is some means of collating the results from a series of duplicate experiments in such a way that the controls over "school" variables of the type described in Designs IV and VI may be taken into consideration in the estimate of error.

The method of analysis which will satisfy this requirement is known as the *analysis of variance*. This method, which has been developed in recent years by R. A. Fisher and his students, represents one of the most important contributions that has yet been made to the techniques of experimental research. It has thus far scarcely been utilized in educational research, and its possibilities are just beginning to be appreciated. It seems destined, however, soon to become the standard procedure in experiments of the general type here considered.

This method will be described in detail in the following chapter, but it may be well to draw attention in advance to some of its most important features. It is essentially a method of analyzing the results from a series of parallel or *duplicated* experiments, each of which is performed under more homogeneous conditions and with more homogeneous groups than prevail in the entire population involved. The estimate of error which it provides eliminates the effects of systematic differences (such as school-differences) from one to another of these duplicated experiments. It will also provide an estimate of the errors due to factors (other than in the treatments) which create systematic differences in the experimental groups within each duplicated experiment, if these factors have been *randomized* within each experiment. For example, suppose that different teachers have taught the various classes in each school in a design like that of number IV in the illustrations just considered. If the teachers in each school were randomly assigned to the methods, the analysis of variance would provide an estimate of error which allows for this uncontrolled teacher variable. The method will thus take into consideration in the estimate of error many important uncontrolled variables for which no estimate can be derived in a single experiment and will permit the utilization of many types of controls (over errors of the second type) which if utilized in a "single experiment" (of the nature of Design IV) only make the results appear less conclusive.

An extension of the analysis of variance, known as the *analysis of covariance*, makes possible all of the precision of designs V and VI, without requiring that the pupils in each school be actually equated with reference to the initial scores. It demands only that an initial measure be available for each pupil, but permits *random* division of the pupils into experimental groups in each school.

This means, of course, that the experimental groups may be organized without waiting for the administration and scoring of a preliminary test and eliminates the difficulties which are met in attempts to "equate" small groups.

There are many interesting and important applications of the analysis of variance and covariance which cannot be suggested here in advance of any detailed consideration of the nature of the methods. Perhaps enough has been said, however, to suggest to the student that these methods of analysis are deserving of his very careful consideration and that it will be worth while for him to persist in his study of them until every detail has been thoroughly mastered.

CHAPTER V

ANALYSIS OF VARIANCE

1. THE FUNDAMENTAL THEOREM IN ANALYSIS OF VARIANCE

THE first step in the development of the methods of analysis of variance is to demonstrate that the variance of a large sample consisting of a number of equal groups may be analyzed into two components: the mean of the variances within the groups, and the variance of the group means. To demonstrate this fact let us suppose that we have a large sample of N cases which consists of r groups of n cases each. We shall call these groups group 1, group 2, ..., group p, ... up to group r, letting p be a general term representing any group. We shall let M represent the mean of the large sample, or the general mean of the r groups taken together, and let M_p represent the mean of a single group. Finally, we shall let d_p' represent the deviation from M of a single measure in group p, and d_p its deviation from the group mean M_p.

It will be observed that this notation is nearly the same as that employed in Section 1 of Chapter III. In this case, however, M represents the observed mean of the large sample, or the general mean of the r groups, rather than a population mean. This, of course, results in a corresponding difference in the meaning of d_p'. Furthermore, we have not here assumed that the r groups are random samples from any population.

Now, in exactly the same manner as in Section 1 of Chapter III, it may be shown that

$$\frac{1}{r}\Sigma\left(\frac{\Sigma d^2}{n}\right) = \frac{\Sigma d'^2}{N} - \frac{\Sigma(M - M_p)^2}{r}. \qquad (12)$$

The steps [1] in the derivation of (12) are algebraically identical with those in the derivation of (6) on page 49, and (12) differs from (6)

---

[1] The student should work through this derivation again, bearing in mind throughout the new meanings of d' and M, to satisfy himself that the change in notation does not disturb the logic.

only in the meaning of d' and M. Let us now, by transposition of terms and change of signs, write (12) as

$$\frac{\Sigma d'^2}{N} = \frac{1}{r}\Sigma\frac{(\Sigma d^2)}{n} + \frac{\Sigma(M - M_p)^2}{r}. \tag{13}$$

We may now note that, since d' represents a deviation from the general mean and since $\Sigma d'^2$ represents the summation of the squares of these deviations over all r groups, the left-hand term in (13) is simply the variance of the large sample of N cases. The first right-hand term in (13) is, as before, the mean of the group variances. The last term is the variance of the group means, since $(M - M_p)$ is the deviation of a single group mean from the mean of all group means, $\Sigma(M - M_p)^2$ is the sum of the squares of these deviations, and r is their number.

We have thus seen (13) that the variance of a large sample consisting of r smaller groups of n cases each may be analyzed into two components: the average variance within groups and the variance of the group means. We may remind ourselves that this is true for any collection of r groups of n cases each, i.e., it does not involve any assumption of random selection. It does, however, suggest a test of the hypothesis that the r groups *are* random samples from the same population.

For large samples, we are accustomed to using the σ of the sample as an estimate of the σ of the population (or the variance of the sample as an estimate of the variance of the population). Accordingly, if we had a number of large samples we could, under the hypothesis that they were all random samples of the same population, use the average variance of the samples as a better estimate of the population variance than the variance of any one sample alone. Similarly, again under the hypothesis of random sampling, we could use the observed variance of the means of these samples as an estimate of the variance of an infinite number of such means. But since the variance of a very large number of means of random samples of the same size is given by

$$\sigma_M^2 = \frac{\sigma_{pop}^2}{n},$$

we could also use n times the observed variance of means $(n\,\sigma_M^2)$ as an estimate of the variance of the population. We would then have two independent estimates of the variance of the population, both derived from our set of r samples of n cases each. One would be based on the variance *within* groups, the other upon the variance of group means, or on the variance *between* groups. If our hypothesis were correct, these two estimates would differ only by chance. If, then, we could show by means of the F-test that the ratio between these estimated variances is larger than chance would allow, we would have reason to believe that our hypothesis is false.

By way of illustration, suppose we had 40 samples of 75 cases each, that we did not know that these were random samples from the same population, but that we wished to test the hypothesis that they were. To apply the test suggested in the preceding paragraphs, we would first compute the variance of each sample separately, and then find the mean of these 40 variances. The result would serve as one of our estimates of the population variance. We would next make up a distribution of the means of these samples, and compute the variance of this distribution. We would then multiply this variance by 75 to secure another estimate of the population variance. We would then compute the ratio (F) between these two estimates of the population variance. If the F then proved significant we would have to reject our hypothesis, i.e., we would say that the variance of the sample means is larger than chance would allow in random sampling.

The test just described would not be exact, since we know that, particularly for small samples, the σ of the sample is not a good estimate of σ_{pop}, or the sample variance is not a good estimate of the true variance. Neither, for a small number of samples, would the observed variance of their means be a good estimate of the true variance of such means. The preceding paragraphs, then, only *suggest* a valid test of our hypothesis. However, if both n and r are small, we can readily secure similar but more valid estimates of the true variance by means of formula (7) (page 50).

According to (7), the best estimate of the true variance which can be computed from a single small group is $\dfrac{\Sigma d_p^2}{n-1}$. The average of these estimates for all r groups would of course constitute a still better estimate of the true variance. This average would be $\dfrac{1}{r}\Sigma\left(\dfrac{\Sigma d_p^2}{n-1}\right)$, which could be more simply written $\dfrac{\Sigma d^2}{r(n-1)}$, in

which Σd^2 represents the grand sum, for all groups, of the squared deviations of the individual measures, *each from the mean of the group to which it belongs*. Similarly, the best estimate of the true variance of the group means would be $\Sigma\dfrac{(M-M_p)^2}{r-1}$, and from

this the best estimate of the variance of the population would be

$$\frac{n\,\Sigma(M-M_p)^2}{r-1}.$$

We now have, under our hypothesis, two estimates of the population variance that are valid even though r and n are both small. These estimates are

$$\text{est'd } \sigma_{pop}^2 = \frac{n\,\Sigma(M-M_p)^2}{r-1} \qquad \text{(based on variance of group means or variance between groups)} \qquad (14)$$

and

$$\text{est'd } \sigma_{pop}^2 = \frac{\Sigma d^2}{r(n-1)} \qquad \text{(based on variance within groups)} \qquad (15)$$

The number of degrees of freedom for the first estimate is $(r-1)$, and for the second is $r(n-1)$. The second estimate is the average of the estimates for the individual groups and since each involves $(n-1)$ degrees of freedom, the average of r of them will involve $r(n-1)$ *d.f.*

These estimates will of course differ by chance, even though the hypothesis is true. However, they should not differ "significantly." That is, if the ratio (F) between these estimates proves significant, we may conclude that our hypothesis is false, or that the differences in group means may not be entirely attributed to fluctuations in random sampling. In other words, in the event of a significant F, we may conclude that there are some *real* differences between the groups.

The foregoing presents the essentials of the logic involved in general in the methods of analysis of variance. *The basic proposition is that from any set of r groups of n cases each, we may, on the hypothesis that all groups are random samples from the same population, derive two independent estimates of the population variance, one of which is based on the variance of group means, the other on the average variance within groups. The test of this hypothesis then consists of determining whether or not the ratio (F) between these estimates lies below the value in the table for F that corresponds to the selected level of significance.*

The application of the basic proposition of analysis of variance in various experimental designs presents many other detailed problems, and the more important of these subsidiary problems will be discussed later with reference to concrete illustrations. Before going on to any consideration of these applications, however, it is essential that the student arrive at a *thorough* understanding of what has been presented in this section and in Section I of Chapter III. There are some things in statistical theory that the research worker can afford to take on faith, but the proof of the basis proposition in analysis of variance is not among them. Unless this proof is fully understood, there is little possibility of intelligent application of the methods to be described in the following sections.

Note on Computational Procedure:

We have seen, in (14) and (15), that the terms Σd^2 and $n\Sigma(M - M_p)^2$ represent the basic quantities needed for our test of significance. It may be well to insert here a description of the manner in which these quantities may be most conveniently computed. We may note first that

$$\Sigma d^2 = \Sigma d'^2 - n\Sigma(M - M_p)^2. \tag{16}$$

The proof of this equality was given in Section 1 of Chapter III, since (16) is identical, except for the meaning of d' and M, with (5) on page 49.

Now d' represents the deviation of any measure from the general mean. Hence, if X represents any measure, $d' = X - M$, and

$$d'^2 = X^2 - 2\,MX - M^2.$$

Summing these expressions for all N measures, we have

$$\Sigma\,d'^2 = \Sigma\,X^2 - 2\,M\,\Sigma\,X - NM^2.$$

But $\Sigma\,X = NM$, hence

$$\Sigma\,d'^2 = \Sigma\,X^2 - 2\,NM^2 - NM^2 = \Sigma\,X^2 - NM^2$$

It will help avoid confusion later to let GT represent the grand total of all the measures $(GT = NM)$, and to let GM, instead of M, represent the general mean. With this notation, we may write

$$\Sigma\,d'^2 = \Sigma\,X^2 - GT\cdot GM. \tag{17}$$

Hence, to compute $\Sigma\,d'^2$, we need only square each of the N measures, sum these squares, and subtract the product of the grand total and the general mean. On an automatic electric computing machine, the X^2's may be cumulated as they are secured, and the grand total may be secured along with the sum of the squares.

It may be shown similarly [1] that the term $\Sigma(M - M_p)^2$ in (16) is equal to

$$\Sigma(GM - M_p)^2 = (M_1^2 + M_2^2 + \cdots\cdots + M_r^2) - GT\cdot\Sigma\,M_p$$

and that therefore

$$n\,\Sigma(GM - M_p)^2 = \frac{T_1^2 + T_2^2 + \cdots + T_p^2 + \cdots + T_r^2}{n} - GT\cdot GM, \tag{18}$$

in which T_p refers to the sum of the measures for a single group.

The equality in (18) may also be written as follows:

$$\Sigma\,n_p(GM - M_p)^2 = (T_1 M_1 + T_2 M_2 + \cdots + T_r M_r) - GT\cdot GM. \tag{18a}$$

This form of the equality will be more convenient to use than (18) in certain types of situations in which the number of cases varies from group to group.

Expressions (17) and (18) or (18a), as we shall see later, will markedly simplify the computation of the terms needed in our final tests of significance. Once $\Sigma\,d'^2$ and $n\,\Sigma(GM - M_p)^2$ have been computed by (17) and (18), we may readily secure $\Sigma\,d^2$ by subtraction according to (16).

[1] The full proof of (18) and (18a) is left as an exercise for the student.

2. ANALYSIS INTO TWO COMPONENTS: ANALYSIS OF RESULTS
IN A SIMPLE METHODS EXPERIMENT

The methods of analysis of variance will perhaps be most frequently applied in educational research to analyze the results of "methods" experiments. The variations in these methods of analysis will therefore be illustrated in terms of such experiments, although other possible applications will be suggested later. Our first illustration will be of the relatively simple design which may be used when the experiment is to be performed in a single school.

Suppose, then, that in a certain school we have conducted an experiment to determine the relative effectiveness of four different methods of instruction for a given unit of content. To make the arithmetic of the illustration simple, we will say that the experiment has involved just 20 pupils. These pupils were originally assigned at *random* to 4 groups of 5 pupils each, one of which was taught by Method A, another by Method B, etc. At the close of the experiment, the same criterion test of achievement was administered to all pupils. The scores on this criterion test are arranged in tabular form as illustrated in Table 6.

TABLE 6
CRITERION SCORES IN A SIMPLE METHODS EXPERIMENT
(Hypothetical Illustrative Data)

	Methods (or Groups)		
A	B	C	D
7	6	4	3
3	7	2	4
4	10	2	5
3	8	1	4
6	5	3	2

Totals (T_p)   23   36   12   18   89.00 = Grand Total
                                                       (GT)

Means (M_p)   4.6   7.2   2.4   3.6   4.45 = General Mean
                                                       (GM)

The purpose of our analysis will be to determine whether the differences in means for the various methods are significant of real differences, or may be explained away in terms of chance fluctuations in random sampling. In other words, we wish to test the hypothesis that the four groups of scores are random samples from the same population. We must then, according to the logic of the preceding section, derive from these data two independent estimates of the variance of this hypothetical population.

The first of these estimates will be based on the group means, as computed by (14). This means that we must first compute $n\,\Sigma(GM - M_p)^2$, noting that in this case M_p is a general term for any of the four group means. According to (18),

$$n\,\Sigma(GM - M_p)^2 = \frac{T_1^2 + T_2^2 + T_3^2 + T_4^2}{n} - GT \cdot GM$$

$$= \frac{529 + 1296 + 144 + 324}{5} - 89.00 \times 4.45$$

$$= 458.60 - 396.05 = 61.55$$

According to (14), this result, divided by $r - 1 = 4 - 1 = 3$, will constitute our first estimated variance. For simplicity, we will call this result the "variance for *methods*," since it is based on the means of the methods groups.

Our second estimate will be based on the variance *within groups*, as computed by (15). This means that we must first compute $\Sigma\,d^2$, which, according to (16), is equal to $\Sigma\,d'^2 - n\,\Sigma(GM - M_p)^2$. Now according to (17),

$$\Sigma\,d'^2 = \Sigma\,X^2 - GM \cdot GT$$

$$= 497 - 396.05 = 100.95$$

This result was obtained by first computing $\Sigma\,X^2$, which is the sum of the squares of the 20 individual scores. That is,

$$\Sigma\,X^2 = 7^2 + 3^2 + 4^2 + 3^2 + 6^2 + 6^2 + \cdots\cdots\cdots + 4^2 + 2^2 = 497.$$

Now, according to (16),

$$\Sigma\,d^2 = 100.95 - 61.55 = 39.40$$

According to (15), this result, divided by $r(n - 1) = 4(5 - 1) = 16$, is our second estimated variance. We will call this the "variance within groups" for simplicity in reference, although strictly it is an estimate of the hypothetical population variance based on the variance within groups.

In practical computation, it is convenient to arrange these results in tabular form, as follows:

	d.f.	Sum of Squares	Variance
Methods	3	61.55	20.517
Within Groups	16	39.40	2.463
Total	19	100.95	

This is the standard form in which we will hereafter array the results of an analysis of variance. "Sum of squares" is simply a convenient abbreviation, which really has different meanings for different rows in the table. The number entered in the first row in the "sum of squares" column is really $n \Sigma (GM - M_p)^2$, or n times the sum of the squared deviations of the methods means from the general mean. The sum of squares for "within groups" is the sum of the squared deviations of the individual scores, each from the mean of the group to which it belongs, or Σd^2. (This sum of squares was secured by subtraction, but the student may find it instructive to check the result by finding the difference between each score and the mean of the group to which it belongs, squaring these 20 differences, and finding their total.) The sum of squares for "total" is the sum of the squared deviations of the individual scores from the general mean, or $\Sigma d'^2$. It is convenient to use "sum of squares" to denote briefly all of these things, but the student should guard against interpreting it literally as a sum of squared scores or means.

We are now ready to apply the test of significance. The ratio (F) between the *methods* and *within groups* variances is 20.517/2.463 = 7.82. Now we find, entering Table 4 with 3 and 16 d.f., that F need only exceed 5.29 to be significant at the 1 per cent level. Hence, it is clear that our hypothesis must be false, and that the differences in methods means could hardly be due to chance alone. This does not mean, however, that the differences in methods means are necessarily due to differences in the relative merits of the methods themselves. All that we have done is to demonstrate that the differences in means could not reasonably be attributed to chance differences in pupil ability resulting from the random division of the total sample into the methods groups. The observed differences in means, although not due to chance in this sense, may be due to some uncontrolled factor, such as the teacher-variable, particularly if different teachers had taught the different groups. The influence of such uncontrolled irrelevant factors may under certain conditions be taken into consideration in the test of significance in other types of experimental designs, but not in a simple design like that employed in this illustration.

Neither does the F-test signify that all methods differences are significant, or that the methods means are ranked in the order of the merits of the methods, even disregarding the possible effect of uncontrolled irrelevant factors. It may be, for example, that three of the methods are equally effective, and that the large F (or large *methods* variance) resulted only from the superiority of *one* method. We would still have to make a separate test, then, of any particular difference in which we were interested.

To test the significance of any particular difference, such as the difference in means for methods A and C, we may apply the t-test to that difference. This test, as we will recall from Section 2 of Chapter III, is a test of the hypothesis that both groups were selected at random from the same population, and requires that we have some estimate of the σ of this hypothetical population. In formula (10), page 57, this estimate was obtained by pooling the squared deviations from both groups. In this case, however, we can get a still better estimate by pooling the sums of squared deviations from all methods groups. If we assume that the variance within a group differs from group to group only by chance, then the "variance within groups" is our best estimate of the population variance, and its square root is our best estimate of the σ_{pop} needed in the formula for the standard error of a mean.

Hence, the best estimate of the standard error of a single methods mean is

$$\text{est'd } \sigma_M = \frac{\text{est'd } \sigma_{pop}}{\sqrt{n}} = \sqrt{\frac{2.463}{5}} = .702$$

To find the standard error of any other methods mean, we divide the variance *within groups* by the number of cases on which the mean is based, and extract the square root of the result. In this case, since each methods mean is based on the same number of cases, each has the same standard error. It should be noted that this estimate of the standard error of a group mean is based on the same $r(n-1)$ degrees of freedom on which the variance *within groups* is based.

The estimated standard error of a difference between any two methods means, such as for A and C, would then be

$$\text{est'd } \sigma_{M_A - M_C} = \sqrt{\sigma_{M_A}^2 + \sigma_{M_C}^2} = \sqrt{2\,\sigma_{M_A}^2}$$
$$= 1.414\,\sigma_{M_A} = 1.414 \times .702 = .992$$

Again this estimate, being based on the variance *within groups*, involves $r(n-1) = 16\ d.f.$ Hence, the value of t for the difference between two methods means, such as A and C, is

$$t = \frac{M_A - M_C}{\text{est'd } \sigma_{M_A - M_C}} = \frac{4.6 - 2.4}{.992} = 2.217$$

For 16 $d.f.$, this t is significant at the 5 per cent, but not at the 2 per cent level.

Since all methods means are equally reliable, we may, if we wish, determine in general what minimum difference between any two means will be significant at any given level. For example, at the 1 per cent level, t must exceed 2.921 for 16 $d.f.$ Hence, from

$$2.921 = \frac{M_1 - M_2}{.992},$$

we find that the difference must exceed $2.921 \times .992 = 2.90$. The differences between the means for A and C, A and D, B and A, and C and D, are not this large. The mean for B, however, exceeds those for C and D by more than this amount. Hence, these are the only differences which are significant at the 1 per cent level.

The student may well ask why it was necessary to apply the F-test at all, if we were subsequently going to test the individual differences anyway. The answer is that the F-test tells us whether it is worth while to test the individual differences at all. If the F-test had not proven significant, we would have known at once that *all* observed differences in methods means could be due to chance alone. In that case it would not only have been unnecessary, but decidedly *improper* [1] to apply the t-test to individual differences.

It may be well to observe here that the F-test which is applied to the *methods* and *within groups* variances may be considered as essentially a way of applying the t-test to all differences in methods means simultaneously. If there are only two methods groups, the F-test becomes the algebraic equivalent of the t-test; in this case $F = t^2$, as the student may note by comparing the values for F (at the 1 per cent level) in the first column of Table 4 with the corresponding values for t in the last column of Table 3.

---

[1] This is particularly true if all of the methods are quantitatively similar, and if the experiment was not designed for any special comparison of two of the methods. An exception to this rule might be defended, however, if one of the methods exhibits marked qualitative differences from all of the others. For example, in an experiment concerned with the relative effectiveness of five types of review procedures upon retention of a "lesson" in geography, four of the review procedures consisted of a 30-minute re-reading of the original lesson. These four procedures differed only in the distribution of time of re-reading: one 30-minute period, two 15-minute periods, etc. The fifth review procedure consisted of a 30-minute written exercise in objective test form. The mean scores on a delayed recall test for the four re-reading groups differed little among themselves, but the mean criterion score for the objective-drill group differed appreciably from the others. The F-test involving all five means fell short of the 5 per cent level of significance. The four re-reading groups were then combined into a single group, whose mean was compared with that of the objective-drill group. The t-test showed this difference to be significant beyond the 1 per cent level. This procedure was legitimate in this case, because the special comparison was suggested by the qualitative characteristics of the methods, and not just by an inspection of the final means. Had all five methods been qualitatively similar, however, it would *not* have been legitimate to select the method with the highest (or lowest) criterion mean for a special comparison with one or with a combination of the others. (See Fisher, *Design of Experiments*, p. 65.)

It is important to note that the evaluation of individual group means and of the individual differences between them involves the assumption that the variance within a group is the same, except for chance, from group to group. In other words, we assume that whatever factor has resulted in significant differences in group *means* will *not* also result in significant differences in group variances. If the group variances do differ fundamentally, then, of course, the standard error of the mean will differ from group to group, even though all groups are of the same size, and it would not be valid to compute the standard error of a mean from the "variance *within groups*." This assumption, known as the assumption of *homogeneity of variance*, may not be very well satisfied in the typical methods experiment, particularly when several schools are involved. It is quite conceivable that the same factor which causes some schools or methods to produce higher mean achievement than others may also cause some schools or methods to produce more variable achievement than others. Evidence will be presented later in this chapter that the variance in educational achievement within *schools* is in fact not constant, but fortunately it is also possible to show that this fact does not seriously disturb the *F*-test of significance in the type of design most frequently employed in educational experiments,[1] and which will later be discussed in Sections 4–6 of this chapter.

[1] If desired, an exact test of the hypothesis of homogeneous variance may be applied to the observed data. It has been shown by M. S. Bartlett that if $s_1'^2 \cdots s_i'^2 \cdots s_k'^2$ represent independent estimates [see (7), page 50] of the population variance derived from k samples drawn at random from the same population (or from equally variable populations), if s'^2 represents the weighted mean of these estimates, if $n_1 \cdots n_i \cdots n_k$ represent the numbers of degrees of freedom for the various samples, and n represents the sum of these numbers ($n = \Sigma\, n_i$), then

$$\frac{2.3026}{C}\left(n \log_{10} s'^2 - \Sigma\, n_i \log_{10} s_i'^2\right),$$

in which

$$C = 1 + \frac{1}{3(k-1)}\left(\left(\Sigma \frac{1}{n_i}\right) - \frac{1}{n}\right),$$

is approximately distributed as χ^2 with $k - 1$ degrees of freedom.

When all samples are of the same size, that is, when $n_1 = n_2 = \cdots = n_k$, we have

$$\frac{1}{C} = \frac{3\,n}{3\,n + k + 1}$$

3. RULES FOR ANALYZING THE RESULTS OF A SIMPLE METHODS EXPERIMENT

It may now be well to summarize the procedure for analyzing the results of a simple methods experiment in terms of a series of brief rules which may conveniently be followed in practice. By a "simple methods experiment," we mean one in which the methods groups are selected at *random* from the same large group at the beginning of the experiment — a condition which usually can be satisfied only when the experiment is performed in a single school — and in which the same criterion test is given to all pupils at the close of the experiment. To analyze these criterion scores by the methods of analysis of variance, the steps in the procedure are as follows:

1. *Compute the total (T) and the mean (M) of criterion scores for each methods group separately.*

2. *Compute the grand total (GT) and the general mean (GM) for all scores taken together.* (Compute *GM* to at least five significant digits.)[1]

3. *Square each individual score, and total these squares for all groups to secure ΣX^2; then subtract $GT \cdot GM$ to secure the sum of squares for* TOTAL *$(\Sigma d'^2 = \Sigma X^2 - GT \cdot GM)$.* (Round this result to five significant digits.) (If the total number of

and hence

$$X^2 = \frac{7.9078\, n}{3\, n + k + 1} \left(n \log_{1} s'^2 - n_i\, \Sigma \log_{10} s^2 \right).$$

For example, in Table 6 on page 93, $n_1 = 5$, $n = 20$, $k = 4$,

$$s_A'^2 = \frac{13.2}{4} = 3.3, \; s_B'^2 = 3.7, \; s_C'^2 = 1.3, \; s_D'^2 = 1.3, \text{ from which}$$

$$s'^2 = \frac{3.3 + 3.7 + 1.3 + 1.3}{4} = 2.4.$$

Hence

$$X^2 = \frac{(7.9078)(20)}{60 - 4 - 1} [(20)(0.38021) - 5(0.51851 + 0.56820 + 0.11394 + 0.11394)] = 2.19$$

This value of χ^2 is obviously not significant for 3 *d.f.*, hence we are justified in retaining the hypothesis of homogeneous variance, and on this hypothesis applying the *F*-test of significance as on page 95.

[1] See E. F. Lindquist, *A First Course in Statistics*, pp. 61–66, for a discussion of significant digits.

scores is quite large, or if a computing machine is not available, the most convenient way of securing the sum of squares for *total* is to prepare a grouped frequency distribution of *all* scores, and to employ the "short" method, using an arbitrary reference point. The formula needed is

$$\Sigma\, d'^2 = i^2 \left[\Sigma\, fd''^2 - \frac{(\Sigma\, fd'')^2}{N} \right]$$

in which $\Sigma\, d'^2$ is the sum of squares for *total*, i is the size of the interval, d'' is the deviation of the midpoint of any interval from the arbitrary reference point and f the frequency in that interval, and in which $\Sigma\, fd''$ is the *algebraic* sum of the products fd''.)

4. *Square the total for each methods group separately, add these squares, divide their sum by the number of cases in a single methods group, and subtract GT · GM to secure the sum of squares for* METHODS. (See (18), page 92.) (Carry this result to the same number of *decimal places* as in the rounded sum of squares for *total*.)

5. *Subtract the sum of squares for* METHODS *from that for* TOTAL *to secure the sum of squares for* WITHIN GROUPS.

6. *Arrange these results in tabular form as indicated below, and divide the sum of squares for* METHODS *and* WITHIN GROUPS *by the corresponding d.f.'s to secure the corresponding variances.* The d.f. for *methods* is one less than the number of methods, and for *total* is one less than the total number of pupils. The d.f. for *within groups* may then be found by subtracting the d.f. for *methods* from that for *total*.

	d.f.	Sums of Squares	Variances
Methods	. . . . . .	. . . .	. . . .
Within Groups (error)	. . . . . .	. . . .	. . . .
Total	. . . . . .	. . . .	

(*Note:* The *within groups* variance is often referred to as the *error* variance in this design, since the standard errors of the means are based on this variance. However, the *within groups* variance is not always used as the *error* variance, as we shall see later in connection with other designs.)

7. *Find the ratio (F) of the* METHODS *and* ERROR *variances, and turn to Table 4 to see if this ratio is significant.* (If the *methods* variance happens to be less than *error* variance, it is obvious that there is no significant difference, and no reference need be made to the table.) If the *F* is not significant, the analysis is usually concluded, since there is then usually no need to investigate individual differences. (See footnote 1 on page 98.)

8. *If the F is significant, and if more than two methods are involved, the individual differences may be evaluated by the t-test.* The standard error of any mean may be estimated by dividing the *error* variance by the number of cases on which that mean is based and extracting the square root of the result. The estimated standard error of the difference in any two independent means is the square root of the sum of the squares of the two standard errors of the means involved. If all methods groups are of the same size, the estimated standard error of any difference is 1.414 times the standard error of any mean. The number of degrees of freedom for *t* in any test involving these estimated standard errors is the same as the *d.f.* for the *error* variance. If all methods groups are of the same size, the minimum value of any difference which will be significant at a selected level may be found by finding in Table 3 the value of *t* needed at that level, and multiplying this value of *t* by the estimated standard error of the difference.

Note: These rules are applicable even though the number of cases may not be the same for all methods groups, so long as these groups were originally selected at random from the same population. In this case we would compute the sum of squares for *methods* according to (18a) on page 92, rather than according to (18), since n is no longer constant from group to group. According to (18a), the sum of squares for *methods* is the sum of the *weighted* squared deviations of the group means from the general mean, the squared deviation of each group mean being weighted by the number of cases on which it is based. This weighted sum divided by $(r - 1)$ is still a valid estimate of the population variance under the hypothesis of random sampling, and may be used as before to test this hypothesis. The sum of squares for *total* may of course be found as before, and the sum of squares *within groups* is still equal to the difference between the sums of squares for *total* and *methods*. If we can assume homogeneity of group variances, we can still compute the standard error of any methods mean by dividing the *error* variance by the number of cases on which that particular mean is based, and extracting the square root of the result.

We may note, finally, that in any methods experiment of this type, performed in a single school, any conclusions drawn are strictly applicable only to that school. In the illustration used (page 93), Method B seemed superior. We have already observed that the apparent superiority of Method B may be due only to the fact that a better teacher was used with Method B than with the others, or that some other extraneous factor operated systematically in favor of Method B in the experiment. Let us assume, however, that all such factors had been very carefully equalized in the experiment, and that Method B really is superior in *this* school. It still does not follow that Method B is the best of these methods in other schools. The pupils in this particular school may previously have been taught by a method similar to Method B, so that they could begin using it at once with full effectiveness, while the other methods may have been strange to them, and much of their time during the experiment may have been spent in becoming acquainted with the method itself. How effective a particular method may be in a particular school depends upon the previous experiences of the pupils, or upon study habits previously acquired by the pupils in that school, and these may differ systematically from school to school. This particular design, then, has certain very serious limitations. In the first place, the error estimate takes into consideration only the first of the two sources of error mentioned on page 79 (the pupil variable), and this may often be the less important of the sources of error present. In the second place, the method which is best in one school may not be best in another, and hence any recommendations concerning methods, which are based on the results of the experiment, must be restricted to the particular school involved. Finally, the number of pupils available in any one school is usually quite small, and hence the degree of precision attained is usually low. We shall therefore be particularly interested in the designs which avoid these limitations, and which are discussed in the succeeding sections.

4. ANALYSIS INTO THREE COMPONENTS: ANALYSIS OF POOLED RESULTS OF DUPLICATED EXPERIMENTS IN RANDOMLY SELECTED SCHOOLS (GROUPS OF UNIFORM SIZE)

In order to attain high precision, to be able to draw conclusions applicable to schools in general, and to secure a comprehensive error estimate, it is necessary in methods experiments to include pupils from a number of different schools. The design usually employed in such instances is like that of Design IV, described on page 82. We shall now consider the appropriate procedure for analyzing the results obtained with this type of design.

This procedure may perhaps be most readily explained with reference to a concrete illustration. Suppose, then, that we have conducted an experimental comparison of 3 methods involving, say, 5 schools, each of which has provided 60 pupils. Suppose that, at the beginning of the experiment, we had in each school divided the pupils into three classes of 20 pupils each, and had assigned these classes at random one to each of the three methods.

Our "experiment" would then really consist of *five duplicate experiments*, one in each school. The results in any one school could, of course, be analyzed as in the illustration of the preceding section, but the same procedure could not be applied to the collected results from all schools.   That is, it would not be valid to throw all results into a single table like Table 6 (page 82), and then apply the F-test to the variances for *methods* and *within groups* in this table.   The reason for this is that the procedure of the preceding section assumes that the pupils under each method were *randomly* selected from *all* pupils involved in the experiment, whereas a "methods group" thus consisting of intact groups from several schools could not be considered as a random sample, even though the pupils in each school were randomly selected from the available pupils in that school.   We must then have some other way of "pooling" the results from our five duplicated experiments that will permit a valid estimate of error for the combined results.

If it were not for the objection already raised, this "pooling" could be effected by analyzing the variance of the 15 class *means* on the criterion test in exactly the same way that we analyzed the variance of the 20 pupil scores in the example accompanying Table 6.   While this procedure would not be valid, it will be worth while to consider it more specifically, since through it we may better arrive at an understanding of a more appropriate procedure.

Let us assume for the moment, then, that we propose to analyze the variance of the 15 class *means* by the method of the preceding section, dealing with class means as we previously dealt with individual pupil scores.   This would involve a tabular arrangement of the means into three columns of five means each, one column for each method.   It should at once be clear that some of the variance in the total distribution of 15 class means would be due to systematic differences in achievement from school to school.   These school differences would make the variance in each methods column (containing class means from 5 schools) considerably larger than if the classes were random samples from all pupils in the schools involved.   In other words, the school differences would increase the variance *within groups* (in this case groups of means) which would be used as the *error* variance in evaluating the *methods* variance.   At the same time, the design of the experiment would tend to eliminate the effect of school differences from differences in methods means, and would thus *reduce* the magnitude of the *methods* variance (as compared to the situation in which all classes were random samples from all pupils in the entire sample of 300). This is because the same 5 schools would be represented in each column, and hence the superiority or inferiority of any one school would tend to affect all methods means alike.

If we followed the procedure of the preceding section with these 15 class means, then, we would be eliminating school differences from the *methods* variance without eliminating them from the *error* variance. Hence, while our experiment would really be more precise than if all pupils were random samples from all pupils involved, our analysis would make it *appear* less precise. This, as we have noted before in connection with Design IV of Chapter IV, is an error that has characterized many methods experiments in the past. It is clear, then, that we must eliminate school differences from our error estimate as well as from our methods differences.

This can be done, without altering our experimental design, by analyzing the results in another way. It involves analyzing the total sum of squares for the class means into *three* components: the sum of squares between methods, between schools, and a "remainder" which is left when the sums for methods and schools are subtracted from the total. As before, the 15 class means would be arranged in a 5 × 3 table, but in this case we would take care to have the three class means for each school in the same row. The three columns would then represent the methods, and the 5 rows the schools. We would find the sum of squares for the *methods* variance exactly as we did in Table 6 (except that we would be dealing with class means instead of pupil scores). We would then write opposite each *row* the total and mean for the row (or school), and then proceed to find the sum of squares for the *rows* just as we did for the columns. In other words, we would find the product of the total and mean for each row, sum these products, and subtract the product of the general mean and grand total. The result would be the sum of squares for *schools*. The sum of squares for *classes* (which corresponds to that for *total* in the example of the preceding section) would be found as before by squaring each class mean, summing these squared means, and subtracting the product of the general mean and grand total. We would then subtract the sums of squares for *methods* and for *schools* from the sum of squares for *classes* to secure the *remainder* sum of squares. The *d.f.* for *schools* would be one less than the number of schools, or 4, just as the *d.f.* for *methods* is one less than the number of methods, or 2. The *d.f.* for *classes* would be one less than the number of classes, or 14. The *d.f.* for *remainder* would then be $14 - 4 - 2 = 8$. The variances for *methods*, for *schools*, and for *remainder* would be found by dividing each sum of squares by its *d.f.* The final step would be to test the *methods* variance by finding its ratio (F) to the *remainder* variance, from which school differences have now been eliminated.

Before continuing further with a discussion of this procedure, it may be well to illustrate the arithmetical processes just described. Suppose that the results for our experiment are as summarized in the following table (Table 7). The scores for the individual pupils are not given, since they are not essential to an understanding of the procedure. The student should have no difficulty in

TABLE 7

ANALYSIS OF VARIANCE OF CLASS MEANS IN A METHODS EXPERIMENT
INVOLVING 5 SCHOOLS AND 3 METHODS

		Method			Schools	
		A	B	C	Totals	Means
	School 1	20.75	20.00	25.45	66.20	22.0667
	" 2	34.60	18.75	29.40	82.75	27.5833
	" 3	29.55	24.05	28.05	81.65	27.2167
	" 4	39.15	22.65	30.60	92.40	30.8000
	" 5	32.40	27.10	28.50	88.00	29.3333
Methods	Totals	156.45	112.55	142.00	$411.00 = GT$	
	Means	31.29	22.51	28.4		$27 40 = GM$

following the computation with the aid of the preceding description.

$GT \cdot GM = 11,261.40$

Total sum of squares (sum of squares for *classes*)

$$= 20.75^2 + 34.60^2 + \cdots + 28.50^2 - 11,261.40 = 446.88$$

Sum of squares for *methods*

$$= \frac{156.45^2 + 112.55^2 + 142.00^2}{5} - 11,261.40 = 200.22$$

Sum of squares for *schools*

$$= \frac{66.20^2 + 82.75^2 + \cdots + 88.00^2}{3} - 11,261.40 = 131.43$$

Sum of squares for *remainder*

$$= 446.88 - 200.22 - 131.43 = 115.23$$

	d.f.	Sum of Squares	Variance
Methods (M)	2	200.22	100.11
Schools (S)	4	131.43	32.86
Remainder (M × S)	8	115.23	14.40
Classes	14	446.88	

$$F = 100.11/14.40 = 6.95$$
$$(d.f. \text{ for } F = 2 \text{ and } 8)$$

(*Note:* Ordinarily the class means would be carried to more decimal places, but in this case, since the divisor for each class was 20, each class mean was even at the second decimal place.)

In terms of this illustration, we may now consider more specifically the nature of the *remainder* variance that is obtained in an analysis of this type. As we have seen, it is the part of the total variance of class means that is left after we have "taken out" the parts due to methods differences and to school differences. In other words, it is due to the differences that still exist between class means after systematic methods and school differences have been

eliminated. It could be computed directly, rather than by subtraction, as follows: *First*, "correct" each class mean so as to eliminate methods differences. Do this by adding to or subtracting
from each class mean in each column the deviation of the mean of
that column from the general mean. For example, in Table 7 the
mean of column A is 3.89 units above the general mean; hence we
subtract 3.89 units from each class mean in column A, thus making
the column mean equal to the general mean. After a similar correction had been made in all columns, all methods means would
be the same, and all would equal the general mean. *Second*, again
correct these once corrected class means so as to eliminate school
differences. This is done by adding to or subtracting from each
class mean in each *row* the deviation of the mean of that row (or
school) from the general mean.

After the first correction, the class means of Table 7 will be as
follows:

	A	B	C	School Means
School 1	16.86	24.89	24.45	22.0667
" 2	30.71	23.65	28.40	27.5833
" 3	25.66	28.94	27.05	27.2167
" 4	35.26	27.54	29.60	30.8000
" 5	28.51	31.99	27.50	29.3333
Methods Means	27.40	27.40	27.40	

After the second correction they will be as follows:

	A	B	C	School Means
School 1	22.1933	30.2233	29.7833	27.40
" 2	30.5267	23.4567	28.2167	27.40
" 3	25.8433	29.1233	27.2333	27.40
" 4	31.8600	24.1400	26.2000	27.40
" 5	26.5767	30.0567	25.5667	27.40
Methods Means	27.40	27.40	27.40	

The student is strongly advised to check for himself the computations involved in these corrections. After the double correction, all row means and column means will equal the general mean, i.e., all systematic school differences and methods differences will be eliminated. It is apparent, however, that these corrections do not make the *class* means equal. The corrected class means will still differ, and the sum of their squared deviations from the general mean is the same as the *remainder* sum of squares previously computed by subtraction. Again, the student is strongly advised to check this last statement for himself in the example given. In actual practice, of course, we never compute the *remainder* sum of squares in this laborious fashion, since, as its name implies, it can be so readily obtained by subtraction. However, it helps considerably to understand the nature of the *remainder* variance if one actually computes the corresponding sum of squares in this fashion in a concrete example.

It is illuminating to note, incidentally, that the variance for *schools* can be computed from the first of the corrected tables just presented (that in which only methods differences have been eliminated) by applying the procedure of Section 2 (pp. 93 ff.) to this table, but dealing with rows instead of columns. (Again the student should check this for himself.) The analysis into three components is then really a simple extension of the method of analysis into two components. That is, the procedure employed in Table 7 consists essentially of an analysis of the total variance into *methods* and *within methods* components by the procedure of Section 2, followed by a second application of the same procedure to analyze the *within methods* variance into the *schools* and *remainder* components.

Let us now consider what it is that causes these doubly corrected class means to differ.

In the first place, such differences might remain because of chance alone. This is clear with reference to our example if we visualize what would happen should a *homogeneous* sample of 300 cases (all of whom had been taught by the *same* method) be randomly divided into 15 equal groups, and the means of these groups arranged at random in a 5 × 3 table. The row means and column means would differ as a result of the random assignment of pupils to the groups, but these differences could be eliminated by corrections such as those which have been described. These corrections, however, would only eliminate differences in row means and column means, and would not eliminate differences in groups means *within* the same row or within the same column. It would be interesting, therefore, to know how much of the *remainder* variance could be attributed to chance alone, and a means of so doing will be explained in the next section (Section 5).

In the second place, our corrected means might differ because of any uncontrolled variables which created real differences in achievement from class to class in the same school quite apart from the effects of the methods. In our illustration, for example, the best teacher in School 1 might have been assigned to Method B and poorer teachers to Methods A and C, and this might account at least in part for the relatively better results for B in School 1 than in the other schools (see the table of corrected means). Any such uncontrolled variables would in general tend to increase the variance in class means, although in some cases they might accidentally *counteract* some of the chance differences. A way of dealing with this latter contingency will be considered in Section 5 following.

In the third place, the corrected class means might differ because of real differences in the relative merits of the methods from school to school. Method B may really be a *relatively* better method (i.e., more nearly equal to A and C) for the pupils in School 1 than for the pupils in School 2, due to differences in the previous educational experiences of the pupils in these schools. Such differences may readily occur, for example, if the relative merits of a method in any one school are dependent upon the methods that have previously been employed in that school, and if these previous methods have differed from school to school.

Since the *remainder* variance may in this type of experiment be due to any or all of these three factors, it is difficult to give it an appropriate name. It is really the result of the interaction of all three factors, and may therefore be referred to in general as an "interaction" variance. Since we shall later have occasion to deal with other interaction variances, we will refer to it specifically as the "methods × schools" variance (read methods *by* schools), or as the interaction of methods and schools, or as the $M \times S$ variance. This notation is quite appropriate, since the number of degrees of freedom for the $M \times S$ variance is equal to the product of the degrees of freedom for *methods* and *schools*.

We may now appreciate more fully the exact nature of the test of significance that we have applied to the *methods* variance. We have just noted that the $M \times S$ variance is in part due to chance, and in part to *any* uncontrolled variables which may create real differences in achievement from class to class in the same school, but which cannot be distinguished in that school from real differences in the relative merits of the methods. *The error estimate* (or the test of significance) *based on the $M \times S$ variance thus takes into consideration all sources of error that have been randomized within each school.* It is for this reason that the methods of analysis of variance represent so great an improvement over the statistical procedures that have heretofore been generally employed in educational research. The older procedures, based on the assumption of simple random sampling, were not only invalid because they were applied to samples that were not random, but they also ignored all sources of error except the pupil variables.

The $M \times S$ variance, of course, does not take into consideration any source of error that has not been randomized, or which operates systematically in favor of a certain method in all schools. Consequently, it is extremely important to exercise great care in insuring that as many as possible of these sources of error are actually randomized. This is perhaps best done by first assigning the classes to the teachers, classrooms, hours, etc., and then employing the "random numbers" procedure (pages 24 ff.) in assigning the methods to the classes. If this is done, then all factors (such as the teacher-variable) will be randomized which are independent of the methods themselves. We shall see later that it is not necessary, except for special purposes, to assign the *pupils* at random to the classes, although it is well to do so if that is convenient.

We have seen that the $M \times S$ variance may be due in part to real differences in the relative merits of the methods from school to school. This possibility is of particular interest with reference to the test of significance based on the $M \times S$ variance. If there are any real differences of this kind, it is particularly appropriate to base our test of significance upon these differential or interaction effects, since if one method is to be recommended for general use, it must be best in all schools and not only in some, or at least it must be best in most schools. If the schools in the experiment are not a *random* sample of all schools to which we wish to generalize, the possibility must also be considered that the total superiority of one method in the experiment is due to biased selection, that is, to an unintentional selection of schools which happened to favor that method. This does not mean that we *must* have a random sample of *schools* to make a methods experiment meaningful, but it does mean that if the sample of schools is not random, we must limit our recommendation to schools *like* those that participated in the experiment.

It may be well to draw specific attention in this example to the effect upon our error-estimate of "taking out" the school differences. On page 105 we had suggested, for developmental purposes, that we analyze the variance of class means by the methods of Section 2, pp. 93 ff. In other words, we had suggested analyzing the total sum of squares into its *methods* and *within methods* components, and using the latter as the basis for the *error* term. Had we done this, since the sum of squares for *within methods* is equal to the sum of squares for *schools* plus that for $M \times S$, our *error* sum of squares would have been $131.43 + 115.23 = 246.66$, with $8 + 4 = 12$ *d.f.* Hence, had we not "taken out" schools, our *error* variance would have been $246.66/12 = 20.55$, whereas with *schools* "taken out" it is 14.40. It is clear, then, that our error-estimate would have been seriously inflated had we not eliminated from it the effect of the school differences.

Reference has been made earlier to the basic assumption of homogeneity of variance. It must be remembered that in the analysis just considered we have been concerned only with class means; in the example used, in fact, we knew nothing at all about the variability of pupil scores within individual classes. In applying the F-test based on the ratio of the M and $M \times S$ variances, we must assume only that the class *means, after having been "corrected" to eliminate school differences*, are homogeneous in variability from method to method. (The $M \times S$ variance is, essentially, the variance of class means *within methods*, school differences having been eliminated by the arithmetic of the analysis.) We do not have to make any explicit assumption, however, that the variance in pupil scores is fundamentally constant from school to school. This is an important feature of this design. Evidence will be presented later (pp. 132 ff.) that the variance (within schools) in educational achievement is in fact heterogeneous, but evidence will also be presented (pp. 139 ff.) to show that the variance in class means may nevertheless remain approximately constant from method to method, and that the test of significance based on the ratio of M and $M \times S$ variances may remain valid in spite of the heterogeneity of pupil variance from school to school.

5. ANALYSIS INTO FOUR COMPONENTS: ANALYSIS OF POOLED RESULTS OF DUPLICATE EXPERIMENTS IN RANDOMLY SELECTED SCHOOLS OF UNEQUAL SIZE

In the analysis of the preceding section we dealt only with class means, and gave all classes the same weight. This was quite proper when all classes were of the same size, but it would not be defensible, except as an approximate procedure demanded by special circumstances, if the classes varied in size from school to school. We will now consider the procedure which is appropriate in the latter situation.

In order to demonstrate that this procedure is essentially the same as that just considered in the preceding section, we shall first apply it to the same data used to illustrate that procedure.

The original data from which the class means of Table 7 were derived were the scores of 300 pupils on the criterion test. We shall now need the total (T) as well as the mean (M) for each class. These totals and means are given in Table 8.

TABLE 8

ANALYSIS OF VARIANCE OF PUPIL SCORES IN A METHODS EXPERIMENT INVOLVING 3 METHODS AND 5 SCHOOLS

(Same data as in Table 7)

	Schools					
	1		2		3	
	T	M	T	M	T	M
Method A	415	20.75	692	34.60	591	29.55
Method B	400	20.00	375	18.75	481	24.05
Method C	509	25.45	588	29.40	561	28.05
School Totals and Means	1324	22.0667	1655	27.5833	1633	27.2167

	4		5		Methods	
	T	M	T	M	Totals	Means
Method A	783	39.15	648	32.40	3129	31.29
Method B	453	22.65	542	27.10	2251	22.51
Method C	612	30.60	570	28.50	2840	28.40
School Totals and Means	1848	30.8000	1760	29.3333	$8220 = GT$	$27.40 = GM$

The arithmetic of computation is now a combination of that in Sections 2 and 3 preceding, as follows:

The sum of squares for *methods*, computed as in Section 2, page 94, is

$$\frac{(3129^2 + 2251^2 + 2840^2)}{100} - (8220)(27.40) = 4004.4$$

The sum of squares for *schools*, similarly computed, is

$$\frac{1324^2 + 1655^2 + 1633^2 + 1848^2 + 1760^2}{60} - 225228 = 2628.6$$

The sum of squares for *classes*, also similarly computed, is

$$\frac{415^2 + 400^2 + 509^2 + 692^2 + \cdots\cdots + 542^2 + 570^2}{20} - 225228$$

$$= 8937.6$$

We may now see that the sums of squares for *methods, schools,* and *classes* bear the same relation to each other that they did in Table 7, although each has been made twenty times as large as before.

The sum of squares for $M \times S$ is obtained as before by subtracting the sums of squares for *methods* and for *schools* from the sum of squares for *classes*. The result is

$$8937.6 - 4004.8 - 2628.6 = 2304.6$$

With these results, we could proceed at once to compute the *methods* and $M \times S$ variances and apply the same test of significance described in the preceding section. However, if the pupils in each school had been assigned at random to the classes in each school, we might wish to know the variance *within classes* in order to evaluate the $M \times S$ variance. We will therefore include the computation of the variance *within classes* in this illustration, although ordinarily it would not be needed.

To compute the variance *within classes*, we must first compute the sum of squares for *total*, that is, for all 300 pupil scores. This is done, as in Section 2, by squaring each of the 300 scores, adding these squared scores, and subtracting the product $GM \cdot GT$. (Without an automatic computing machine, a more convenient procedure is to construct a frequency distribution of the 300 scores and find the sum of squares by the short method, as was suggested on page 101.) The sum of squares for *total* in this case is 49,674.

The sum of squares for *total* may be considered, after the manner of Section 2 of this chapter, as consisting of two components, one of which is that for differences *between* classes, and the other for differences *within* classes. In other words, we may think of the variance of the 300 scores as having been analyzed only into the "between classes" and "within classes" components, just as we analyzed the variance of the 20 scores in Table 6 into "between methods" and "within methods" components. Hence, the sum of squares for *within classes* is equal to the difference of the *total* sum of squares and the sum of squares for *classes*, as follows:

$$49764 - 8937.6 = 40826.4$$

The *d.f.'s* for methods (M), schools (S), and $M \times S$ are the same as before. The *d.f.* for *total* is one less than the number of pupils, or 299. The *d.f.* for *within classes* is the *d.f.* for *total* minus the *d.f.* for *classes*, or $299 - 14 = 285$.

We may now arrange our results in tabular form, as follows:

	d.f.	Sum of Squares	Variance
M	2	4004.4	2002.2
S	4	2628.6	657.1
$M \times S$	8	2304.6	288.1
Within Classes	285	40826.4	143.3
Total	299	49764.	

We now see that the ratio between the M and $M \times S$ variances is exactly the same as the analysis of Table 7. (This would be true only when all classes are the same size.) Hence, our test of significance is the same as before, and all that was said about the $M \times S$ variance in the preceding section still applies here, whether or not the classes are of equal size. However, we now know the variance *within classes*, and if the pupils have been assigned at random to the classes in each school, this variance may be used to evaluate the $M \times S$ variance. We have noted earlier that the $M \times S$ variance is due in part to the pupil-variable (variance *within classes*), in part to uncontrolled variables outside the classes, and in part to possible real differences in the relative merits of the methods from school to school. If all extraneous variables were completely equalized or controlled, and if the relative effects of the methods are the same in all schools, the $M \times S$ variance should be the same (except by chance) as the variance *within classes*.

In this particular case, however, we see that the $M \times S$ variance is larger than the *within classes* variance. The ratio (F) between these variances is 2.011. For 8 and 285 *d.f.*, an F of 2.58 is required for significance at the 1 per cent level, and of 1.97 at the 5 per cent level. Hence, the interaction variance may be considered significantly larger than chance would allow. This indicates (although not conclusively) either that we have failed to control the extraneous variables (such as the teacher-variable) or that there are real differential effects of the methods in different schools, or both. If we could be certain that the extraneous factors had been completely equalized, we could take this as evidence of the presence of a real differential effect. In practice, since complete control is impossible, we cannot distinguish between the effects of these two factors.

It may sometimes happen that the $M \times S$ variance turns out to be smaller than the variance *within classes*. This is particularly likely to happen if only a few schools are involved, since then the $M \times S$ variance will be based on only a few degrees of freedom, and will be quite unstable in relation to the *within classes* variance. If all extraneous factors were perfectly controlled, and if there were no *real* interaction of methods and schools, then, under the hypothesis of random sampling which we wish to test, the $M \times S$ variance and the *within classes* variance are both estimates of the same thing, and will differ only by chance. Since the extraneous factors are never fully controlled, and since some interaction is likely, we would always expect the $M \times S$ variance to be the larger. If it is less, it is so only by chance, and in this case the *within classes* variance constitutes a better estimate of error than the $M \times S$ variance. The *methods* variance may then be divided by this (*within classes*) *error* variance to secure the F for the test of significance.

It may also quite frequently happen in experiments of this type, as is true in our example, that the *methods* variance is significantly larger than the *within classes* variance, but not significantly larger than the $M \times S$ variance. This would have the same meaning as in the analysis of Section 2.   That is, it would mean that the methods differences are almost certainly not due entirely to the *pupil* variable — although they might be due to uncontrolled variables, or to the accidental selection of schools which happened to favor certain methods.   In this situation, *if* the extraneous variables had been very effectively equalized, one might safely conclude that there are real differences between methods so far as the particular schools involved are concerned, although we could still not safely generalize concerning other schools.   In general, it is not of very much practical value to know the variance *within classes*, although if the pupils have been randomized it is best to compute it in order to cover the contingency that the $M \times S$ may by chance be too small to provide a good error estimate.   Our principal interest in the procedure of this section, then, is not that it permits us to compute the *within classes* variance when the pupils have been randomized, but that it allows for differences in size of class from school to school in the F-test based on the $M \times S$ variance.

It may be well to mention here still one other reason why we would ordinarily have relatively little interest in the *within classes* variance.   The use of this variance as an *error* term involves the assumption of homogeneity of variance *within classes* from school to school.   Evidence will be presented in Sections 8 and 9 that this assumption will probably not be satisfied in the typical methods experiment, and that the validity of the F-test involving the *within classes* variance will be appreciably lowered as a result.

6. RULES FOR ANALYZING POOLED RESULTS OF DUPLICATED EXPERIMENTS IN RANDOMLY SELECTED SCHOOLS

We shall now apply the procedure of the preceding section in a concrete illustration involving differences in size of class from school to school.   For the later convenience of the student, we shall provide, along with this illustration, a set of definite rules which may be conveniently followed in practical applications.   It will be assumed in these rules that the experiment has been properly designed and controlled. The essential elements in the design are that the classes are of equal size in each school (but not necessarily from school to school), that the classes, teachers, rooms, etc. have been randomly assigned to the methods, and that comparable criterion measures are secured for all pupils at the close of the experiment. These rules are so organized as to cover both the situation in which the pupils in each school have been randomly assigned to the classes within that school and that in which they have not been so assigned.

The parenthetical remarks following each rule are concerned with the concrete example used to illustrate them. This concrete example is based on an experiment performed with four methods in five schools. There are a total of 440 pupils, 40 in School 1, 120 in School 2, 76 in School 3, 152 in School 4, and 52 in School 5. The pupils in each school were randomly assigned to four classes of equal size, thus resulting in 20 classes in the whole experiment. The actual scores of the 440 pupils on the criterion test are not given, since these are not essential to an understanding of the procedure.

In this example we shall let T_c represent the sum of the scores for a single class, T_s the total for a single school, T_m for all pupils under a single method, and GT the grand total. The numbers of pupils on which these totals are based will be represented by n_c, n_s, n_m and N, respectively.

Step 1: *Find the total (T_c) of the criterion scores for the pupils in each* CLASS *separately.*

      For the example, these totals are given in the following table. For instance, the total for the A-class in School 1 is 603.

Step 2: *Find the total for each school, for each method, and for the entire sample (grand total) by adding class totals.* This may be done most conveniently if the class totals have been arranged in a table like that above. The grand total (GT) should equal both the sum of the methods total and of the school totals.

		Methods							
	A	B	C	D	T_s	$\Sigma\, T_c{}^2/n_c$	$T_s{}^2/n_s$	n_s	n_c
School 1	603	571	558	592	2324	135147.8	135024.4	40	10
School 2	1711	1624	1586	1619	6540	356715.1	356430.0	120	30
School 3	1120	1082	1006	1083	4291	242634.2	242272.1	76	19
School 4	2052	1975	1939	1937	7903	411132.1	410904.0	152	38
School 5	741	716	678	700	2835	154724.7	154562.0	52	13
T_m	6227	5968	5767	5931	23893 = GT			440 = N	
Methods Means	56.61	54.25	52.43	53.92	$GM \times GT = \dfrac{GT^2}{N} = \dfrac{23893^2}{440} = 1297444.2$				

These totals for the example are given in the preceding table.

Step 3: *Square each methods total, add, divide the sum by the number of pupils under each method, and subtract GT^2/N (= $GT \times GM$) to secure the sum of squares for* METHODS. *(Carry the result to at least four significant digits.)*

$$\frac{\Sigma\, T_m{}^2}{n_m} - \frac{GT^2}{N} = \frac{6227^2 + 5968^2 + 5767^2 + 5931^2}{110}$$
$$- 1297444.2 = 988.6$$

In machine computation, the squared totals may be *cumulated* in the lower dial for division by the number of cases. Hence, no squared total need be recorded.

Step 4: *For each school separately, square the total (T_s) and divide by the total number of pupils in the school. (Carry each result to the same number of decimal places as in the final result of Step 3.)*

For School 1, $T_s^2/n_s = 2324^2/40 = 135024.0$. The results for the other schools are similarly computed, and are given in the T_s^2/n_s column of the preceding table.

Step 5: *Add the results of Step 4 for all schools and subtract GT^2/N to secure the sum of squares for* SCHOOLS.

$$\Sigma(T_s^2/n_s) - GT^2/N = (135024.4 + \cdots + 154562.0)$$
$$- 1297444.2 = 1748.3$$

Step 6: *For each school separately, square each class total, add, and divide the sum by the number of pupils per class in that school.* (Carry each result to the same number of *decimal places* as in the final result of Step 3.)

$$\text{For School 1, } \Sigma\, T_c^2/n_c = \frac{603^2 + 571^2 + 558^2 + 592^2}{10}$$
$$= 135147.8$$

Step 7: *Add the results of Step 6 for all schools and subtract GT^2/N to secure the sum of squares for* CLASSES. (Carry to same number of *decimal places* as in result of Step 3.)

$$\Sigma(\Sigma\, T_c^2/n_c) - GT^2/N = 135147.8 + \cdots + 154724.7$$
$$- 1297444.2 = 2909.7$$

Step 8: *Subtract the sums of squares for* METHODS *and* SCHOOLS *from that for* CLASSES, *to secure the sum of squares for* M × S.

In the example:

$$2909.7 - 1748.3 - 988.6 = 172.8$$

Step 9: *Divide the sum of squares for* METHODS *by one less than the number of methods to get the variance for* METHODS. *The divisor is the d.f. for* METHODS.

$$988.6/3 = 329.5$$

Step 10: *Divide the sum of squares for* M × S *by the product of the degrees of freedom for* METHODS *and* SCHOOLS *to get the* M × S *variance. The divisor is the d.f. for* M × S.

$$172.8/(4 \times 3) = 172.8/12 = 14.40$$

Step 11: *Divide the variance for methods by the variance for* M × S. *The result is the* F *used in the test of significance.*

$$F = 329.5/14.40 = 22.88$$

Step 12: *Compare the* F *just found with values given in Table 4 for the corresponding d.f. to determine the significance of the methods differences.*

[In the example, the *d.f.'s* for the F computed are 3 and

12. In Table 4 we see that for these *d.f.* an *F* of 5.74 is required for significance at the 1 per cent level. Hence, the *F* is clearly significant.]

> *Note:* This is as far as the computation need be carried if the *F* is not significant, and if the pupils were not assigned at *random* to the classes in each school. If the *F* is significant, and there are more than two methods, one would wish to evaluate the individual differences in methods means, as in steps 13 to 15 following.

Step 13: *To find the standard error of a difference between means for any two methods, divide the* M × S *variance by the total number of pupils under one method, multiply the quotient by 2, and extract the square root of the result.*

$$\left[\sqrt{2\ (14.40/110)} = \sqrt{.2618} = .512 \right]$$

Step 14: *Compute the mean for each method.*

[Given in the table.]

Step 15: *To find the maximum error at the 1 per cent level in a difference in methods means, find the value of t in the last column of Table 3 for the d.f. of the* M × S *variance, and multiply the standard error of the difference by this value of t.*

[The *d.f.* for $M \times S$ is 12. For this *d.f.*, a *t* of 3.005 is required for significance at the 1 per cent level. Hence, the maximum error (at 1 per cent level) in the difference of two methods means is 3.005 × .512 = 1.54. Hence, the mean for method A is significantly higher than for any other method, the mean for B is significantly higher than for C but not for D, and the mean for C is almost significantly higher than for D.]

> *Note:* This is as far as the computation would be carried in any case in which the pupils had not been randomized in each school (including the case

of matching within schools). It is apparent, then, that in spite of the complexity of the theory, the actual computational procedure in an analysis of variance is really quite simple. (For example, the time required by the writer to complete the preceding steps in the illustrative problem, using an electrical computing machine, was under one hour.) In fact, the time required for computation in an analysis of this type is less than that formerly required in similar situations when the random sampling formulas were (incorrectly) used.

If the pupils have been randomized in each school, and one wishes to evaluate the $M \times S$ variance, the procedure continues as follows:

Step 16: *Secure the sum of the squared scores of all pupils on the criterion test and subtract GT^2/N to secure the* TOTAL *sum of squares.* If an automatic computing machine is not available or the number of cases is large, use the "short" method with a grouped frequency distribution of the scores. (See page 101.)

In the example, the sum of squares for *total* was 5891.2.

Step 17: *Subtract the sum of squares for* CLASSES *from the sum of squares for* TOTAL *to secure the sum of squares for* WITHIN CLASSES.

$$5891.2 - 2909.7 = 2981.5$$

Step 18: *Divide the sum of squares for* WITHIN CLASSES *by the number of pupils less the number of classes to secure the variance for* WITHIN CLASSES. *The divisor is the d.f. for* WITHIN CLASSES.

$$2981.5/(440 - 20) = 2981.5/420 = 7.10$$

Step 19: *To evaluate the* M $\times$ S *variance, divide the variance for* M $\times$ S *by the variance for* WITHIN CLASSES, *and evaluate* the F *as in Step 12, remembering that the* D.F.'S *are those for* M × S *and* WITHIN CLASSES.

$$14.40/7.10 = 2.03 = F$$

For 12 and 420 *d.f.* an F of 1.78 is required for significance at the 5 per cent level and of 2.23 at the 1 per cent level. Hence, the $M \times S$ variance may in this case be considered significantly larger than the *within classes* variance. This indicates that the relative effectiveness of the methods is not the same from school to school, and that the method which is best in one school may not be best in another.

Step 20: *If the $M \times S$ variance is less than the within classes variance, use the within classes variance as the error term in testing the methods differences.* That is, divide the methods variance by the *within classes* variance, and evaluate the F as in Step 12, taking care to use the *d.f.'s* for *methods* and for the *within classes* variance. If this test proves significant, the individual methods differences may be evaluated as in Steps 13 and 15, except that the *within classes* variance (and *d.f.*) is substituted for the $M \times S$ variance (and *d.f.*).

Note: Steps 16 to 20 involve the assumption of homogeneous variance *within schools* — an assumption which may be generally questioned on an *a priori* basis. (See Section 8, pp. 132 ff.) Before placing much reliance on the probabilities read from the F-table for Steps 19 and 20, therefore, one should make an objective test of the reasonableness of this assumption. The test needed is described in the footnote on page 99. To apply this test, one must first analyze the results for *each school separately* (by the method described in Section 3, pp. 100 ff.) to secure the *within classes* (within groups) variance for each school.

The test on page 99 may then be applied to these variances, the *within classes* variances from the separate schools being represented by $s_1'^2$, $s_2'^2$, $\cdots$, $s_k'^2$ in the test, k representing the number of schools. The corresponding degrees of freedom for the *within classes* variances will then be represented by n_1, n_2, etc., and s'^2 will be equal to $\dfrac{\Sigma(n_i s_i'^2)}{\Sigma n_i}$. These values may then be substituted in the expression for χ^2 at the beginning of the footnote on page 99. If the value of χ^2 is not significant, one is justified in assuming homogeneous variance in Steps 16 to 20 (although a non-significant χ^2 does not *prove* that the variances are homogeneous). If the value of χ^2 is very significant, i.e., if the school variances are very heterogeneous, special methods of analysis should be employed, but these are beyond the scope of this book. The student interested in this possibility should read "The Analysis of Groups of Experiments," by F. Yates and W. G. Cochran, *Journal of Agricultural Science*, Vol. XXVIII, Part IV, October, 1938 (Cambridge University Press).

The foregoing rules have been adapted particularly to the type of experiment in which the pupils have *not* been assigned at random to the classes within each school (and in which steps 16 to 20 would not be involved). This type of experiment seems to the writer to deserve first consideration, since in the actual school situation it is rarely practicable to re-assign pupils (at random) to special classes for experimental purposes, and thus to disrupt the existing school organization. It is possible, however, that the analysis here recommended does not do justice to the case in which the pupils within each school are divided into classes at random. Where this type of experiment is practicable, considerably more information can be derived from it than is suggested by the preceding rules. In this type of experiment, the first step (as is suggested in the preceding note) should be to do an analysis of variance separately for each school. (This may have some political as well as statistical value, since any co-operating schools may appreciate receiving an independent report on its own particular experiment.) If the result of Step 19 then shows the $M \times S$ variance to be significant, one may want to know *why* certain schools behave differently from others, and the individual school analysis will help to pick out the anomalous schools. Unless one method happens to be best in all schools, the correct deduction from the experiment may be that one method is best for certain types of schools (whose distinguishing characteristics may be recognized and specified) and another method is best for other types of schools. Whether or not it may be possible to thus typify the schools within an experiment remains to be seen as we accumulate more experience with these analytical procedures, but it is a possibility that is worth keeping in mind.

7. MODIFICATIONS OF DESIGN AND ANALYSIS IN METHODS
EXPERIMENTS INVOLVING SEVERAL SCHOOLS

We are now ready to consider more fully a fact of considerable importance in methods experiments of the general type described in the preceding sections. We assumed in Section 2 (page 93) that the pupils in the single school involved were randomly assigned to the experimental classes. This assumption is still essential in the more complicated design for several schools if the *within classes* variance is to be used to evaluate the $M \times S$ variance, but it is not essential if we have no interest in the *within classes* variance, and intend to use only the $M \times S$ variance as the error term. In the latter situation, when we use $M \times S$ as *error*, we are considering the class as the unit of sampling, even though we do weight each class according to size. Since the class is the unit, the only assumptions involved are: (1) that the classes are randomly assigned to the methods, (2) that the variance in "corrected" class means is fundamentally constant from method to method, (3) that the distribution of "corrected" class means is fundamentally normal in form, and (4) that all classes in the same school are of the same size. Our generalizations then really apply to the population of *schools* from which the schools involved in the experiment were presumably selected at random, rather than to a population of pupils. If, then, we are not going to use the *within classes* variance to test the interaction, we need not consider the random assignment of *pupils* to the experimental classes as an essential element in the design of a methods experiment involving a random selection of schools. There should be no misunderstanding, however, as to the importance of randomizing the classes (and the associated error variables) with reference to methods in each school separately.

One important implication of the foregoing is that we may, if we wish, or if no other procedure seems feasible, utilize the classes as they are found already organized in the schools which are to participate in the experiment, if these classes are of the same size (or very nearly so) within each school. In general, this would not be desirable, although it may often be necessary. The classes as found are likely to show large systematic differences in achievement or ability, either because of a deliberate or unconscious grouping according to ability, or because of systematic differences in educational experience up to the time of the experiment. The precision of the experiment will of course depend on the magnitude of the $M \times S$ variance (or upon the variance of class means after school and methods differences have been eliminated). Hence, the use of classes as found would result in a relatively large $M \times S$ variance and a relatively low precision, some of which could be avoided by reorganization of the classes. The purpose of reorganization is of course to reduce the variance in mean ability from class to class within the same school. *One* means of doing this, and in general a very good way, is to assign the pupils at random to the experimental classes in each school. A still more effective way of reducing the $M \times S$ variance is to *match* the classes in each school separately on the basis of some initial measure of ability.   It is *not* necessary that this matching be in any sense *exact*, or that it must be done on a pupil-to-pupil basis.   Any procedure that is likely to result in a more nearly equal *mean* achievement of the classes (within the same school) than would result from random grouping would be so much to the good.   If the matching is to be done on the basis of an objective measure of ability, such as the score on an initial achievement test, perhaps the best procedure is first to assign the pupils "on paper" to tentative experimental classes *at random*, then compute the mean of each of these tentative classes on the initial test, and then to exchange pupils between classes so as to make the means as nearly alike as possible.   If the correlation between the initial and criterion test is high, this matching may very markedly increase the precision of the experiment. It is important that the matching be equally well done in all schools, otherwise the variance of the class means will be greater in some schools than others, and hence a basic assumption will be violated.   If the matching *is* equally well done in all schools, it is likely that the assumption of homogeneous variance will be even more nearly satisfied than if random grouping within schools were employed.   In general, then, an objective matching procedure, which can be made equally effective in all schools, is better than a subjective or inexact procedure, although any procedure may be employed that makes the classes more alike in mean ability than random classes would be.

We have already noted that if it is necessary to utilize the classes as found, the method of analysis here described is still valid so far as the test based on the $M \times S$ variance is concerned.   This is fortunate, since sometimes no reorganization of any kind is practicable.   While it is often possible to find schools willing to cooperate in an experiment to the extent of permitting their regular classes to be used, relatively few schools are willing to allow any physical reorganization (of extended duration) of the classes for experimental purposes.   It may be noted, however, that the necessity of dealing with intact school classes as found is not always a very serious handicap.   If the classes are all in the same building, if there was no deliberate ability grouping in the original assignment to classes and if the class organization of the previous year had not been retained, and if the experiment is performed early in the year before differences in teachers and other factors had had time to create large class differences in the same school, the precision of this type of experiment might be practically as high as if the pupils were actually assigned at random to the classes at the beginning of the experiment.   However, if the classes in the same "school," now meaning school *system*, were drawn from different buildings, if these buildings were characterized by marked differences in environmental and cultural patterns, and if the experiment were performed late in the school year when teacher differences had produced still further variability, the precision of the experiment would be relatively low — perhaps as low as if "system" differences were not eliminated at all.

When intact classes are used, it will seldom happen that all classes in the same school are of uniform size.   If the size of class does not differ widely (and they usually will not) this difficulty may be overcome by proceeding as follows in each school separately: (1) Compute the actual mean of each class; (2) Find the average size of class in that school, and round the result to the nearest whole number; (3) Multiply each mean by this number to secure a "corrected" total; and (4) Use these "corrected" totals in place of the actual totals in the analysis (see pages 152 ff.).   The analysis will still allow for systematic differences in class size from school to school, but ignores such differences within schools.   This procedure, and the test of significance involved, will be only approximate in character, but in most instances will probably be just as satisfactory, for all practical purposes, as if the classes in each school were actually uniform in size.   If the classes vary markedly within schools, for example, if some classes are several times as large as others in the same school, the validity of this procedure might be appreciably lowered, but this situation can usually be avoided in planning the experiment.

The preceding paragraph suggests also what to do about "missing cases." Very frequently, although the experiment was originally planned so as to provide equal classes in each school, some pupils may drop out of school during the course of the experiment, or for some other reason fail to take the criterion test. In this case, if the $M \times S$ variance is to be used as the only error term, the data may be analyzed in exactly the same manner as was just described.

It may be well, before closing this discussion, to draw specific attention to certain possible *misconceptions*. In the first place, there is some danger that the student may conclude, since the $M \times S$ variance takes into consideration or provides a valid error estimate for all uncontrolled but randomized errors, that there is no need to control any sources of error that may be randomized. We have already seen the advantage of *equalizing* the pupil variable by matching the classes. Equally important advantages may be gained by equalizing any other error-variables. For example, if the classes within each school are taught by teachers of widely varying ability, this fact will tend to increase the $M \times S$ variance, and hence lower the precision of the experiment. Randomization of teachers only insures that the teacher-variable will not operate systematically in favor of a certain method. Any means of equalizing the teacher-variable, such as having the same teacher teach all experimental classes in the same school, or trying to select teachers of equal ability, will tend to reduce the $M \times S$ variance and increase the precision of the experiment. In designing and conducting a methods experiment, then, every practicable precaution should be taken to render the experimental conditions or extraneous factors as much alike as possible from class to class within the same school.

A second possible misconception has to do with the significance of school differences in an analysis of this kind. It may seem that the worthwhileness of taking *schools* into consideration at all depends entirely upon the magnitude of these differences. The sum of squares for *classes* is equal to the sum of the sums of squares for

M, S, and $M \times S$. Hence, it is true that "taking out" the sum of squares for *schools* reduces the sum of squares for *error* $(M \times S)$, and thus increases the precision of the experiment, by an amount dependent upon the magnitude of the variance for *schools*. (See page 113.) If the variance for *schools* is no larger than could be attributed to chance fluctuations in random sampling (that is, no larger than the variance *within classes*), then "taking out" school differences will not reduce the $M \times S$ or *error* variance. (The sum of squares for $M \times S$ will be reduced, but the *d.f.* will also be reduced, so that the variance for $M \times S$ will remain undiminished, or may even be increased if the variance for *schools* is less than that for $M \times S$.) This does not mean, however, that the method of analysis here described would not be needed if, in a given experiment, there were no systematic differences between the participating schools (i.e., if the variance for *schools* were no larger than that for *within classes*). Even though the variance for *schools* were no larger than chance would permit, we would still have to employ this method of analysis in order to take into consideration in the error $(M \times S)$ term any extraneous variables which operated within each school to create systematic differences from one methods group to another. It is quite conceivable that the variance for *schools* could fail to be significant, and that there also may be no *real* interaction of methods and schools, but that we might nevertheless have a significant $M \times S$ variance due to uncontrolled variables such as the teacher variable. Hence, we would still have to use $M \times S$ as *error* to take these sources of error into consideration. Whether or not school differences are significant, the type of analysis based on the familiar standard error formulas designed for large random samples (see page 83) will not provide a valid *comprehensive* error estimate in an experiment of the type IV design involving several schools.

8. THE ASSUMPTION OF HOMOGENEITY OF VARIANCE

One of the cardinal sins of educational research workers in the past has been that of taking too lightly the assumptions underlying the derivations of statistical techniques. It would be particularly unfortunate if, in becoming acquainted with a technique which seems as promising for educational research as that presented in the preceding section, we should perpetuate this unfortunate tendency to pass over the basic assumptions without any very critical consideration of them.

In the method of analysis just considered, one of the most important underlying assumptions is that of homogeneity of variance. This assumption entered into the analysis at two points. In the test of significance based on the ratio of M and $M \times S$ variances, it was assumed that the variance of the "corrected" class means is fundamentally constant from method to method. In the test of significance of the interaction, based on the ratio of the $M \times S$ and *within classes* variances, it was assumed that the variance of pupil scores, after methods differences have been eliminated, is the same from *school* to *school*. The latter assumption would also be involved if we were to test the school differences on the basis of the ratio of the S and *within classes* variances, as well as in a test of the M variance against an *error* variance consisting of *within classes*, which would be used if the $M \times S$ variance turned out to be less than the variance *within classes*.

If either of these assumptions is not satisfied, there is a danger that the sampling distribution of the observed F's will not be given by the table for F, or that the F-tests of significance based on this table will be invalidated. As was noted on page 99, there is good reason to suspect each of these assumptions in the typical methods experiment, particularly the assumption of homogeneity of variance from school to school. However, if only the latter assumption is not satisfied, the situation may not be serious so far as the usefulness of the procedure of the preceding section is concerned. We have noted (page 114) that the variance of "corrected" class means might be homogeneous from method to method, even though the variance *within schools* is heterogeneous. In other words, it has been suggested that the test of significance based on the ratio of the M and $M \times S$ variances might be valid even though the variance *within schools* is heterogeneous. Whether or not it actually *is* valid under these conditions, however, remains to be proved.

There are, then, two crucial questions that should be answered before the procedure of the preceding section may be safely recommended for wide-spread use in methods experimentation. These questions are: (1) For examinations of the type usually employed to secure the criterion measures in methods experiments, do the *variances* of pupil scores, as well as the means, differ more from *school* to *school* than could be explained by fluctuations in random sampling?; and, (2) If the variances *within schools* are in fact heterogeneous, to what extent will this condition disturb the tests of significance based on variance ratios (F's)?

An attempt will be made to provide at least a partial answer to these questions in this section and in that following (Section 9). To answer the first question, the writer analyzed the scores made on certain of the objective achievement tests that had been administered in a very large number of Iowa schools in the 1938 Iowa Every-Pupil Testing Program. As will be seen later, the tests used are quite representative of those that are generally employed to secure the criterion measures in experiments concerned with the relative effectiveness of methods of instruction in established school subjects, and the number of schools and pupils involved is so large as to render the results very highly dependable. The procedure with each examination, briefly stated, consisted of computing the actual variance of pupil scores within each school separately, constructing a frequency distribution of these observed variances, and comparing this distribution with that which theoretically should be found for *random* samples of the same size as the school groups used. The procedure will be explained in detail for one of the examinations and the results for the remaining examination will then be more briefly reported.

The first examination considered is Test D of the 1938 Iowa Every-Pupil Tests of Basic Skills. This is a carefully constructed objective examination of achievement in arithmetic, intended for use at the sixth- to eighth-grade levels. The test requires 90 minutes for its administration. This test was administered, in the 1938 Iowa Every-Pupil Testing Program, to the seventh-grade pupils in over 200 schools, in 94 of which 20 or more seventh-graders were tested. From each of these 94 schools 20 seventh-grade pupils were selected at random by the method described on page 27. Only 20 pupils were used from each school in order to simplify the problem of determining the theoretical distribution of variances. For the 20 pupils in each school, the variance of the total scores was computed, and a distribution made of these variances. This distribution is given in Table 9, in the f_o column. The computation of the theoretical frequencies (f_t) in this table was based on the fact [1] that for random samples of N cases each the sampling distribution of the ratio $\dfrac{Ns^2}{\sigma^2}$, in which s^2 is the variance of a sample $(s^2 = \Sigma\, d^2/N)$ and σ^2 is the variance of the population, is the same as the sampling distribution of χ^2 for $N - 1$ degrees of freedom, and that s^2 is therefore distributed as $\left(\dfrac{\sigma^2}{N}\right) \cdot \chi^2$. In other words, the theoretical frequencies are based on the hypothesis that the school variances are homogeneous, that is, that they differ no more than would the variances of *random* samples of 20 cases each. In this case, σ^2 was estimated by estimating the true variance, according to (4), from the data for each school separately, and taking the mean of these estimates. This best estimate of σ^2 was 265.54. For 19 *d.f.*, the value of χ^2 which should be exceeded in 20 per cent of all random samples is 23.900. Hence, if we multiply this value by $\dfrac{\sigma^2}{N} = \dfrac{265.54}{20} = 13.277$, we should have $(23.900 \times 13.277 = 317.32)$ the value of the variance which should be exceeded in 20 per cent of our samples. This value, it will be noted, constitutes the lower limit of the fifth interval (from the

---

[1] Karl Pearson, "On the Distribution of Standard Deviations of Small Samples," *Biometrika*, Volume 10 (1914–15), pp. 522–529.

top). The limits of the other intervals were similarly computed from the χ^2 table, and the observed variances were tabulated with reference to these intervals. The theoretical relative frequencies (f_t) were then readily derived from the χ^2 table, and the observed frequencies were then expressed as relative frequencies $\left(f'_o = \dfrac{100\,f_o}{N}\right)$ so as to make them comparable.

It is at once apparent from Table 9 that the "spread" of the observed variances is greater than in the theoretical distribution. The observed frequencies (f'_o) are systematically smaller than the theoretical in the middle of the distribution and larger at the extremes. To determine whether or not this divergence is greater than can be attributed to chance, the χ^2 test (described on pages 37–40) was applied. The value of χ^2 was 30.827. For 7 d.f. this value of χ^2 would be exceeded less than 0.1 per cent of the time if

TABLE 9

DISTRIBUTION OF VARIANCES OF SCORES OF SEVENTH-GRADE PUPILS ON A COMPREHENSIVE TEST OF ACHIEVEMENT IN ARITHMETIC (TEST D OF 1938 IOWA EVERY-PUPIL TESTS OF BASIC SKILLS) IN 94 SCHOOLS (20 PUPILS FROM EACH SCHOOL), COMPARED WITH DISTRIBUTION EXPECTED ON HYPOTHESIS OF RANDOM SAMPLING

Variances	f_o	$f'_o \left(= \dfrac{100\,f_o}{N}\right)$		f_t		Differences	
480.51 and above	4	4.255		1			
447.27 − 480.50	1	1.064	19.148	1	10	(+)	9.148
400.22 − 447.26	4	4.255		3			
361.19 − 400.21	9	9.574		5			
317.32 − 361.18	3	3.191		10		(−)	6.809
287.97 − 317.31	12	12.766		10		(+)	2.766
243.48 − 287.96	8	8.511		20		(−)	11.489
203.83 − 243.47	14	14.894		20		(−)	5.106
182.11 − 203.82	12	12.766		10		(+)	2.766
154.69 − 182.10	9	9.574		10		(−)	0.426
134.32 − 154.68	8	8.511		5			
113.75 − 134.31	5	5.319	19.149	3	10	(+)	9.149
101.34 − 113.74	1	1.064		1			
101.33 and below	4	4.255		1			
	94	99.999		100			

our hypothesis were true; hence, we may very confidently reject the hypothesis of homogeneous variance.[1]

Table 10 presents the results of similar analyses for other examinations administered in the Iowa Every-Pupil Testing Programs. The manner in which this table may be read may be illustrated in the case of Part A of the table. The abbreviated title for Part A gives the title of the test involved, and indicates that the variance of pupil scores on this test was computed for 20 randomly selected seventh-grade pupils in each of 89 schools. Only the lower limits of the variance intervals are given in the first column (except for the bottom interval, whose upper limit only is given). Only the *relative* observed frequencies are presented, in the f'_o column, opposite the theoretical frequencies (f_t) expected on the hypothesis of random sampling. For the distribution in Part A, the value of x^2 computed in the test of goodness of fit would be exceeded by chance less than ten per cent of the time, i.e., χ^2 was significant beyond the 10 per cent level. According to the Neyman-Pearson λ-test, the probability of exceeding the observed heterogeneity by chance is approximately the same as the probability that a measure selected at random from a normal distribution will deviate 12.24 standard deviations from the mean of the distribution. This probability is obviously too small to be read from available tables of the normal probability integral.

It may be noted in Table 10 that there is an apparent tendency toward increased heterogeneity of variance at the higher grade levels. This is reasonable, since the factors tending toward heterogeneity have had more time to operate by the time the pupils reach the upper high-school grades. Part I of the table is of particular interest, since it is the only instance in which there is

---

[1] A more rigid test of the hypothesis of homogeneous variance was applied to the same data. This is the λ-test devised by Neyman and Pearson. ("The Problem of K Samples," J. Neyman and E. S. Pearson. *Bulletin of the Polish Academy of Science*, 1931.) No attempt will be made to explain this test here. It will be sufficient to say that the test is very much like that described on page 99, and that according to this test, if the hypothesis of homogeneous variance were true, the probability of getting a distribution as heterogeneous as that observed is too small to be computed from available tables.

TABLE 10
DISTRIBUTIONS OF VARIANCES OF SCORES ON VARIOUS EDUCATIONAL ACHIEVEMENT TESTS, EACH COMPARED WITH DISTRIBUTION EXPECTED ON HYPOTHESIS OF RANDOM SAMPLING

A. Vocabulary Test (Part I, Test B, 1938 Iowa Tests of Basic Skills); 20 Seventh-Grade Pupils in Each of 89 Schools			B. Test of Work-Study Skills (Parts II–VI, Test B, 1938 Iowa Tests of Basic Skills); 20 Seventh-Grade Pupils in Each of 89 Schools			C. Test of Language Skills (Test C of 1938 Iowa Tests of Basic Skills); 20 Seventh-Grade Pupils in Each of 87 Schools		
Variances	f'_0	f_t	Variances	f'_0	f_t	Variances	f'_0	f_t
105.2–	3.37	1	518.0–	1.12	1	4324.9–	3.45	1
97.9–	2.25	1	482.1–	1.12	1	4025.7–	0.00	1
87.6–	5.62	3	431.4–	6.74	3	3602.3–	4.60	3
79.1–	2.25	5	389.4–	5.62	5	3251.0–	11.49	5
69.5–	8.99	10	342.1–	7.87	10	2856.1–	6.90	10
63.0–	11.24	10	310.4–	6.74	10	2591.9–	6.90	10
53.3–	20.23	20	262.5–	20.23	20	2191.4–	11.49	20
44.6–	11.24	20	219.7–	14.61	20	1834.6–	13.79	20
39.9–	4.49	10	196.3–	13.48	10	1639.1–	4.60	10
33.9–	15.73	10	166.8–	8.99	10	1392.3–	16.09	10
29.4–	3.37	5	144.8–	5.62	5	1209.0–	10.35	5
24.9–	6.74	3	122.6–	1.12	3	1023.8–	6.90	3
22.2–	0.00	1	109.2–	4.49	1	912.2–	2.30	1
–22.2	4.49	1	–109.2	2.25	1	–912.2	1.15	1

χ^2-test: $.20 < P < .10$
λ-test: $x = 12.24$

χ^2-test: $.60 < P < .50$
λ-test: $x = 9.04$

χ^2 test: $.01 < P < .001$

D. 1937 Iowa Every-Pupil Test in English Correctness; 30 Ninth-Grade Pupils in Each of 107 High Schools			E. 1938 Iowa Every-Pupil Test in English Correctness; 30 Twelfth-Grade Pupils in Each of 85 High Schools			F. 1938 Iowa Every-Pupil Test in American History; 30 Pupils in Each of 99 High Schools		
Variances	f'_0	f_t	Variances	f'_0	f_t	Variances	f'_0	f_t
2343.4–	2.80	1	1047.0–	1.18	1	102.2–	9.09	1
2206.6–	0.94	1	985.9–	5.88	1	102.9–	2.02	1
2011.1–	1.87	3	898.5–	1.18	3	93.8–	5.05	3
1847.1–	4.67	5	825.3–	8.24	5	86.1–	3.03	5
1660.6–	8.41	10	741.9–	8.24	10	77.4–	5.05	10
1534.0–	14.95	10	685.4–	8.24	10	71.5–	7.07	10
1339.1–	14.02	20	598.3–	14.12	20	62.4–	8.08	20
1161.4–	23.36	20	518.9–	11.77	20	54.1–	11.11	20
1062.1–	6.54	10	474.5–	12.94	10	49.5–	13.13	10
934.2–	8.41	10	417.4–	11.77	10	43.5–	12.12	10
836.8–	5.61	5	373.9–	10.59	5	39.0–	6.06	5
736.0–	2.80	3	328.8–	2.35	3	34.3–	11.11	3
673.7–	1.87	1	301.0–	1.18	1	31.4–	4.04	1
–673.7	3.74	1	–301.0	2.35	1	–31.4	3.03	1

χ^2-test: $.60 < P < .50$
λ-test: $x = 9.87$

χ^2-test: $10 < P < .05$
λ-test: $x = 9.74$

χ^2-test: $.01 < P < .001$

TABLE 10 — *continued*

G. 1938 Iowa Every-Pupil Test in Ninth-Year Algebra; 30 Ninth-Grade Pupils in Each of 94 High Schools			H. 1938 Iowa Every-Pupil Test in Biology; 30 Tenth-Grade Pupils in Each of 64 High Schools			I. 1938 Iowa Every-Pupil Test in English Correctness; 30 Ninth-Grade Pupils in Each of 122 High Schools		
Variances	f'_o	f_t	Variances	f'_o	f_t	Variances	f'_o	f_t
90.2-	7.45	1	156.7-	3.13	1	1320.0-	2.46	1
85.0-	1.06	1	147.5-	0.00	1	1242.9-	0.82	1
77.4-	3.19	3	134.4-	4.69	3	1132.9-	3.28	3
71.1-	3.19	5	123.5-	7.81	5	1040.5-	4.10	5
63.9-	6.38	10	111.0-	4.69	10	935.4-	9.84	10
59.1	9.57	10	102.6-	6.25	10	864.1-	9.02	10
51.6-	12.77	20	89.5-	20.31	20	754.3-	21.31	20
44.7-	18.09	20	77.6-	21.88	20	654.2-	16.39	20
40.9-	5.32	10	71.0-	7.81	10	598.3-	10.66	10
36.0-	14.89	10	62.5-	12.50	10	526.2-	11.48	10
32.2-	7.45	5	55.9-	6.25	5	471.4-	6.56	5
28.3-	2.13	3	49.2-	1.56	3	414.6-	2.46	3
25.9-	5.32	1	45.0-	1.56	1	379.5-	1.64	1
-25.9	3.19	1	-45.0	1.56	1	-379.5	0.00	1
χ^2-test: $.05 < P < .02$			χ^2-test: $.40 < P < .30$			χ^2 test: $.90 < P < 1.00$		
λ-test: $x = 15.63$			λ-test: $x = 7.25$					

no evidence of heterogeneity. It should be noted, however, that for a similar test administered in 1937 (Part D of the table), a marked degree of heterogeneity was found at the same grade level. These data, then, leave little room for doubt that in the typical methods experiment we may expect to have some heterogeneity of variance from school to school. It will therefore be of particular interest to know the effects of such heterogeneity upon the validity of the F-test of significance employed in the method of analysis of Sections 4 to 6 preceding. This will be considered in the following section.

9. THE EFFECT OF HETEROGENEOUS VARIANCE WITHIN SCHOOLS UPON THE F-TEST OF SIGNIFICANCE IN METHODS EXPERIMENTS

To secure some quantitative description of the effect of heterogeneous variance within schools upon the validity of the tests of significance employed in methods experiments of the type described in Section 4 of this chapter, the writer and Mr. R. H. Godard determined the actual distribution of F's for a very large

number of experiments of this type, and compared the actual
F-distribution with that which theoretically should be obtained if
all assumptions were satisfied.[1]

The first step in this empirical study was similar to the procedure
described in the preceding section. The basic data were the scores
made on Test A of the *1938 Iowa Every-Pupil Tests of Basic Skills*
by the sixth-grade pupils in 151 Iowa schools. This test was a
55-minute objective test of silent reading comprehension. Fifteen
pupils were selected at random from each school, and the variance
of the scores of these 15 pupils was computed for each school separately. The distribution of these variances showed some heterogeneity, but not as pronounced as in some of the distributions presented in the preceding section. Since a markedly heterogeneous
distribution was desired, 47 schools of near-average variance were
discarded. The distribution of variances for the remaining 104
schools is given in Table 11. The actual frequencies (f_o) are ex-
pressed as relative frequencies in the f_o' column $\left(f_o' = \frac{100 f_o}{N} \right)$, and
the corresponding theoretical frequencies are given in the f_t col-
umn. The differences in the last column indicate that the observed
distribution contains many more very large and very small variances than would be found in random samples of 15 cases each.
This degree of heterogeneity is perhaps more pronounced than
would be found in most school subjects (compare with the distributions in Table 10).

The next step was to divide the 15 pupils in each school into
three groups of 5 pupils each. This division was made at random
by the method described on page 28. One of these groups was
then considered, for the purposes of this study, as having been
taught by Method A, another by Method B, and the third by
Method C, although actually, of course, all had been taught alike
in each school.

[1] The results of this study are reported in complete detail in an unpublished Mas-
ter's thesis "The Effect of Heterogeneous Variance Upon Certain F–Tests of Significance," by R. H. Godard. State University of Iowa, M. A. Thesis in Education,
1939.

TABLE II

DISTRIBUTIONS OF OBSERVED AND THEORETICAL VARIANCES OF SCORES
OF SIXTH-GRADE PUPILS ON A TEST OF SILENT READING COMPREHENSION
IN 104 IOWA SCHOOLS (15 PUPILS FROM EACH SCHOOL)

Variances	f_o	$f'_o \left(= \frac{100 f_o}{N} \right)$	f_t	Differences	
328.108 and above	5	4.81 ⎫	1 ⎫		
302.572 — 328.107	2	1.92 ⎪ 17.31	1 ⎪ 10	(+)	7.31
266.677 — 302.571	5	4.81 ⎪	3 ⎪		
237.167 — 266.676	6	5.77 ⎭	5 ⎭		
204.368 — 237.166	11	10.58	10	(+)	0.58
182.649 — 204.367	8	7.69	10	(−)	2.31
150.188 — 182.649	11	10.58	20	(−)	9.42
121.837 — 150.187	11	10.58	20	(−)	9.42
106.592 — 121.836	9	8.65	10	(−)	1.35
87.710 — 106.591	14	13.46	10	(+)	3.46
73.985 — 87.709	7	6.73 ⎫	5 ⎫		
60.440 — 73.984	4	3.85 ⎪ 21.16	3 ⎪ 10	(+)	11.16
52.468 — 60.439	5	4.81 ⎪	1 ⎪		
below 52.468	6	5.77 ⎭	1 ⎭		
	104	100.00	100		

The next step was to divide the 104 schools into 26 random sets
of 4 schools each, again by the procedure described on page 28.
New "random numbers" were then employed, and 26 *different*
random combinations or sets of 4 schools each were secured. This
was repeated until 1000 random sets of 4 schools each had been
selected from the 104 schools. It is highly improbable that any
one of these sets contained the same four schools as any other.
The data for each of these 1000 sets of 4 schools then constituted
the basis for an analysis of variance in an "experiment" of the
type described in Sections 5 and 6 of this chapter. Each of these
1000 "experiments" involved four schools and three "methods,"
with a total of 60 pupils, 20 under each "method." For each
experiment the variance for *methods* (M), for $M \times S$, and for
within classes was computed. For each "experiment," also, the
ratios (F) between M and $M \times S$, M and *within classes*, and
$M \times S$ and *within classes* were computed. It was thus possible

to make up a distribution of 1000 observed F's for each of these three ratios.

We shall first consider the distribution of observed F's for the M and $M \times S$ variances, in which ratio we are, of course, most interested. In each "experiment," the $d.f.$ for *methods* was 2 and for $M \times S$ was 6. Hence, according to Table 4, if all assumptions underlying the F-test were satisfied, we should expect 5 per cent of the F's to exceed 5.14 if there were no real methods differences. In this case there can be no real methods differences, since there are no real methods. Each of the so-called "methods" groups was selected at random from pupils that had been taught alike, and any differences in "methods" means could be due only to chance. Hence, if the known heterogeneity of variance did not disturb the F-test, we should expect 5 per cent of our 1000 F's, or 50 F's, to exceed 5.14. Actually, 64 of the observed F's exceeded this value. Similarly, 1 per cent or 10 of our observed F's should exceed 10.92, whereas 15 actually exceeded this value. The 20 per cent point in the F-distribution, according to Fisher and Yates *Statistical Tables*, is 2.13 for 2 and 6 $d.f.$ Hence we should expect 200 of our F's to exceed 2.13, whereas 215 actually exceeded this value. These data are summarized in the table below.

F's $(M/M \times S)$	f_o	f_t
10.92 and above	15	10
5.14 — 10.91	49	40
2.13 — 5.13	151	150
below 2.13	785	800
	1000	1000

If we compute χ^2 for these observed and theoretical frequencies, we find a value of $\chi^2 = 4\ 813$. For three degrees of freedom, this value of χ^2 would be exceeded almost 20 per cent of the time under a true hypothesis. Hence, according to this test, this divergence of observed from theoretical frequencies is no larger than would be found about once in five in studies like this, even though the underlying assumptions were exactly satisfied in each. A more adequate or more rigid test than the χ^2 test would undoubtedly show that this divergence could not so readily be attributed to chance, but even so, the absolute divergence in this case is clearly not large. These data, so far as they go, are quite in agreement with the suggestion made earlier that real differences in variance from school to school will not seriously affect the validity of the test of significance of methods differences based on the ratio of the M and $M \times S$ variance.

The findings for the other two ratios are of a somewhat different character. For the ratio of the $M \times S$ and *within classes* variances, the distributions of observed and theoretical F's are as follows (6 and 48 *d.f.*):

F's ($M \times S$/within classes)	f_o	f_t
3.20 and above	21	10
2.30 — 3.19	89	40
1.41 — 2.29	195	150
below 1.41	695	800

For the ratio of the M and *within classes* variances, the distributions are (2 and 48 *d.f.*):

F's (M/within classes)	f_o	f_t
5.08 and above	27	10
3.19 — 5.07	62	40
1.67 — 3.18	212	150
below 1.67	699	800

In each case, it may be shown by the χ^2 test that the divergence of observed from theoretical frequencies is significant far beyond the 1 per cent level. There is little question, then, that heterogeneity of variance *within schools* will result in a considerably larger proportion of high F's for these tests of significance than the proportions given in the table for F. Even so, the divergence of observed from theoretical frequencies is not large enough to render the F-test completely meaningless for these ratios. Even with the very marked degree of heterogeneity produced in the data used in this study, one would not go far wrong, for most practical purposes, in using the table for F to evaluate the significance of the F obtained for these variances. It should be observed, however, that these data are by no means conclusive. It might be that in experiments involving more schools, and hence with larger $d.f.$'s for $M \times S$ and *within classes*, the divergence would be less marked, or it may be that the validity of the F-test would be even more seriously affected. However, the tentative conclusion seems justified that in the typical methods experiment one may safely employ the F-test as an *approximate* test of the $M \times S/within classes$ ratio, particularly if one insists on a high level of significance before generalizing from the results obtained.

It is very important to observe that these data, even though we assume that they are generally representative, do not completely establish the validity of the F-tests in experiments of the type with which we are here concerned. In this study, only the effect of real differences in variability of pupil scores from *school* to *school* was considered. Nothing has been shown about the effect of possible differences in variability from *method* to *method*. If it should happen that certain methods produce greater variability than others, either in pupil scores within the same school, or in "corrected" class means from method to method, there is again the danger that the F-test will be seriously invalidated. This latter possibility seems relatively remote, since the differences found between *mean* scores on the criterion test in most methods experiments have been quite small in relation to the variabilities of the distributions. It seems unlikely, therefore, that methods incapable of producing large differences in central tendency would produce sufficiently large differences in variability to disturb the F-tests seriously.

10. GENERAL POSSIBILITIES OF ANALYSIS OF VARIANCE
IN EDUCATIONAL RESEARCH

The preceding illustrations have dealt only with "methods" and "schools," since it is perhaps in the instructional experiment that analysis of variance will find its most important single type of application in educational research.   There are many other types of situations, however, in which the methods of analysis of variance may be used to great advantage by the research worker in education.   A few of these situations will be suggested in the following discussion; the purpose of the discussion, however, is not to exhaust these possibilities, but to stimulate the student to discover many other possible applications for himself with the aid of the suggestions offered.

The simplest of the methods thus far discussed is that involving only one classification (such as methods), and in which the hypothesis to be tested is that the differences in means among the various groups in this classification are due only to chance fluctuations in random sampling.   This method of analysis may be applied either to experimental or observational data.   (Observational data are those obtained from investigations of existing populations, i.e., not derived from experiments.)

One illustration of this method of analysis as applied to experimental data was given in Section 2 (pages 93 ff.), the purpose of the experiment being to evaluate the effects upon achievement of certain methods of instruction.   The same general procedure could be followed in any experiment of the same general design. For example, it could be used in experiments intended to discover the relative effects of various sizes of type upon reading rate, or of different amounts (or distributions) of drill upon retention, or of various types of propaganda upon attitude toward a social issue, or of different environmental conditions upon measured intelligence, or of different diets upon body weight, different lighting conditions upon eye-strain, different drugs upon sense discrimination, etc. In other words, the term "treatments" may include any series of variations in any factor which may influence any type of measurable performance or any trait. The term "individuals," similarly, is obviously not restricted to school pupils, but may include such units as libraries in an experimental study of use of library facilities, or schoolrooms in a study of ventilating conditions, or rats in an animal-learning experiment, etc. With these suggestions, then, the student should be able to supply any number of further illustrations of the use of simple analysis of variance in experimental situations in his own field of interest.

The same method of analysis is appropriate for *observational* data when each of the groups compared may be considered as a random sample of a specified *type* or *class* of individuals. For example, one might evaluate differences in the mean achievement in high-school physics of pupils grouped according to amount of previous training in mathematics. Again, one might select samples of individuals from different vocational groups and evaluate differences in the mean intelligence of the samples. Further examples would be found in investigations purporting to evaluate differences in: mean expenditure per pupil in schools of various types; average grade-points earned by college freshmen coming from different high schools; mean achievement of pupils with different vocational interests; mean life of brooms supplied by different manufacturers; mean tenure of teachers with different amounts of professional training; mean amounts of training for teachers in different counties or states; mean persistence in school of pupils from families in different income brackets; etc. It is in situations like these that the feature noted on page 102 — that the method is applicable whether or not the groups are equal in size — is of most value.

The second general type of design, in order of complexity, is that in which there are two classifications, but in which it is desired to *evaluate* (i.e., determine the significance of) differences in group means only within one of these classifications. The second or cross-classification is introduced merely in order to increase the precision of the major comparisons or to permit a valid estimate of error. In other words, there are in this design only two major sources of variation (aside from chance), and only one of these is to be evaluated, the other is to be equalized in the major comparisons and its effects eliminated from the error estimate. In the illustrations already given of this design (Sections 4 to 6 of this chapter), these major sources of variation were *methods* and *schools*, *methods* being the factor to be evaluated and *schools* that to be equalized. In more general terms, this design involves a number of *homogeneous groups* (of which schools is only one example), each of which is divided into a number of equal or proportional [1] subgroups with reference to the major classification. In agricultural research, in which it was first widely used, this design is known as a "randomized blocks" design; hence, in educational research, it seems appropriate to refer to it as a "randomized groups" design.

The randomized groups design, as here defined, is in general appropriate only in *experimental* situations. It consists essentially of a number of duplicate experiments, each of which has been performed independently with a relatively homogeneous group. The accompanying analysis is therefore essentially a means of evaluating the pooled results for a number of duplicate experiments. In educational research, each of the homogeneous groups would most frequently consist of pupils under the same teacher, or in the same school, or in the same community, and hence the basic experiment would be duplicated in different classes, or in different schools, or in different communities. In such cases, the experimenter finds the groups already organized for him, and since they must be left intact, he has no choice but to take group differences into consideration in his analysis if he is to have a valid estimate of error. Quite often, however, the homogeneous groups are organized *by* the experimenter, especially for the pur-

---

[1] The interaction or "remainder" sum of squares may be computed by subtraction (see page 106) only if the sizes of the subgroups within each homogeneous group are in the same *proportion* for all homogeneous groups. The case of *equal* subgroups is then only a special case of proportional subgroups.

poses of the experiment, to secure increased precision. For example, he might organize the pupils into groups of the same age, or same level of intelligence, or same level of achievement, and in effect duplicate the basic experiment with each level or group. In other words, the various "treatment" classes would be "equated" with reference to age, or intelligence, or achievement.

It may be well to consider in some detail the procedure to be followed when the homogeneous groups are organized by the experimenter, rather than simply identified and used by him. Suppose, for example, that the object of an experiment is to determine the effect of color of light upon the accuracy with which a worker performs a certain task. Our plan is to have one set of workers perform the task with a blue light, another set with a yellow light, etc., and to compare measures of accuracy for the various light conditions. Suppose 5 light conditions or "treatments" are to be tested. If we are to use the randomized groups design, the homogeneous groups would have to be specially organized for the purposes of the experiment. In selecting or organizing these groups, our object would be to select the workers in each group so that their criterion measures would be as nearly alike as possible. We must then group them on the basis of some measure which is as highly related as possible to the criterion of accuracy. The most obvious way of doing this would be to test first the accuracy of each individual when all are working under the *same* light conditions. We would then *rank* all workers in order of these initial measures, and let the first five constitute group or "level" 1, the second five level 2, etc. We would then assign the workers in each level one to each of the five treatments *at random*. If the number of levels is not too small, the workers under the various treatments would then be closely "equated" with reference to our initial measure (although not on a man-to-man basis), and hence the precision of the treatment comparisons would be increased. The analysis of the criterion measures would then be made in the manner of Section 4, pages 104 ff. (with only one worker in each subgroup). Assuming 20 "levels" or 100 workers, we should have

	d.f.
Treatments	4
Levels	19
Treatments × Levels (Error)	76
Total	99

By substituting other "treatments" for "color of light," and levels of intelligence, or of initial achievement, or of chronological age, etc., for "levels of accuracy," the student should be able to supply many other illustrations of possible applications of this procedure. It may be noted, however, that the methods of analysis of covariance (Chapter 6) will suggest a way of securing equal precision in an experiment of this kind without having to go to the trouble of arranging the individuals into "levels" in advance.

It is not necessary to have the same number of individuals in each "level" as there are treatments to be evaluated. For example, in an experiment involving 210 pupils, we might divide the pupils into just ten levels, say on the basis of scores on a general intelligence test, 21 pupils at each level. Suppose that three "treatments" are involved, and that the pupils in each level are divided at random into three subgroups of 7 pupils each, one subgroup for each method. We would then have

	d.f.
Treatments	2
Levels	9
Treatments × Levels	18
Within subgroups	180
Total	209

One feature of this design deserves special consideration. Ordinarily, it is not appropriate to use an interaction variance as an *error* variance unless one of the effects involved in the interaction is a random effect (in the $M \times S$ variance of Sections 4 to 6, "schools" is a random effect, i.e., the schools were selected at random from a population of schools). In the designs just considered, however, we may justify the use of the *treatment* $\times$ *levels* interaction as an error term in a special sense. The justification of this procedure is given in the following paragraph.

Suppose, first, that the *treatments* $\times$ *levels* variance is significantly larger than the *within-subgroups* variance. This suggests that the relative effectiveness of the treatments depends upon the level of intelligence of the pupils to which they are applied. Hence, even though the *treatments* variance proved significantly larger than the interaction variance, we could not necessarily recommend one treatment for use at all *individual* levels. We could, however, recommend it for use with any other sample made up of the same levels of intelligence as the sample used in the experiment, i.e., with any sample drawn at random from the same population as our sample. The levels of intelligence which we have used do not, it is true, constitute a *sample*, random or otherwise, from any large number of such levels. On the contrary, we have *all* levels represented in our sample that are represented in the population, and the fact that the *treatment* variance significantly exceeds the interaction variance is evidence that certain treatments work better than others at *most* levels, even though they do not for all. Of course, if there is no significant interaction, or if the interaction variance is less than the *within-subgroups* variance, we would use the latter as *error*.

In general, then, when the "homogeneous groups" are organized especially by the experimenter by dividing the individuals in a sample into "levels" with reference to some continuous variable, so that all possible levels are represented, the interaction variance may be used as an *error* term for the purpose of generalizing about the population from which the total sample was drawn. It should be noted, also, that while this design may be duplicated in a number of randomly selected schools, we would not in that case introduce "levels" into our analysis. As was noted on page 129, the

$M \times S$ variance is still valid as *error* even though the groups have been matched within each school.

The student may have observed that when the homogeneous groups are already organized and must be left intact (as when they are school classes), it is not always feasible to divide each of them at random into subgroups which are equal or proportional in size and which may be physically separated for experimental purposes. This is a serious obstacle in some types of research, but it must not be overlooked that many of the "treatments" we may wish to compare may be simultaneously administered to all of the subgroups in each of the homogeneous groups. For example, we may wish to determine the relative effects upon reading rates of four sizes of type, and may have to work with a sample of several school classes, each of which must be left intact. To do this, we might prepare four editions of the same rate-of-reading test, each in one of these sizes of type. We could then make up a pile of tests for each class, each pile containing an equal number of each of the four editions. We would then *randomize* the papers in each pile separately. For each class, we could then hand out the tests (in the random order in which they appear in the pile) to the pupils, and then administer all tests simultaneously. The pupils in each class would then be divided into four random subgroups of equal size, but the procedure would involve no disturbance of the administrative organization of the school. The precautions about randomizing the papers are not essential, since the *treatments* $\times$ *schools* interaction is to be used as *error*, but it will avoid any larger-than-chance differences between subgroups that might otherwise increase the interaction variance and thus lower the precision of the experiment, and it would make possible an evaluation of the interaction. Other illustrations of "treatments" which may be simultaneously administered should readily occur to the student.

The method of analysis (pp. 119-127) used with "randomized groups" designs is not appropriate for direct application to observational data, since with such data the subgroups would not ordinarily be proportional in size from group to group. For example, if we wished to evaluate the difference in mean achievement of boys and girls in a number of schools, we would almost certainly not find the ratio of boys to girls to be the same for all schools. As a result, the difference in general means for the sexes (and also the differences in school means) would in part depend upon the way in which the sexes were distributed in the various schools. For instance, suppose that the scores on an achievement test administered in three schools gave the following totals and means for boys and girls separately:

	School 1			School 2			School 3			Total Sample		
	n	T	M	n	T	M	n	T	M	n	T	M
Boys	30	380	19.0	10	165	16.5	10	255	25.5	40	800	20.0
Girls	15	273	18.2	15	237	15.8	20	490	24.5	50	1000	20.0
Difference			+ 0.8			+ 0.7			+ 1.0			0.0

In this table, the mean for all boys is identical with that for all girls, in spite of the fact that the mean for boys exceeds that for girls in each of the three schools. This, of course, is due to the fact that the school in which the general level of achievement is the highest is also that which contains the highest proportion of girls. The difference between the sexes is obviously not measured by the difference in the general sex means, and the method of analysis of Section 6 (pages 119–127) would therefore not enable us to evaluate the sex factor. Because of the disproportionate class numbers, it would also be impossible to compute the variance for *schools* from the school means, or to compute the *interaction* (sex × schools) variance by the remainder theorem (page 107).

However, Snedecor [1] has presented empirical evidence indicating that if the subgroup numbers are not too disproportionate, usefully accurate results may be secured by applying the ordinary methods of analysis of variance (Section 6, pp. 119 ff.) to adjusted

[1] Snedecor, G. W., "The Method of Expected Numbers for Tables of Multiple Classification with Disproportionate Subclass Numbers," *Journal of American Statistical Association*, Vol. 29, pp. 389–393, December, 1934.

or "expected" numbers and sums instead of to the actual numbers and sums for the subgroups. Since this procedure appears to have considerable value in educational research, it will be described in detail in relation to a concrete example.

We shall illustrate this method as applied in an analysis of sex differences in performance on a high-school language test administered in a number of schools. The following table summarizes the results obtained from the administration of the 1939 *Iowa Every-Pupil Test in English Correctness* in seven high schools randomly selected from all schools below 100 in enrollment that participated in the 1939 Iowa Every-Pupil Testing Program.

	Boys			Girls			Schools		
	n	T	M	n	T	M	n	T	M
School 1	12	2097	174.7500	19	3228	169.8947	31	5325	171.7742
School 2	9	1145	127.2222	9	1455	161.6667	18	2600	144.4444
School 3	10	1705	170.5000	14	2629	187.7857	24	4334	180.5833
School 4	5	839	167.8000	13	2348	180.6154	18	3187	177.0556
School 5	8	1174	146.7500	19	3302	173.7895	27	4476	165.7778
School 6	11	2036	185.0909	16	2745	171.5625	27	4781	177.0741
School 7	6	841	140.1667	7	1173	167.5714	13	2014	154.9231
	61	9837	161.2623	97	16880	174.0206	158	26717	169.0949

We note, as might be expected, that the ratio of boys to girls differs considerably from school to school, and that hence the methods of Section 6 (pp. 119 ff.) may not be applied directly to these data.

The first step in the procedure is to adjust the "class" numbers (each "class" consisting of pupils of the same sex in the same school) so as to make them proportional. These "expected" numbers are computed in exactly the same way as we computed the "theoretical" frequencies in a contingency table in applying a test of independence or homogeneity (pp. 43 ff.). For example, the "expected" number of boys in School 1 is $(61 \times 31)/158 = 11.9684$. The expected numbers thus computed are given in the table on the following page, together with the actual numbers. The sum of expected numbers of course exactly equals the sum of actual numbers for any row or column.

The second step is to apply the χ^2 test to the table of actual

	Boys		Girls	
	Actual	Expected	Actual	Expected
School 1	12	11.9684	19	19.0316
School 2	9	6.9494	9	11.0506
School 3	10	9.2658	14	14.7342
School 4	5	6.9494	13	11.0506
School 5	8	10.4240	19	16.5760
School 6	11	10.4240	16	16.5760
School 7	6	5.0190	7	7.9810
Total	61	61.0000	97	97.0000

and expected frequencies. This is essential, since if the discrepancy between actual and expected numbers is larger than could be attributed to random selection, the procedure later described is not likely to give accurate results. In this case,[1] the value of X^2 is

$$X^2 = (12 - 11.9684)^2/11.9684 + \cdots\cdots + \\ (7 - 7.9810)^2/7.9810 = 3.254.$$

Since this X^2 has 6 $d.f.$, its value is no larger than could result by chance selection $(.8 > P > .7)$. Had X^2 proved highly significant, we would not be justified in continuing with this procedure.

The third step, granting that the X^2 test is not significant, is to compute an expected *sum* for each class by multiplying the actual mean by the expected number. For example, the expected sum for boys in School 1 is $174.7500 \times 11.9684 = 2094.623$. A new table, containing expected class numbers and sums and actual class means is then prepared, as below.

School	Boys			Girls			Schools		
	n'	T'	M	n'	T'	M	n'	T'	M'
1	11.9684	2094.623	174.7500	19.0316	3233.368	169.8947	31	5327.991	171.8707
2	6.9494	884.118	127.2222	11.0506	1786.514	161.6667	18	2670.632	148.3684
3	9.2658	1579.819	170.5000	14.7342	2766.872	187.7857	24	4346.691	181.1121
4	6.9494	1166.109	167.8000	11.0506	1995.909	180.6154	18	3162.018	175.6677
5	10.4240	1529.722	146.7500	16.5760	2880.735	173.7895	27	4410.457	163.3503
6	10.4240	1929.388	185.0909	16.5760	2843.820	171.5625	27	4773.208	176.7855
7	5.0190	703.497	140.1667	7.9810	1337.387	167.5714	13	2040.884	156.9911
	61.0000	9887.276	162.0865	97.0000	16844.605	173.6557	158	26731.881	169.1891

[1] In a $2 \times n$ table, X^2 is most easily computed by the method described on page 44.

The marginal totals in this table were secured by adding the expected sums within the body of the table. The marginal means were secured from the marginal totals.

The fourth step is to compute the variances for *sex*, *schools*, and *sex × schools* from this table of adjusted data. Since class and marginal means are available, it will be more convenient [1] to compute the sums of squares for *classes*, *sex*, and *schools* by means of formula (18a), page 92, than of (18). In other respects the computational procedure is the same as that described on pages 120–122.

The fifth step is to compute the sum of squares for *within classes* from *the table of original data*, by subtracting the sum of squares for *classes* from that for *total*. In the example, the sum of squares for *total* (from unadjusted data) was 126146.58, and that for *classes* (also from unadjusted data) was 35680.16, leaving 90466.42 as the sum of squares *within classes*.

The results for the example are summarized in the table below.

	d.f.	Sum of Squares	Variance	
Sex	1	3009.71	3009.71	
Schools	6	16606.33	2767.72	From adjusted data
Sex × Schools	6	12258.27	2043.05	
Within Classes	144	90466.42	628.24	From original data
	157			

The results may now be interpreted as in a randomized groups experiment. We note first that the variance ratio for *sex × schools* and *within classes* is $F = 2043.05/628.24 = 3.25$. This ratio, for 6 and 144 *d.f.*, is significant well beyond the 1 per cent level. This indicates that the true sex difference varies from school to school, hence it is not appropriate to test *sex* against *within classes* if we wish to generalize about all schools. We note, however, that for this *particular* set of seven schools, girls seem superior

---

[1] For example, the sum of squares for *schools* is

$$(5327.991 \times 171.8707 + \cdots\cdots + 2040.884 \times 156.9911) - 26731.881 \times 169.1891$$
$$= 16606.33$$

to boys in the trait measured, since $F = 3009.71/628.24 = 4.79$ (1 and 144 $d.f.$) is significant beyond the 5 per cent level. If we wish to generalize about all schools, we may, on the assumption that these seven schools are a random sample from the population of schools, test *sex* against *sex* $\times$ *schools*. This variance ratio, $F = 3009.71/2043.05 = 1.47$ (1 and 6 $d.f.$), is not significant. Hence these results are consistent with the interpretation that in the population of schools boys and girls are equal in mean achievement, but that in some schools there are real sex differences, and that we just happened in this small sample to get a majority of schools in which the girls were superior. This interpretation may in part appear unreasonable on other grounds, but there is nothing in the results of *this* investigation to enable us to reject it with any high confidence. We note, finally, that there are real differences between schools (apart from sex), since $F = 2767.72/628.24 = 4.41$ (6 and 144 $d.f.$) is highly significant.

A procedure similar to that just illustrated could be followed in the analysis of any observational data which may be arranged in a two-way table, *if* the sub-class numbers are not too disproportionate from row to row (as indicated by the χ^2 test of homogeneity) and if the variance within classes is homogeneous. For example, we might analyze the variance of scores on an attitudes scale for a random sample of persons classified with reference to both religious affiliations and political party affiliations. We would first have to assume that in the population the proportions in the various religious classes are roughly the same for the different political groups, and would test this assumption by the χ^2 test. We would then prepare a table of adjusted numbers and totals for the subgroups, and would interpret the results much as in the preceding illustration, *religious affiliations* taking the place of *sex* and *political affiliations* that of *schools*. The interpretation would differ in that the political or religious affiliations involved in the sample may not be considered as random samples from populations of such affiliation groups, but we might nevertheless interpret the results as suggested for the treatment of *levels* on pages 148–150.

If the investigation is such as to render the latter type of interpretation inappropriate, the type of interpretation suggested for factorial designs (pages 163–173) might be applied.

Before concluding the discussion of analysis of two-way classifications with disproportionate subgroup numbers, it may be well to emphasize that the method of "expected" numbers is an *approximate* method only, and may safely be employed only when it seems reasonable to suppose both on *a priori* grounds and in consideration of the results of a x^2 test, that in the whole population the subgroup numbers *are* proportional, or nearly so. If this assumption seems unreasonable, or if the x^2 test proves significant, other methods [1] of analysis are available, but these are beyond the scope of this book.

We noted in Chapter I (pages 5 and 6), that the use of "controlled" and "stratified" samples appears to offer very important (but hitherto largely neglected) possibilities in educational and psychological research. If we are to use such samples, it is of course important that we have unbiased objective measures of the precision or reliability of the results obtained from them, and, particularly, that we be able to secure an unbiased estimate of the standard error of the mean of a sample of this type. One solution to this problem is directly suggested by the methods of analysis of variance.

Suppose, for instance, that we are studying some trait in which it is known or suspected that there are systematic sex differences in the population to be sampled. Assuming that these differences concern only the means of the sexes, and not their variabilities, we might draw our sample so that it contains an equal number of each sex, rather than allow chance to determine the proportion of sexes in our sample. In other words, our sample would consist of two random samples of equal size, one from each sex, and the total sample would be a controlled sample rather than a simple random sample. We could now compute the standard error of the weighted

[1] See Yates, F., "The Analysis of Multiple Classifications With Unequal Numbers in the Different Classes," *Journal of American Statistical Association*, Vol. 29, pp. 51–66, March, 1934.

mean of the total sample by analyzing the total variance into *between sexes* and *within sexes*, divide the latter variance by the total number of cases, and extract the square root of the result. The *d.f.* for this standard error would be the same as for the *within sexes* variance, or $N - 2$. This standard error would indicate the variability in the sampling distribution of the means of a large number of similar samples, all of which had been "controlled" in exactly the same fashion. It is important to note, however, that this procedure assumes homogeneous variance within sexes.

It may be well to indicate in more general terms the procedure that may be followed in evaluating the mean of a controlled or representative sample. Suppose that for a given population we are interested in a variable x, which is known to be related to a variable y. Suppose that the distribution of y in the whole population is already known, and that the whole population may therefore be divided into definite classes or categories with reference to y. If the relative frequencies in these categories for the population are not exactly known, we may *assume* certain relative frequencies on the basis of available information and subjective opinion. We will then select our sample so that the relative frequencies in the y categories conform to the known or assumed relative frequencies in the population. If we may assume that we have a random sample from each category, and if we may also assume homogeneous variance in x within these categories, we may compute the standard error of the observed x mean for the total sample. The procedure, as already suggested, would be to analyze the total variance of the x distribution into *between categories* and *within categories*. The square root of the quotient obtained by dividing the latter variance by the total number of cases would be the standard error of the observed x mean. If the relative frequencies in the categories has been assumed, rather than known, this procedure of course introduces the danger of bias. In the latter case, however, the standard error is still valid with reference to a hypothetical population with the same distribution of y as we have in our sample. Where the true y distribution is not known, therefore, any generalizations based on the sample should be confined to this hypothetical population. Again, it should be emphasized that this procedure assumes homogeneous variance *within categories* — an assumption which should always be carefully examined in light of the observed data.

To illustrate the procedure just described, suppose we wish to know the mean annual expenditure per pupil in rural one-room schools in the state of Iowa. Suppose we know or suspect that there are systematic differences from one part of the state to another. We could then divide the state into geographical districts, and select a random sample of schools from each district. The number selected from each district would be proportional to the known total number of schools in that district. "Districts" would then constitute our *y* categories. We would then determine the expenditure per pupil in each school in the total sample, and analyze the total variance of the distribution of these data into *between districts* and *within districts* variances, in the manner of Section 2 of this chapter (see particularly the NOTE on page 102). We would then divide the latter variance by the total number of schools in our sample, and extract the square root of the result, to determine the standard error of the general mean. The *d.f.* for this standard error would be the number of schools minus the number of districts (the *d.f.* of the *within districts* variance). This standard error would validly describe the reliability of our mean if the variance in per-pupil-expenditures were fundamentally constant from district to district. If the differences in mean per-pupil-expenditure from district to district were marked, the mean of this type of sample might be considerably more reliable than the mean of a simple random sample selected from the state at large.

By way of further illustration, and also to exemplify the computational procedure, suppose we have administered a test of information about contemporary affairs to a sample of students in a certain university, this sample having been made representative with respect to the distribution by departments and colleges, such as

Law, Medicine, Engineering, etc. Specifically, the sample has been taken so that the number selected from each department is proportional to the total number in that department in the whole university. Suppose the results are as summarized below (the last column containing the sums of squares of individual scores).

Department or College	n	T	M	Σx^2
#1	27	2009	74.4074	179925
#2	13	709	54.5385	47411
#3	18	810	45.0000	49840
#4	22	1757	79.8636	157987
#5	39	2877	73.7692	236103
Total	119	8662	68.5882	671266

The sum of squares for *total* is
$$671266 - 8662 \times 68.5882 = 111449.11,$$
and for *departments* is
$$(2009 \times 74.4074 + \cdots + 2877 \times 73.7692) - 8662 \times 68.5882$$
$$= 17339.71,$$
leaving 94109.40 as the sum of squares *within departments*. The variance for *within departments* is then $94109.40/114 = 825.521$. Accordingly, the estimated standard error of the general mean is $\sqrt{825.521/119} = 2.633$. Hence, since for 114 *d.f.* the value of t at the 1 per cent level is about 2.58, we may be highly confident that the sample mean does not differ from the population mean by more than $2.58 \times 2.633 = 6.79$, or that the population mean lies between 75.38 and 61.80. It is worth noting that had we considered the total sample as a simple random sample, we would have estimated the standard error [1] of the mean as $\sqrt{111449.11/119^2}$ $= 2.805$. Hence, our control resulted in an appreciable increase

---

[1] Had we actually taken a simple random sample of 119 cases, with a subsequent chance variation in the subgroup numbers, the estimated standard error of the mean of this random sample would tend to be less than 2.805. The advantage of controlled sampling is therefore not as great as seems indicated by the comparison of 2.58 with 2.805.

in precision. The fact that the control was worth while is also demonstrated by the fact that the variance for *departments*, 17339.71/4 = 4334.85, is significantly larger (F = 4344.85/825.51 = 5.26) than that *within departments*.

It is important to note that the procedure just described assumes homogeneous variance within groups (see test on page 99, footnote). If this assumption cannot be made, the preferred procedure is that described in the following paragraphs.

Suppose we have a sample whose members have been classified into certain categories with reference to which it is possible to classify all members in the population. Suppose also that the members in each category may be considered a random sample from all such members in the population, but that the numbers in the categories of the sample are *not* proportional to those in the population. This would be a "stratified," but not a "representative" sample. Suppose, further, that we know the numbers in these categories in the whole population, or know that they are in a certain proportion. We may then secure from this stratified sample an unbiased estimate both of the population mean and of the standard error of this estimate. How this may be done may be illustrated with the data used in the preceding example.

Suppose that this sample had been drawn by taking any convenient number (n_p) of students at random from each department separately, but with no attempt to make these numbers proportional to those in the population. Suppose, however, that we know that in the population (that is, in the whole university) 35 per cent of the students are enrolled in department #1, 15 per cent in #2, 8 per cent in #3, 20 per cent in #4, and 22 per cent in #5. The formula for estimating the population mean is then

$$\text{est'd } M_{pop} = \frac{n_1' M_1 + n_2' M_2 + \cdots + n_p' M_p + \cdots + n_r' M_r}{n_1' + n_2' + \cdots + n_r'}$$

$$= \frac{\Sigma n_p' M_p}{\Sigma n_p'},$$

in which r is the total number of categories, M_p is the observed mean of category p of our total sample, and $n_1', n_2', \cdots n_r'$ are numbers which are *proportional* to the numbers in these categories in the whole population. (Similarly, n_1, n_2, etc. denote the actual numbers in the sample.) In our example, then, the estimate of the population mean is

$$\text{est'd } M_{pop} = \frac{74.4074 \times 35 + 54.5385 \times 15 + \cdots + 73.7692 \times 22}{100}$$

$$= 70.0253.$$

The standard error of this mean may then be secured by first estimating the variance of the observed mean of each category, using formula (8) on page 51 (but noting that the n in the formula refers to the actual number in the category of the sample). For our example, since Σd^2 for department #1 is $179925 - 74.4074 \times 2009 = 30440.54$, the estimated variance of the observed mean of department #1 is $s_1^2 = 30440.54/(27 \times 26) = 43.3626$. The estimated variances of the means for the other categories are 56.0462, 43.7582, 38.2395, and 16.1059, respectively. Each of these variances is then multiplied by the *square* of the weight used with the mean, and the sum of the products is divided by the square of the sum of the weights. The result is the estimated variance of the weighted general mean. If s^2_p represents the estimated variance of the mean of category p and if n'_p has the same meaning as before, then

$$\text{est'd } \sigma_M^2 = \frac{\Sigma n_p'^2 s_p^2}{(\Sigma n_p')^2}.$$

For our example,

$$\text{est'd } \sigma_M^2 = \frac{35^2 \times 43.3626 + 15^2 \times 56.0462 + \cdots + 22^2 \times 16.1059}{100^2}$$

$$= 9.1621$$

and hence the estimated standard error of the mean is the square root of this result, or 3.027. This mean is of course less stable than in the first example given, since we have given relatively little weight to the most stable group mean (that for department #5), and relatively heavy weight to some of the less stable. This last estimate (3.027) is an unbiased estimate under the conditions given, but a better estimate of the population mean (i.e., a smaller standard error of the mean) would have resulted from the same size (119) sample if the category numbers in the sample had been proportional to those in the population. The possibility of securing an unbiased estimate of the standard error of the mean of a stratified but not representative sample therefore does not reduce the desirability of making the sample representative whenever possible. We may note again that the procedure last described is valid even if the variances within groups are heterogeneous. Hence, even though the sample is representative, this latter procedure may sometimes be the appropriate one to use.

In concluding this discussion of general possibilities of analysis of variance in educational research, it may be well to repeat that the foregoing has been intended to be suggestive only. There are many other variations of these methods which have not been presented here. (One of these, the *factorial* design, will be given special consideration in the next two sections, and an extension of these methods, known as analysis of covariance, will be presented in Chapter VI. Other variations, such as the Latin square design and the Graeco-Latin square design, may be found described in Fisher's *Design of Experiments*.) Thus far, our experiences with these methods in the field of education have been extremely limited — so much so, in fact, that the writer has been forced to use many hypothetical illustrations. As our experience accumulates, it is probable that many of the suggestions here made will be in need of revision, or almost certainly of a redistribution of emphasis, and the student is therefore urged to retain a highly critical attitude in relation to them.

11. SIMPLE FACTORIAL DESIGNS IN METHODS EXPERIMENTS

It may sometimes be desirable to design a methods experiment so as to permit an evaluation, not only of certain methods, but also of certain variations in procedure which may be tried with all of these methods. For example, in addition to evaluating several ways of distributing drill in arithmetic, we may wish to evaluate several types of drill materials (each of which may be used in conjunction with any of the distributions of drill) and may wish also to determine which particular combination of type and distribution of drill is most effective. If we followed the procedure which has heretofore been customary in educational research, we would experiment separately with the distributions and the types of drill, each experiment being of the familiar "single variable" type. However, we can often serve the same ends much more efficiently by employing analysis of variance with what is known as a *factorial* design — a factorial design being one that permits comparisons of two or more factors in all combinations.

For the purposes of concrete illustration of the analytical procedure to be followed in factorial designs, let us suppose that we have planned an experiment to determine the relative effects upon reading rate of three different *sizes* of type and four different *styles* of type (such as Old English, Gothic, etc.). We thus have twelve possible combinations of style and size of type. Suppose we have accordingly prepared twelve different editions of the same rate-of-reading test, one in each of these combinations. Suppose our experiment has involved 120 pupils (all in the same school) and that we assigned these pupils at random to twelve equal groups, ten pupils per group. All groups were tested simultaneously and under the same conditions, but each took a different edition of the reading test. Suppose the results are as given in the table at the top of the opposite page, the measures being the number of words read per unit of time. In the following tables the Roman numerals represent the *styles* of type and the capital letters the *sizes*. Thus, in the group which was presented with style II and size B, the fastest reader read 225 words per unit of time, the next fastest 213 words, etc.

The arithmetic of computation [1] in the analysis of these data is the same as that described on pages 119 ff. The procedure can be facilitated in this case by subtracting 100 from each measure before beginning computation (this will have no effect on the final variances or variance ratios). The totals for the twelve groups

---

[1] The student is strongly urged to check these results as an exercise.

Style I			Style II			Style III			Style IV		
A	B	C	A	B	C	A	B	C	A	B	C
171	169	162	191	225	228	175	215	231	222	204	219
170	169	156	185	213	198	167	197	219	202	201	217
161	168	142	177	211	175	154	185	191	174	195	207
142	162	137	176	208	167	153	184	188	171	174	196
130	151	137	157	165	152	151	176	172	170	172	187
127	151	131	146	163	148	138	168	165	164	168	181
123	141	127	132	163	144	133	153	162	157	165	174
118	132	123	132	153	129	132	150	159	147	162	168
104	119	108	131	142	125	121	146	157	145	160	152
102	115	105	127	141	114	115	120	150	116	152	150

and the general totals and means for sizes and styles are given below (in terms of reduced scores).

	I	II	III	IV	Size Totals	Size Means
A	348	554	439	668	2009	50.23
B	477	784	694	753	2708	67.70
C	328	580	794	851	2553	63.83
Style Totals	1153	1918	1927	2272		
Style Means	38.43	63.93	64.23	75.73		

The results of the analysis of variance are as follows.

	d.f.	Variances
Size	2	3369.1
Style	3	7446.9
Size × Style	6	1020.3
Within Groups	108	668.5

The variance ratios in which we will be particularly interested are as follows (the numbers in parentheses after each F being the values needed for significance at the 5 per cent and 1 per cent levels, respectively, for the given d.f.):

Size/Within Groups: $F = 5.04$ $(3.09, 4.82)$

Style/Within Groups: $F = 11.14$ $(2.70, 3.98)$

Size × Style/Within Groups: $F = 1.53$ $(2.19,\ 2.99)$
Size/Size × Style: $F = 3.30$ $(5.14, 10.92)$
Style/Size × Style: $F = 7.30$ $(4.76,\ 9.78)$

We note first that the variances for both *style* and *size* are highly significant when tested against *within groups*. This tells us at once that the differences in general *size* means, or in general *style* means, cannot reasonably be attributed entirely to fluctuations in random sampling within the experiment. Had neither of the main effects proved significant when tested against *within groups*, our analysis would of course have been concluded.[1] What kind of general conclusions we may draw about the influence of type size (or style), however, depends upon whether or not there is any real interaction between these factors.

Before proceeding further with the interpretation of these results, it may be well to distinguish, for expository purposes, between two general kinds of situations in which we may resort to the use of factorial designs in experimentation. The first, and perhaps the more common, is that in which there is *a priori* reason to suspect that there is an interaction between the factors investigated, and in which one of the purposes of the experiment is to establish the presence of an interaction if it does exist. The second is that in which there is no reason to suppose, in advance of the experiment, that the factors are inter-dependent, and in which the major purpose in using the factorial design is to make multiple use of the experimental material.

The example we have taken is perhaps a better illustration of the latter than of the former type of situation. There does not appear to have been any strong reason to suspect, in advance of this experiment, that if one style of type proves best in one size it will not also prove best in another. We might therefore be disposed in this experiment to interpret the results on the assumption

---

[1] It is possible, although unlikely, that the interaction may prove significant even though the main effects are not significant. In this case, it would be well to test *between groups* (main effects and interaction combined) before accepting the interaction as significant. If both *between groups* and interaction prove significant, the appropriate analysis and interpretation would be that suggested on pages 168–170.

that there is no real interaction, unless, of course, the experimental data present convincing evidence to the contrary. That they do not is evident when we test *size* × *style* against *within groups*. The interaction variance is appreciably larger than the *within groups* variance, but not by an amount greater than could reasonably be attributed to chance fluctuations in random selection of the experimental groups. We may feel justified, therefore, in retaining the hypothesis that there is *no* real interaction, and proceed with our interpretation on that basis.

If we assume no interaction we may, if we wish, proceed to test differences in individual size (or style) means by the *t*-test, basing our error estimate on the *within groups* variance. For instance, our estimate of the standard error of the difference in any two *size* means would, on our assumption, be $1.414 \sqrt{668.5/40} = 5.77$. Hence, for 108 *d.f.* a difference in size means would have to exceed $1.96 \times 5.77 = 11.31$ to be significant at the 5 per cent level. We thus see that the difference in *size* means for A and B and for A and C are significant at the 5 per cent level, but that the difference for B and C could easily be due to chance. Similarly, a difference in *style* means would have to exceed 13.07 to be significant at the 5 per cent level. Thus, on the assumption of no interaction, we could safely recommend B and C over A, and could feel sure that style I is inferior to the others for the population sampled.

These recommendations, let us not forget, would be based upon the assumption of no interaction. While it may seem reasonable in this particular example, in general we would hesitate to rest so heavily upon this assumption. This would be particularly true if the interaction variance, although not significant, turned out to be so much larger than the *within groups* variance as it did in this example. In general, then, we would feel it necessary, in situations like this, to consider the results further in light of the possibility that there is, after all, a real interaction. Before doing so in this case, however, let us pause to consider the advantages of the factorial design in situations in which the assumption of no interaction appears reasonable on both *a priori* and experimental grounds.

The advantage, in this example, is that we have used the same experimental material for two independent purposes — to determine whether *size* of type influences reading rate, and to determine if *style* of type influences reading rate — and have accomplished each purpose as effectively as if it had been the *sole* purpose of the experiment. In other words, our comparisons of *size* means have been just as precise as if *style* had been held constant for all pupils, and our comparisons of *style* means as precise as if only one *size* had been used. Our experiment has therefore yielded essentially the same results as would two independent experiments of the single variable type, each using 120 pupils. We have thus secured twice as much information per pupil as if we had conducted two independent experiments. Furthermore, we have demonstrated that the assumption of no interaction is tenable, which could not have been learned at all from independent experiments. Finally, we are in a position to compare any size-style combination with any other (by applying the *t*-test to differences in individual group means) which again would have been impossible in two single-variable experiments. All of this, let us remind ourselves, is on the assumption of no interaction.

Let us now reconsider the results for the example in light of the possibility that there *is* a real interaction — which in general would be the safer point of view when the observed interaction variance is appreciably larger than the *within groups* variance. Let us first remind ourselves of what, in general, is meant by saying that an *interaction* exists between two classifications. It may mean that the *rank order* of the categories within one classification *differs* from category to category of the other, or it may mean that the rank order is the *same*, but that some differences within the first classification are larger or smaller in certain categories of the second classification than in others. With reference to our example, it may mean that the rank order of the *styles* differs from size to size, or it may mean that the rank order of styles is the same for all sizes, but that the superiority or inferiority of some styles is more pronounced in certain sizes than in others. The student should not get the idea that a significant interaction *necessarily* means a variation in rank order.

We may now recall that in a situation somewhat similar to this, the methods-schools type of experiment, we tested the *methods* differences against the interaction ($M \times S$) variance. In that situation, we had no interest in school differences other than to eliminate them from the *methods* and *error* variances. In other words, we introduced "schools" into the analysis only in order to make possible a valid test of the methods differences, and to increase the precision of the test, and not because we were interested in the particular schools involved. In that situation, also, the particular schools used were considered as a random sample of all schools in a specified population of schools. For the purpose of generalizing about all schools in the population, it was therefore appropriate to use the *methods* $\times$ *schools* variance as the *error* term, since it measured fluctuations due to the *random* selection of schools.

We have no very close parallel to this interpretation in our factorial design. We are now interested in evaluating differences in the means of both rows and columns, instead of only in one, and the particular *styles* (or *sizes*) involved may not strictly be considered as a random sample from a "population" of *styles* (or *sizes*). The interaction variance in a factorial design is therefore usually not strictly a measure of normally distributed *random* fluctuations, which theoretically must be true of the *error* term in any *F*-test or *t*-test. However, so far as our *style* comparisons are concerned, we may take somewhat the same position as that suggested on page 150 with reference to the treatment-level type of experiment. We may be able to say that we have included all sizes in which we are interested, or as wide a *range* in sizes as that in which we are interested. Similarly, while our sample of styles may not be considered as the equivalent of a random sample of all styles in which we are interested, it may include *all* the styles in which we are interested. That is, we may have no desire to generalize about other styles from the results of this experiment. If this position seems reasonable (and there will be some factorial experiments in which it is not), it will be meaningful to test the variances for *style* and *size* against that for *size* × *style*, even though the latter is not strictly a measure of random variations, and though we may not interpret the probabilities from the F or t tables so literally as otherwise. In other words, if the variance for *style* is "significantly" larger than that for *size* × *style*, we may be reasonably confident that the rank order of the styles does not differ greatly from size to size, and we may be running relatively little risk in recommending certain styles for all sizes (although recognizing that there may be a few exceptions to the general rule). Similarly, if the variance for *size* is "significantly" larger than that for *size* × *style*, we may quite safely recommend one size for all styles (or, as in the example, conclude that a certain size is inferior to the others for all styles). Furthermore, this procedure would be fairly safe *even though the interaction variance proved significant*, although in that case we would perhaps be more cautious, and before generalizing to all styles or all sizes, would insist that the main effects be more highly "significant" when tested against interaction. Actually, in this example, only one of the main effects is "significant," even at the 5 per cent level, when tested against interaction, but because of the lack of *a priori* reasons for suspecting a real interaction, we need hardly modify at all the conclusions earlier based on the tests against *within groups* alone. In other situations presenting similar experimental results, it might be safer to follow the procedure suggested in the following paragraphs. Before concluding this paragraph, however, let us emphasize again that the procedure just recommended is arbitrary in character, although wide experience in agricultural research indicates that it is usually satisfactory.

We have now left to consider the case in which the variances for the main effects are not "significantly" larger than the interaction variance, and in which the interaction variance *is* significantly larger than the *within groups* variance. In this case the suggestion would be strong that the rank order of the categories of the first classification may differ markedly from category to category of the second, and we could not hope to extend our recommendations concerning one classification to all categories of the other.   We might nevertheless be able to reveal significant differences within one classification for specific categories of the other.   How this may be done may be illustrated in the case of our example.

Let us suppose, for the sake of illustration, that the *size* × *style* variance had proved significant, and that the *size* and *style* variances had not been much larger than that for *size* × *style*.   We would then have to restrict our recommendations (if any) concerning styles to certain sizes, and those for sizes to certain styles. That is, we would have to consider the observed style differences for each size separately and the observed size differences for each style separately.   Suppose, then, we raise the question of whether there are real differences in *style* for size A alone.   We would then compute the sum of squares for *style* means *within* size A alone, as follows:

$$\frac{348^2 + 554^2 + 439^2 + 668^2}{10} - \frac{2009^2}{40} = 5184.5$$

The variance estimated from style means within size A would then be $5184.5/3 = 1728.2$.   The ratio of this variance to the *within groups* variance is $F = 1728.2/668.5 = 2.57$.   For 3 and 108 *d.f.* this F is not significant, hence all differences in style means within size A could be attributed to chance, and we may not feel justified [1] in testing differences in individual style means within size A by the *t*-test.   For size C, however, a similar test reveals that there are significant differences in *style* means, and we are clearly justified in applying the *t*-test to individual differences in style means within that size.   The estimated standard error of a difference between two means of 10 cases each is $1.414 \sqrt{668.5/10} = 11.58$, and hence for 108 *d.f.* a difference of $11.58 × 1.96 = 22.6$ would be required for significance at the 5 per cent level.   We thus see that for size C the mean for style I is significantly lower than for

---

[1] This, of course, depends on the arbitrary standards we choose to employ.   This particular F, for example, barely falls short of the 5 per cent level, and many research workers would feel justified in testing individual differences.

all other styles, and that IV is significantly above I and II, though not III. In a similar fashion it may be shown that the variance for *size* means within style I is not significant, but that it is within style III, and that for this style size A is significantly below both B and C. We are thus able to make a number of recommendations of styles for certain sizes and of sizes for certain styles, and have 108 *d.f.* available [1] for each test. It will be noted then, that we are essentially viewing the whole experiment as consisting of three independent or parallel single-variable experiments with *styles*, each employing 40 pupils, or of four independent single-variable experiments with *sizes*, each employing 30 pupils, except that our *error* term is in each case derived from all 120 pupils.

The preceding illustration should offer a reasonably close parallel to most of the applications likely to be made of simple factorial designs in educational research.[2] When applied in instructional experiments, one of the factors will usually be "methods," the other will be some variable such as time spent in study, or distribution of class time (double *vs.* single period), or type of motivation, which may vary in *degree* within each method. While the particular methods involved may not be considered as a random sample of any "population" of methods, it may frequently be true that they do include *all* of the methods in which we are interested at the moment. Hence *methods* would be analogous to *styles* in our illustration. While the categories or levels based on the second factor may also not be considered a random sample from a population of such categories, we may nevertheless often be able to include as wide a *range* in these categories or levels as is of any practical interest, with several well-distributed intermediate levels, and hence may follow the type of interpretation of the interaction term which has been here suggested in evaluating *sizes*.

It is highly important to note finally, that in any such experiment, performed in a single school, any conclusions drawn would

[1] On the assumption of homogeneous variance *within groups*.

[2] The student is urged, as a very valuable exercise, to invent or discover for himself as many specific illustrations as possible of further applications of this design in educational research.

strictly apply only to the one school involved.   Different results might be obtained in other schools, just as was pointed out on page 103 with reference to the simple methods experiment.

12. FACTORIAL DESIGN DUPLICATED IN RANDOMLY SELECTED SCHOOLS

The simple factorial design considered in the preceding section may find many useful applications, but its general usefulness in educational research is restricted by the facts that ordinarily one would not wish to confine his generalizations to a single school, and that a single school would seldom provide sufficient numbers for high precision even though the first restriction were acceptable. The preceding section, then, was presented in part in order to lead the student more gradually to an understanding of the procedure — now to be considered — which is appropriate when several schools are involved.

Let us suppose, for the sake of illustration, that we wish to evaluate three methods of instruction, and two motivating devices that may be used in conjunction with any of these methods.   We thus have six possible combinations of method and device.   Suppose that our experiment is to involve seven schools.   Suppose that within each school we have been able to assign the pupils at random to six equal groups, one for each combination of method and device.   These groups would of course differ in size from school to school.   We will assume that a total of 560 pupils is involved in all schools.   The experiment is conducted under the same controlled conditions in all schools.   At the close of the experiment, all groups in all schools take the same criterion test.   Within each school, then, we have an experiment of the type described in the preceding section.   Our problem is to analyze and interpret the pooled results from these duplicated experiments.

The basic data needed for the analysis would be the sum of the criterion scores for each of the 42 groups, and the sum of the squared scores for the entire sample.   From these totals, all other necessary totals, and all required means and sums of squares, may be computed. For convenience, we will use a notation in which numerical subscripts refer to schools, lower case subscripts to motivating devices, and capital subscripts to methods; T will stand for total, ss for "sum of squares," and n for the number of cases in a group or set of groups. Thus T_{aB3} would be the total for all pupils in the group using device a and method B in school 3; T_{bc} would be the total for all groups using device b and method C, T_{b2} for all pupils using device b in school 2, T_4 for all pupils in school 4, etc.

The sum of squares for *methods* would then be

$$ss_M = \frac{T_A^2 + T_B^2 + T_C^2}{n_A} - \frac{T^2}{N},$$

T without a subscript being the grand total, N the total number of cases, and $n_A = n_B = n_C$ the number of pupils under any one method.

The sum of squares for *schools* would be

$$ss_S = \frac{T_1^2}{n_1} + \frac{T_2^2}{n_2} + \cdots\cdots + \frac{T_7^2}{n_7} - \frac{T^2}{N},$$

and the sum of squares for *devices* would be

$$ss_D = \frac{T_a^2 + T_b^2}{n_a} - \frac{T^2}{N}.$$

In this case there would be a number of interaction terms. The sum of squares for *methods* × *schools* would be computed by disregarding *devices*, and dealing only with 21 sets of pupils, each set consisting of the two groups that used the same method but different devices in a certain school. The sum of squares for these sets corresponds to the sum of squares for "classes" in the problem of Sections 4 to 6 of this chapter, and will here be referred to as the sum of squares for *methods within schools* (notation: $ss_{M \text{ in } S}$). This sum of squares would be

$$ss_{M \text{ in } S} = \frac{T_{A1}^2 + T_{B1}^2 + T_{C1}^2}{n_{A1}} + \cdots\cdots + \frac{T_{A7}^2 + T_{B7}^2 + T_{C7}^2}{n_{A7}} - \frac{T^2}{N}.$$

The sum of squares for *methods* × *schools* would then be

$$ss_{M \times S} = ss_{M \text{ in } S} - ss_M - ss_S.$$

The sum of squares for *methods × devices* would similarly be found by disregarding schools, finding the sum of squares for *methods within devices* (based on 6 sets of pupils, each set consisting of the 7 groups which used the same combination of method and device), and subtracting the sums of squares for *methods* and *devices*. The sum of squares for *methods within devices* would be

$$SS_{M \text{ in } D} = \frac{T_{aA}^2 + T_{bA}^2 + \cdots\cdots + T_{bC}^2}{n_{aA}} - \frac{T^2}{N},$$

and for *methods × devices* would be

$$SS_{M \times D} = SS_{M \text{ in } D} - SS_M - SS_D.$$

The sum of squares for *devices × schools* would be found by subtracting the sums of squares for *devices* and *schools* from the sum of squares for *devices within schools* (based on 14 sets, each set consisting of the 3 groups using the same device but different methods in a certain school). The latter sum of squares would be

$$SS_{D \text{ in } S} = \frac{T_{a1}^2 + T_{b1}^2}{n_{a1}} + \cdots\cdots + \frac{T_{a7}^2 + T_{b7}^2}{n_{a7}} - \frac{T^2}{N}$$

and the sum of squares for *devices × schools* would be

$$SS_{D \times S} = SS_{D \text{ in } S} - SS_D - SS_S.$$

In this case there would also be a *triple* interaction whose sum of squares would be the remainder left when all primary and double-interaction sums of squares are subtracted from the sum of squares for *groups*. The latter sum of squares (based on the 42 groups) would be

$$SS_{\text{groups}} = \frac{T_{aA1}^2 + T_{aB1}^2 + T_{aC1}^2 + T_{bA1}^2 + T_{bB1}^2 + T_{bC1}^2}{n_{aA1}}$$

$$+ \cdots\cdots + \frac{T_{aA7}^2 + \cdots\cdots + T_{bC7}^2}{n_{aA7}} - \frac{T^2}{N}.$$

The sum of squares for *methods × devices × schools* would then be

$$SS_{M \times D \times S} = SS_{\text{groups}} - SS_M - SS_D - SS_S - SS_{M \times S} - SS_{M \times D} - SS_{D \times S}.$$

The sum of squares for *total* (ss_t) is the sum of all squared scores minus T^2/N, and for *within groups* is

$$SS_{\text{within groups}} = SS_t - SS_{\text{groups}}$$

(This sum of squares *within groups* would not be meaningful and would therefore not be computed unless the pupils had been assigned at random to the various groups in each school.)

The *d.f.*'s for *methods*, *devices*, and *schools* and for the double interaction terms are found as before. The *d.f.* for *methods within schools* (based on 21 pairs of groups) is $21 - 1 = 20$. Hence, the *d.f.* for $M \times S$ is $20 - 2 - 6 = 12$. The *d.f.* for *methods within devices* (based on 6 sets of groups) is $6 - 1 = 5$, hence the *d.f.* for $M \times D$ is $5 - 2 - 1 = 2$. The *d.f.* for *devices within schools* (based on 14 sets of groups) is $14 - 1 = 13$. Hence the *d.f.* for $D \times S$ is $13 - 6 - 1 = 6$. The *d.f.* for *groups* is $42 - 1 = 41$, hence the *d.f.* for $M \times D \times S$ is $41 - 2 - 1 - 6 - 12 - 2 - 6 = 12$. The *d.f.* for *total* is $560 - 1 = 559$. Hence, the *d.f.* for *within groups* is $559 - 41 = 518$. These data [1] may be arranged as follows:

	d.f.	ss	Variance
M	2	—	—
D	1	—	—
S	6	—	—
$M \times D$	2	—	—
$M \times S$	12	—	—
$D \times S$	6	—	—
$M \times D \times S$	12	—	—
Within groups	518	—	—
Total	559	—	—

As in the simpler design of the preceding section, how we may interpret the results depends upon whether or not we may assume that there is no real interaction between *methods* and *devices*. Our first step, then, will be to test $M \times D$. In this case, however, it is not sufficient to test $M \times D$ against *within groups*. This is for the same reason that in the simpler methods-schools type of experiment (Sections 4 to 6) it was insufficient to test *methods* against *within schools*. In the latter type of experiment, we recog-

---

[1] It may be more convenient to think of the *d.f.* for $M \times D$ as the product of the *d.f.*'s for *M* and *D*, and of the *d.f.* for $M \times S$ as the product of the *d.f.*'s for *M* and *S*, etc. The *d.f.* for $M \times D \times S$ is the product of the *d.f.*'s for *M*, *D*, and *S*.

nized that while there might be real differences in the methods means for individual schools, these differences might differ in magnitude or even in direction from school to school, and that in the whole population the general methods means might be equal. We therefore found it appropriate to test *methods* against the interaction of methods with *schools*, and if the *methods* variance did not prove significantly larger than the interaction (with schools) variance, we recognize that the observed difference in general methods means might be due to the chance selection of schools that favored certain methods. Similarly, in the situation we are now considering, it is possible that there is a real $M \times D$ interaction in some schools, but that this interaction varies in intensity or even in direction from school to school. Hence it is appropriate in this case, before generalizing about all schools, to test $M \times D$ against the interaction of $M \times D$ with *schools*, that is, to test $M \times D$ against $M \times D \times S$. If this test does not prove significant, we may retain the hypothesis that in the whole population of schools the interactions of $M \times D$ within individual schools may in effect counteract one another, with the result that the general population means for methods may have the same relationship for both devices, or the devices have the same relative effectiveness for all methods.

In our example, the test of $M \times D / M \times D \times S$ is based on 2 and 12 *d.f.* If $M \times D$ does not prove significantly larger than $M \times D \times S$, the hypothesis is tenable that there is no real overall $M \times D$ interaction, and we may proceed on this hypothesis to test *methods* (and *devices*) on the basis of the total results. On that hypothesis we may (as in Section 5) evaluate the variance for *methods* against that for $M \times S$, and that for *devices* against that for $D \times S$. It is conceivable, however, that there is no *real* interaction of schools with either M, D, or $M \times D$, and that the observed interactions involving schools are due to uncontrolled variables (such as the teacher variable) or to chance alone. (See pp. 110–111.) It is also conceivable, although generally improbable, that the interactions of *schools* with M, D, and $M \times D$ are real but of equal strength. In either case, the variances for $M \times S$, $D \times S$, and $M \times D \times S$ would differ only by chance, or would all be estimates of the *same* true value. At any rate, if there are no appreciable differences between the three interaction variances involving schools (S), the hypothesis is tenable that they are fundamentally the same, and on this hypothesis a combination of the three of them will provide a better error estimate than any one alone. The usual procedure, therefore (before testing even $M \times D$), is to first examine the $M \times S$, $D \times S$, and $M \times D \times S$ variances. If they are all of approximately the same magnitude (no differences significant at the 5 per cent level), the *error* variance is obtained by adding the sums of squares for $M \times S$, $D \times S$, and $M \times D \times S$, and dividing the total by the sum of the corresponding *d.f.*'s (in this case $12 + 6 + 12 = 30$). We would thus have

	d.f.
M	2
D	1
$M \times D$	2
Error	30

The interpretation of the results would then be exactly like that in Section 11, with the difference that the conclusions would apply to schools in general (in the specified population) rather than only to a single school. If, however, large or significant differences were observed between the $M \times S$, $D \times S$, and $M \times D \times S$ variances, we would evaluate $M \times D$ against $M \times D \times S$, and, if $M \times D$ proved insignificant, would evaluate M against $M \times S$ and D against $D \times S$ as suggested earlier.

If a significant $M \times D$ interaction were found (or if the $M \times D$ interaction were appreciably larger than *error* and the hypothesis of no interaction were otherwise doubtful) we would test M and D against $M \times D$ (just as we tested *styles* and *sizes* against *size* × *style*). If these tests prove insignificant, we would have to test the differences for methods separately for each device, and those for devices separately for each method, using as the *error* term either $M \times D \times S$ or the pooled error term described in the preceding paragraph. Specifically, to evaluate the methods differences for the first device, we would consider all groups using that device as constituting a separate experiment (with 280 pupils) in which the variance for *methods* could be computed as in Section 6 preceding. For example, the sum of squares for *methods* with reference to device *a* only would be

$$\frac{T_{aA}^2 + T_{aB}^2 + T_{aC}^2}{n_{aA}} - \frac{T_a^2}{n_a},$$

which when divided by the number of *d.f.* (2) would give the variance for *methods* within device *a*. This variance could then be tested against the *error* term derived from the whole experiment. A similar procedure would be followed to evaluate the methods differences in relation to the second device, and to evaluate the devices in relation to each of the methods.

The factorial design may be extended, in theory at least, to any number of factors, and to any number of levels within each factor. Thus, we could experiment simultaneously, for example, with three methods, two motivating devices, and two sets of reading materials, duplicating the experiment in a number of schools. If the interactions involving S were all of approximately the same magnitude, the *error* term would then be the sum of all of these interactions, and the primary and interaction variances involving the other factors would be computed in the manner already explained. However, as the number of factors and levels increases, the combinations may become so numerous that few schools could provide even one pupil for each combination, and hence in practice these more complex designs will perhaps seldom be employed, and need not be considered here.

CHAPTER VI

ANALYSIS OF COVARIANCE

I. INTRODUCTORY

THE use of "matched" or equated groups to secure increased precision in methods experiments has long been widely practiced in educational research. (See Designs V and VI of Chapter IV.) This practice has usually resulted in a very worthwhile increase in precision, but often at the cost of considerable administrative inconvenience. If the equating of groups is done at the beginning of the experiment — as it should be — time must be taken to administer an initial test, to score these tests, and to organize the equated groups before the experiment can get under way. The organization of the equated groups involves disrupting the classes as they are found already organized, and this again is often very inconvenient, if not quite impracticable. To avoid these difficulties, the device has sometimes been employed of doing the "matching" at the close of the experiment. The experiment is conducted with the classes as they are found already organized in the school, and then, at the close of the experiment, the results for such pupils are discarded from the final analysis as is necessary to make the means and standard deviations of initial scores alike for all classes. This of course means a loss of valuable information, and this loss may sometimes offset any advantage gained by the use of equated groups. It is therefore fortunate for the educational experimenter that the methods of analysis of *covariance* — an extension by R. A. Fisher of his methods of analysis of variance — now enable us to dispense with these inconvenient matching procedures and to secure the same increase in precision by the use of statistical controls.

2. THE ESSENTIAL NATURE OF ANALYSIS OF COVARIANCE

The essential nature of the methods of analysis of covariance may perhaps best be made clear in terms of a concrete illustration.

We shall first consider the relatively simple case in which the experiment is conducted in a single school, and in which the experimental groups are selected at random from the available pupils. The more complex case in which the experiment is duplicated in a number of schools will be considered later.

Suppose that in a certain school we have conducted an experimental comparison of three methods (A, B, and C) of teaching a given unit of content in seventh-grade arithmetic. Suppose that three equal experimental groups have been taught, one by each of the methods, and that the pupils were originally assigned to these groups strictly at random. Suppose that for each pupil we have a measure of initial ability in arithmetic secured at the beginning of the experiment, as well as a criterion measure of final achievement secured at the close of the experiment.

Broadly stated, the hypothesis that we wish to test is that there are no real differences in methods, and that any differences in final mean scores of the methods groups, *after allowances have been made for chance differences in initial mean scores*, are due entirely to chance fluctuations in random sampling. This is not an exact statement of the null hypothesis, since we have not specified the manner in which the allowances for initial differences are to be made, but we will supply that deficiency later. The important point is that we hope through such allowances to attain the same precision as would have been attained had the groups been actually matched on the basis of the initial measures.

The allowances for initial differences are to be made in terms of the regression of final on initial measures. If we were actually to compute the regression coefficient for the pupils in each group (or under each method) separately, the result would of course differ from group to group, but under our hypothesis these differences would be due only to chance. In other words, according to our hypothesis there is one true regression of final on initial measures which is the same for all groups. This regression may be referred to as the regression *within groups*. We shall see later how we may secure a valid estimate of this regression. For the moment, let us suppose that we have this estimate, and consider how it would be used to "correct" the final means for initial differences.

The student will recall, from simple correlation theory, that if one knows the regression coefficient of Y on X for a sample, and knows also the amount x by which a given X deviates from the mean of the X's, one can estimate the deviation of the corresponding Y from the mean of the Y's by multiplying the known x by the regression coefficient. Hence, given the regression coefficient and knowing the deviation of the initial score of any pupil from the initial general mean, we can compute the amount by which his final score would be expected to deviate from the final mean ("expected" because of his initial ability only, regardless of the method by which he had been taught). If, then, we subtract [1] this expected deviation (or correction) from his *actual* final score, we should have an "adjusted" criterion score whose relative status would be independent of the pupil's initial ability. This adjusted score may be defined as Y-bx, in which Y is the pupil's actual final score, x the deviation of his initial score from the general mean, and b the regression of final on initial scores. This adjusted score would then be such that any two pupils, regardless of their initial scores, would have the same *adjusted* score if their actual final scores exceeded (or fell short of) their expected final scores by the same amount.

Suppose, then, that we had thus computed an adjusted criterion score for each pupil in the experiment. (As we shall see later, we need not actually adjust the score of each individual pupil in order to compute the mean of the adjusted scores.) If we then computed the mean of these adjusted scores for the pupils under each method separately, these means would be independent of chance differences in mean initial ability of the experimental groups. These means of adjusted scores, or these adjusted means, should then have the same relative magnitude as if the experimental

[1] If the expected deviation were positive in sign, we would subtract it from the actual final score; if the correction were negative, its absolute value would be added to the final score.

groups had been alike in initial ability, or had actually been matched with reference to the initial measures. Finally, by applying the methods of analysis of variance to these *adjusted* scores, we could test the hypothesis that the differences in adjusted methods means are due entirely to chance.

While the foregoing is not an exact indication of the specific procedures involved in the methods of analysis of covariance, it should make clear to the student the essential nature of these methods. Essentially, the methods of analysis of covariance will enable us: (1) to estimate the true regression of final on initial measures (on the assumption that there is no real difference in regression from group to group or method to method), (2) to use this regression coefficient to correct or "adjust" the final methods means so as to allow for differences in the initial measures, and (3), to test the significance of the differences remaining in the adjusted methods means. The detailed steps in the procedure will be described later, but before going on to their description, it might be well first to consider the derivation of certain formulae which will be required.

3. DERIVATION OF BASIC FORMULAS

These formulae will be derived for a sample consisting of m groups of n cases each. The notation employed will be as follows:

X represents a raw score on an initial test

Y represents a raw score on a final (criterion) test

T_X and T_Y represent the sums of all initial and final scores respectively, and M_X and M_Y represent the corresponding means.

$x = X - M_X$ and $y = Y - M_Y$ represent deviations from the general means for any individual.

$\bar{x} = \dfrac{\Sigma x}{n}$ and $\bar{y} = \dfrac{\Sigma y}{n}$ represent the means of x's and y's for any *group*.

The correlation r_{xy} for the total sample would then be

$$r_{xy} = \frac{\Sigma xy}{N \sigma_x \sigma_y}$$

or, for any single *group* it would be

$$r_{xy} \text{ (within any group)} = \frac{\dfrac{\Sigma(x - \bar{x})(y - \bar{y})}{n}}{\sigma(x - \bar{x})\,\sigma(y - \bar{y})}$$

Again, if the correlation within the group were computed from M_X and M_Y as arbitrary origins, we could write

$$r_{xy} \text{ (within any group)} = \frac{\dfrac{\Sigma xy}{n} - \bar{x} \cdot \bar{y}}{\sigma_{(x - \bar{x})}\,\sigma_{(y - \bar{y})}}$$

Hence for any one group

$$\frac{\Sigma(x - \bar{x})(y - \bar{y})}{n} = \frac{\Sigma xy}{n} - \bar{x} \cdot \bar{y}$$

from which

$$\Sigma xy = \Sigma(x - \bar{x})(y - \bar{y}) + n\bar{x}\bar{y}$$

Summing these expressions for all m groups we have

$$\Sigma\Sigma xy = \Sigma\Sigma(x - \bar{x})(y - \bar{y}) + n\Sigma\bar{x}\bar{y}$$

which may be more simply written

$$\Sigma xy = \Sigma(x - \bar{x})(y - \bar{y}) + n\Sigma\bar{x}\bar{y} \qquad (19)$$

if we understand that the summation is for the total sample.

Thus we see that the total sum of the *products* (of deviations) may be analyzed into two components, just as the total sum of *squares* (of deviations) may be analyzed for either variable considered alone. The components of the total sum of products (of deviations from the general mean) are the sum of the products of deviations from the group means and n times the sum of the products of the group means (each mean expressed as a deviation from the general mean).

The *covariance* of two variables for a sample is the mean of the *products* of their deviations from their means, just as the *variance* of a single variable is the mean of the *squares* of the deviations. The best estimate of the covariance of a population that may be derived from a sample of n cases is $\dfrac{\Sigma xy}{n - 1}$, and the best estimate of the covariance of the means of such samples that may be derived from m means is $\dfrac{\Sigma \, \bar{x}\bar{y}}{m - 1}$. The best estimate of the covariance of the population that may be derived from the means of m samples of n cases each is $\dfrac{n \Sigma \, \bar{x}\bar{y}}{m - 1}$. The argument supporting these statements is of the same character as in the case of analysis of variance.

We have seen [formulas (17) and (18) on page 92] how $\Sigma \, x^2$ and $\Sigma \, \bar{x}^2$ may be computed from the raw scores. We shall need similar expressions for the computation of $\Sigma \, xy$ and $\Sigma \, \bar{x}\bar{y}$. We may note first that

$$xy = (X - M_X)(Y - M_Y)$$
$$= XY - XM_Y - YM_X + M_X M_Y.$$

It follows that for a sample of N cases

$$\Sigma \, xy = \Sigma \, XY - M_Y \Sigma \, X - M_X \Sigma \, Y + NM_X M_Y.$$

Now, since each of the last three terms is equal to $\dfrac{\Sigma \, X \Sigma \, Y}{N}$, two of them will cancel, leaving

$$\Sigma \, xy = \Sigma \, XY - \frac{\Sigma \, X \Sigma \, Y}{N} = \Sigma \, XY - \frac{T_X T_Y}{N} \qquad (20)$$

Similarly, for m groups,

$$n \Sigma \, \bar{x}\bar{y} = T_{X_1} M_{Y_1} + T_{X_2} M_{Y_2} + \cdots\cdots + T_{X_m} M_{Y_m} - T_X M_Y,$$

from which, multiplying and dividing the right-hand terms by n_1, n_2, etc., respectively, and noting that $M_{Y_1} = T_{Y_1}/n_1$, we get

$$n \Sigma \, \bar{x}\bar{y} = \frac{T_{X_1} T_{Y_1}}{n_1} + \frac{T_{X_2} T_{Y_2}}{n_2} + \cdots\cdots + \frac{T_{X_m} T_{Y_m}}{n_m} - \frac{T_X T_Y}{N} \qquad (21)$$

in which the numerical subscripts refer to the groups.

Let us now recall that r_{xy} for the total sample may be written

$$r_{xy} \text{ (total)} = \frac{\Sigma \, xy}{\sqrt{\Sigma \, x^2 \cdot \Sigma \, y^2}} \qquad (22)$$

and that in the corresponding regression equation of Y on X the regression coefficient $(b_{y \cdot x})$ may be written

$$b_{y \cdot x} \text{ (total)} = r_{xy} \frac{\sigma_y}{\sigma_x} = \frac{\Sigma xy}{\sqrt{\Sigma x^2 \cdot \Sigma y^2}} \cdot \frac{\sqrt{\dfrac{\Sigma y^2}{N}}}{\sqrt{\dfrac{\Sigma x^2}{N}}} = \frac{\Sigma xy}{\Sigma x^2} \qquad (23)$$

The correlation and regression coefficients *within* any one group may similarly be written

$$r_{xy} \text{ (within any group)} = \frac{\Sigma(x - \bar{x})(y - \bar{y})}{\sqrt{\Sigma(x - \bar{x})^2 \cdot \Sigma(y - \bar{y})^2}} \qquad (24)$$

and

$$b_{x \cdot y} \text{ (within any group)} = \frac{\Sigma(x - \bar{x})(y - \bar{y})}{\Sigma(x - \bar{x})^2} \qquad (25)$$

If we think of the summations as extending over all groups, expression (24) may be considered as representing an "average" correlation *within groups* for the entire sample, and (25) as representing the "average" regression within groups. This average regression *within groups* is our best estimate (on the assumption that the regression is fundamentally the same from group to group, or that the groups are random samples from the same population) of the true regression of final on initial measures for all groups. It is the regression on the basis of which we shall "adjust" the final scores so as to allow for initial differences.

If we now let $Y - bx$ (in which b is the average $b_{y \cdot x}$ *within groups*) represent what we have called an "adjusted" final score, we may note that the mean of these adjusted scores for the total sample will be

$$\frac{\Sigma(Y - bx)}{N} = \frac{\Sigma Y}{N} - \frac{b}{N} \Sigma x = M_Y, \qquad (26)$$

since $\Sigma x = o$ and $\Sigma Y/N = M_Y$. Furthermore, since the deviation of a single adjusted score from the general mean of adjusted scores is

$$(Y - bx) - M_Y = y + M_Y - bx - M_Y = y - bx \qquad (27)$$

it follows that the mean of these deviations *for any single group* is

$$\frac{\Sigma(y - bx)}{n} = \frac{\Sigma y}{n} - \frac{b \Sigma x}{n} = \bar{y} - b\bar{x}, \tag{28}$$

which is also the deviation of the group mean of adjusted scores from the general mean of adjusted scores. Accordingly, the sum of the squares of these deviations for all m groups would be

$$\Sigma(\bar{y} - b\bar{x})^2 = \Sigma \bar{y}^2 - 2 b \Sigma \bar{x}\bar{y} + b^2 \Sigma \bar{x}^2 \tag{29}$$

Now if we assume that all m groups are random samples from the same population, our estimate [see (14), page 90] of the variance of adjusted scores for the population would be $n \Sigma(\bar{y} - b\bar{x})^2/m - 1$, and the "sum of squares" used to compute this variance would be $n \Sigma(\bar{y} - b\bar{x})^2$. From (29),

$$n \Sigma(\bar{y} - b\bar{x})^2 = n \Sigma \bar{y}^2 - 2 bn \Sigma \bar{x}\bar{y} + b^2n \Sigma \bar{x}^2 \tag{30}$$

We now note that the first right-hand term, $n \Sigma \bar{y}^2$, is the sum of squares for variance *between groups* in an analysis of the variance of the Y scores. Similarly $n \Sigma \bar{x}^2$ is the sum of squares for variance *between groups* in an analysis of the X scores, and $n \Sigma \bar{x}\bar{y}$ is the expression whose computation is given by (21). From (30) we can then compute the sum of squares for variance *between groups* for the adjusted scores.

For any one group, the sum of the squared deviations of the adjusted scores from their mean for the group would be

$$\Sigma[(y - \bar{y}) - b(x - \bar{x})]^2 = \Sigma(y - \bar{y})^2 - 2 b \Sigma(x - \bar{x})(y - \bar{y}) + b^2 \Sigma(x - \bar{x})^2$$

$$= \Sigma(y - \bar{y})^2 - 2 \frac{\Sigma(x - \bar{x})(y - \bar{y})}{\Sigma(x - \bar{x})^2} \cdot \Sigma(x - \bar{x})(y - \bar{y})$$

$$+ \left[\frac{\Sigma(x - \bar{x})(y - \bar{y})}{\Sigma(x - \bar{x})^2}\right]^2 \Sigma(x - \bar{x})^2$$

$$= \Sigma(y - \bar{y})^2 - \frac{[\Sigma(x - \bar{x})(y - \bar{y})]^2}{\Sigma(x - \bar{x})^2} \tag{31}$$

This expression (31) may also be used to represent the sum of squares *within groups* for the total sample, again considering the summations as extending over all groups.

We may now return to our illustration of the methods experiment. We had noted that if we could estimate the true regression of Y on X for all methods groups, we could compute an adjusted score for each individual such that the effect of differences in initial ability would be eliminated from these adjusted scores. We have now seen (25) that we can compute this regression coefficient if we have the sum of products and the sum of squares of initial scores *within* groups. The needed sum of squares *within groups*, $\Sigma(x - \bar{x})^2$, for initial scores may be found by analyzing the variance of the initial scores by the method of Section 2 of Chapter V. The needed sum of products *within groups*, $\Sigma(x - \bar{x})(y - \bar{y})$, may be found by analyzing the *covariance* of the initial and final scores. The procedure for the analysis of covariance is the same as for the analysis of variance, except that at each step we deal with products (of deviations) of two variables rather than with *squares* (of deviations) of only one.

The sum of *products* $(\Sigma\, xy)$ for the total sample would be secured, according to (20), by first finding the product of initial and final scores (XY) for each pupil, summing these products for all pupils $(\Sigma\, XY)$, and subtracting from this sum the product of the *initial* grand total and the *final* grand mean, or the product of the grand totals divided by the total number of cases.

The sum of products $(n\Sigma\, \bar{x}\bar{y})$ for methods means would be found, according to (21), by multiplying the *initial* total (T_{X_A}) for the group under Method A by the *final* mean (M_{Y_A}) for that group, by securing a similar product for each of the other methods groups, summing these products, and subtracting the product of the initial grand total and the final grand mean.

We would then have the sums of *products* for *total* and for *methods* to correspond to the sums of squares for *total* and for *methods* for either initial or final scores. The sum of products *within groups*, $\Sigma(x - \bar{x})(y - \bar{y})$, would then be found, according to (19), by subtracting the sum of products for *methods* from the sum of products for *total*, just as we secure the sum of squares *within groups* by subtracting the sum of squares for *methods* from the sum of squares for *total*. The ratio (25) between the sum of products *within groups* (error) and the initial sum of squares *within groups* would then be the regression coefficient needed to adjust the final scores.

An analysis of the variance of the final scores would similarly yield a sum of squares *within groups*, $\Sigma(y - \bar{y})^2$, for final scores. The sum of squares *within groups* for the adjusted scores could then be computed from (31). This sum of squares may then be used to compute the *variance* of adjusted scores *within groups* for the total sample, which would represent the "adjusted" error-variance used in evaluating differences in final adjusted means for the methods. It is important to note, however, that this *error* variance must be computed with one less *d.f.* than before, since one *d.f.* was utilized to compute the regression coefficient involved in (28).

To evaluate the methods differences for adjusted scores, we must first find the adjusted variance for *methods*. We have already found the adjusted sum of squares *within groups*. If we can now find the adjusted sum of squares for the total sample, we can then secure the adjusted sum of squares for *methods* by subtraction.

It should be noted that an adjusted sum of squares for *methods* (between groups) could be found, by means of (30), from the sums of squares for *methods* secured in the analyses of initial and final scores, and by computing b from (25) and $n \Sigma \bar{x} \bar{y}$ from (21). This sum of squares, however, would not be appropriate for testing the significance of the methods differences. The adjusted sum of squares for *methods* which is estimated from (30) is inflated by sampling errors in the estimate of b which is utilized, and may make the *methods* variance appear more significant than it really is.

To test the significance of the methods differences in adjusted scores we therefore use a "reduced" estimate of the *methods* variance, which is derived as follows: we first compute the total sum of squares that would have been found for adjusted scores had the regression coefficient used in the adjustment been that derived from the total sample.   In this case the b used would be that of (23), and the sum of squares of deviations from the general mean for the adjusted scores $(Y - bx)$ would be

$$
\begin{aligned}
\Sigma[(Y - bx) - M_y]^2 &= \Sigma(y + M_y - bx - M_y)^2 \\
&= \Sigma(y - bx)^2 \\
&= \Sigma y^2 - 2b\Sigma xy + b^2\Sigma x^2 \\
&= \Sigma y^2 - 2\frac{\Sigma xy}{\Sigma x^2}\cdot\Sigma xy + \frac{(\Sigma xy)^2}{(\Sigma x^2)^2}\cdot\Sigma x^2 \\
&= \Sigma y^2 - \frac{(\Sigma xy)^2}{\Sigma x^2} \quad\quad (32)
\end{aligned}
$$

Having calculated the total sum of squares for adjusted scores from (32), we subtract the sum of squares *within groups* computed from (31), to secure a "reduced" sum of squares for *methods*. We then compute a reduced variance for *methods* from this reduced sum of squares, and then apply the F-test to the ratio between this reduced variance for *methods* and the *error*-variance for the adjusted scores.

If this test indicated that there are real differences between methods, we could proceed to compute each adjusted methods mean by finding the deviation of the initial mean for that method from the general initial mean, multiplying this deviation by the b computed from (25), and subtracting the result from the final mean for the method.   In other words, each methods mean would be adjusted in the same way we would adjust a single score.   We could then find the difference between any pair of adjusted means. The standard error of an adjusted methods mean would be the square root of the adjusted *error* variance divided by n, and the standard error of a difference between two such means would be 1.414 times the standard error of a single adjusted mean.

It should be noted that all this would have been accomplished without actually having computed the adjusted score for any individual.   The only datum needed in addition to those required for analyses of variance of the initial and final scores is the sum of products (ΣXY) of initial and final scores for all individuals.

Even so, the student is hardly to be blamed if at this point he considers analysis of covariance as extremely complicated. Much of this *apparent* complexity has perhaps resulted from the writer's attempt to *simplify* the discussion by showing every step of the derivations, in order that they may be followed by one not skillful in mathematics. The applications of the end results of these derivations in an actual computational problem is not at all difficult, as the following illustration will show.

4. ANALYSIS OF COVARIANCE IN A SIMPLE METHODS EXPERIMENT

Suppose that a methods experiment involving three methods has been performed in a single school, and, for the sake of simplicity of illustration, that only 12 pupils were involved in the experiment. Suppose that the pupils were assigned at random to 3 groups of 4 pupils each, one group for each method. We will use the letters A, B, and C to refer both to the methods and the corresponding groups. Suppose, finally, that measures of achievement in the subject taught (using different tests) were secured both at the beginning and the end of the experiment, and that the scores on the initial (X) and final (Y) tests were as follows:

A		B		C	
X	Y	X	Y	X	Y
33	18	34	31	34	15
42	34	55	45	4	8
40	22	9	1	12	18
31	24	50	33	16	15

The steps in the analysis are as follows:

1. *Find the sums of initial scores, squared initial scores, final scores, and squared final scores, and the sum of products of initial and final scores for the entire sample.*

The results for the illustrative problem are as follows:

$$\Sigma X = 360 \qquad \Sigma Y = 264$$
$$\Sigma X^2 = 13748 \qquad \Sigma Y^2 = 7454$$
$$\Sigma XY = 9832$$

(These five terms may all be secured in a single operation on an automatic Monroe computing machine.)

2. *Compute the total and mean for each group for initial and final scores separately.*

    Results for illustrative problem:

	Initial Scores		Final Scores	
	Total	Mean	Total	Mean
A	146	36.5	98	24.5
B	148	37.0	110	27.5
C	66	16.5	56	14.0

3. *Analyze the total "sum of squares" for initial scores into the* METHODS *and* WITHIN GROUPS *components, following the procedure of Section 2 of Chapter V. Do the same for the final scores.*

    Results for illustrative problem:

	Σx^2	Σy^2
Methods	1094.0	398.0
Within Groups	1854.0	1248.0
Total	2948.0	1646.0

4. *Compute the total sum of products [according to (20)].*

$$\Sigma XY - GT_X \cdot GM_Y = 9832 - (360)(22.0) = 1912$$

5. *Compute the sum of products for* METHODS *[according to (21)].*

$$(146)(24.5) + (148)(27.5) + (66)(14.0) - 7920 = 651$$

6. *Subtract the sum of products for* METHODS *from that for* TOTAL *to secure the sum of products* WITHIN GROUPS *(error).*

$$1912 - 651 = 1261$$

7. *Compute the adjusted sum of squares* WITHIN GROUPS *[according ing to (31)].*

$$1248 - \frac{(1261)^2}{1854} = 390.4$$

8. *Compute the adjusted total sum of squares [according to (32)].*

$$1646 - \frac{(1912)^2}{2948} = 420.9$$

9. *Subtract the adjusted sum of squares* WITHIN GROUPS *from that for* TOTAL *to secure the reduced sum of squares for* METHODS.

$$420.9 - 390.4 = 30.5$$

10. *Compute the reduced variance for* METHODS.

$$\frac{30.5}{2} = 15.25$$

11. *Compute the adjusted error* (WITHIN GROUPS) *variance, noting that the d.f. is one less than for the* WITHIN GROUPS *variance of either initial or final scores.* (One d.f. is used in computing the regression coefficient from the *within groups* sums of squares and products.)

$$\frac{390.4}{8} = 48.80$$

12. *Divide the reduced methods variance by the adjusted error variance to secure the F used to test the adjusted methods differences.*

$$\frac{15.25}{48.80} = .3$$

Since the F is less than 1, it is obvious that the methods differences are not significant.

It is instructive to note that the *error* variance for the unadjusted final score is $1248/9 = 138.7$. Hence, through analysis of covariance we have reduced the *error* variance from 138.7 to 48.8, or almost tripled the precision of the experiment.

The extent to which the use of the methods of analysis of covariance increases the precision of an experiment of this type depends upon the *within groups* correlation between initial and final scores. The ratio between the adjusted *error* variance and the unadjusted *error* variance is very nearly equal [1] to $(1 - r^2)$, r being the *within*

---

[1] It would be exactly equal if it were not for the loss of 1 *d.f.* for the adjusted error variance.

groups correlation. In the illustration here used, according to (24),

$$r_{xy} \text{ (within groups)} = \frac{1261}{\sqrt{(1854)(1248)}} = .83.$$

The ratio between the adjusted and unadjusted error variances is $\frac{48.8}{138.7} = .35$, which is very nearly equal to $(1 - .83^2)$. The correlation of .83 which is found in this example is of course higher than would be found in most actual methods experiments. Ordinarily, the *within groups* correlation between initial and final scores will not exceed .70, hence the use of analysis of covariance will seldom more than double the precision of the experiment.

It will also be instructive to compute the adjusted methods means in the illustrative problem. To do this, we must first find the value of *b*. From (25),

$$b = \frac{1261}{1854} = .6796.$$

The initial mean for Method A deviated from the general mean by $36.5 - 30.0 = 6.5$. Hence the adjusted final mean for Method A is

$$24.5 - (.6796)(6.5) = 20.08$$

Similarly the adjusted mean for Method B is

$$27.5 - (.6796)(7.0) = 22.74$$

and for Method C is

$$14.0 - (.6796)(- 13.5) = 23.17.$$

Thus we see that the differences between the methods means for adjusted scores is very much less than for the unadjusted scores. This tells us, then, that the differences in the methods means of unadjusted final scores is very largely accounted for by chance differences in the initial ability of the pupils in the experimental groups. We note particularly how much the unadjusted mean for Method C was lowered by the low initial ability of the pupils in the C group. After adjustment, the C mean is higher than the others, where before it had been much lower.

If the differences between methods had proved significant, we would have wished to compute the standard error of a methods mean and the standard error of the difference between two means to evaluate the individual differences between adjusted methods means. The standard error [1] of an adjusted mean would be the square root of the adjusted error-variance divided by 4, or

$$\sigma_M = \sqrt{\frac{48.80}{4}} = 3.49.$$

The d.f. for this standard error is the same as for the adjusted error variance, or 8. The standard error of a difference between adjusted methods means is $(1.414)(3.49) = 4.92$. Since for 8 degrees of freedom a t of 3.36 would be required at the 1 per cent level of significance, a difference between adjusted methods means would have to be larger than 16.5 to be significant at that level.

It may be well, finally, to remind ourselves of the various assumptions — some of which have not heretofore been stated explicitly — that are involved in an analysis of the type just illustrated. They are:

1) That the methods groups were selected at random from the same population.

---

[1] This method of computing the standard error of the difference between two adjusted means is not quite correct, although near enough for most practical purposes. Actually, the variance of the difference between the adjusted final means is given by

$$\sigma^2_{diff} = \left[\frac{2}{n} + \frac{(\overline{X}_A - \overline{X}_B)^2}{\Sigma x^2} \right] s^2,$$

in which s^2 is the adjusted error sum of squares, n is the number of pupils per class, $\overline{X}_A$ is the initial A-mean, and Σx^2 is the initial sum of squares within groups. For methods A and B this result is

$$\left[\frac{2}{4} + \frac{(00.5)^2}{1854.0} \right] 48.80 = 24.406.$$

The standard error of the difference is the square root of this, or 4.96, which is almost the same as the value (4.92) computed above. For methods A and C, however, the standard error of the difference thus computed is 5.91, and for B and C is 5.96. The two methods of computing the standard error of the difference will obviously yield nearly the same result if the corresponding initial means are close together, as they ordinarily would be if the groups were randomly selected, but may differ markedly if the groups are not so selected.

2) That the distribution of adjusted scores *within groups* is fundamentally normal.

3) That the groups are homogeneous in variability.

4) That the regression of final on initial scores is fundamentally the same from group to group.

5) That the regression is linear.

5. ANALYSIS OF COVARIANCE IN DUPLICATE EXPERIMENTS IN RANDOMLY SELECTED SCHOOLS

We may now see how the methods of analysis of covariance may be applied in a more complex experimental design involving duplications, in each of a number of different schools, of an experiment of the type just considered. The procedure in this case will be much the same as before, the principal difference being that our error estimate will be based on the interaction $(M \times S)$ variance, rather than on the *within groups* variance of the adjusted scores. The "adjustment" of the criterion scores will accordingly be based on a regression coefficient derived from the sums of squares and products for $M \times S$, rather than for *within groups*.

There will also be certain changes in the assumptions involved. In the problem of the preceding section we assumed that the true regression of final on initial *scores* was the same from one methods group to another, and that this regression was linear. We shall now have to assume that the true regression of final on initial *class means*, with methods and school differences eliminated, is the same from method to method, and is linear. That is, we assume that after the class means for both initial and final scores have been "corrected" (see page 109) so as to eliminate methods and school differences, the true regression of final on initial values (weighted) of these corrected means is the same from method to method. In the problem of the preceding section, we assumed also that the pupils were assigned at random to the various methods groups. This assumption is not now necessary, but we must assume that the classes in each school were assigned at random to the methods. (The exception would be if we wished to test the adjusted interaction variance itself, in which case we would have to randomize the pupils.)

We will first illustrate the computational procedures in a concrete example in which our only objective is to test the significance of the differences between methods, using the interaction $(M \times S)$ term as the error term. Later we will consider the modifications in procedure that would be necessary if we wished to test the hypothesis that there is no real interaction of methods and schools.

The data used in this example were obtained from an experimental comparison of two methods of improving punctuation ability at the fifth-grade level. The initial measure (X) was the score on a general English usage test administered at the beginning of the experiment. The criterion measure (Y) was the score on a punctuation test administered at the close of the experiment. The experiment was planned as in the example of the preceding section. In each of five schools one of two classes of equal size was taught by Method A, the other by Method B, for a period of 18 weeks. (The scores of all pupils on the initial and final tests are given in Table 12, on page 198. The student is urged to check all computations as an exercise.)

The steps in the analysis are as follows:

1. *For both initial and final scores, compute the total and mean for each class, for each school, and for each method.*

For the example:

TOTALS AND MEANS OF INITIAL SCORES

	Method A		Method B		Schools		Number of Pupils
	Totals	Means	Totals	Means	Totals	Means	
School 1	2269	70.9063	1995	62.3438	4264	66.6250	64
School 2	1832	96.4211	1698	89.3684	3530	92.8947	38
School 3	824	54.9333	859	57.2667	1683	56.1000	30
School 4	839	76.2727	731	66.4545	1570	71.3636	22
School 5	414	59.1429	424	60.5714	838	59.8571	14
Methods	6178	73.5476	5707	67.9405	$11885 = GT_X$		$N = 168$

$\Sigma X^2 = 910289$	$GM_X = 70.7441$	$GT_X \cdot GM_X = 840,794$

TABLE 12

SCORES ON INITIAL (X) AND FINAL (Y) TESTS FOR PUPILS WHO STUDIED UNDER METHODS A AND B IN AN EXPERIMENT IN FIFTH-GRADE LANGUAGE INSTRUCTION

School 1

A		B	
X	Y	X	Y
64	41	77	59
55	41	69	59
77	64	82	71
71	42	67	53
68	39	40	48
81	49	83	51
66	67	76	36
74	53	62	30
30	21	79	62
81	44	53	26
88	66	62	25
66	40	60	55
86	61	51	19
74	57	64	54
69	38	74	64
54	37	29	52
75	45	70	55
52	26	52	21
85	47	24	52
80	58	32	28
67	37	37	18
81	69	26	33
50	34	71	69
92	74	85	62
76	49	60	63
97	67	96	77
73	43	66	43
70	35	55	42
74	23	55	41
72	56	86	61
56	32	71	59
65	71	81	55

School 2

A		B	
X	Y	X	Y
66	43	90	68
94	74	99	84
85	33	93	74
107	59	95	59
97	56	98	68
102	62	87	60
101	44	90	71
98	42	68	65
98	61	87	56
102	62	87	78
107	67	101	85
105	66	87	82
92	38	96	77
87	52	77	55
88	60	77	68
108	77	93	84
94	66	98	84
105	68	80	52
96	47	95	80
9	12	45	38
66	29	54	39
68	19	56	39
58	33	56	30
35	16	75	71
95	65	39	33
61	42	47	35

School 3

A		B	
X	Y	X	Y
55	48	55	49
49	30	43	35
39	26	92	72
23	12	50	29
71	38	67	36
81	53	65	43
70	37	39	41
44	25	76	32

School 4

A		B	
X	Y	X	Y
74	64	78	61
90	75	55	54
72	56	77	70
100	64	87	85
57	46	53	41
78	69	31	39
93	73	75	43
101	75	75	72
73	56	63	43
50	29	68	55
51	44	69	42

School 5

A		B	
X	Y	X	Y
44	17	87	71
54	24	61	50
49	26	42	49
87	59	41	36
75	36	68	43
63	46	76	66
42	49	49	43

TOTALS AND MEANS OF FINAL SCORES

	Method A		Method B		Schools		Number of pupils
	Totals	Means	Totals	Means	Totals	Means	
School 1	1526	47.6875	1543	48.2188	3069	47.9531	64
School 2	1077	56.6842	1350	71.0526	2427	63.8684	38
School 3	485	32.3333	622	41.4667	1107	36.9000	30
School 4	651	59.1818	605	55.0000	1256	57.0909	22
School 5	257	36.7143	358	51.1429	615	43.9286	14
Methods	3996	47.5714	4478	53.3095	$8474 = GT_Y$		$N = 168$

$$\Sigma Y^2 = 477432 \qquad GM_Y = 50.4405 \qquad GT_Y \cdot GM_Y = 427,432.8$$

2. *For the initial and final scores separately, find the sums of squares for M and for $M \times S$.*

(Follow the procedure of steps 1 to 7 on pages 120–122.)

	Σx^2	Σy^2
M	1319.5	1382.5
$M \times S$	904.7	2033.9

3. *Compute the sums of products for M, S, and CLASSES.*

[According to (21), page 185.]

Sum of products for *methods* equals:

$$[(6178)(47.5714) + (5707)(53.3095)] - 599486 = -1352.6$$

Sum of products for *schools* equals:

$$[(4264)(47.9531) + (3530)(63.8684) + (1683)(36.9000)$$
$$+ (1570)(57.0909) + (838)(43.9286)] - 599486 = 18989.7$$

Sum of products for *classes* equals:

$$[(2269)(47.6875) + (1832)(56.6842) + (824)(32.3333)$$
$$+ (839)(59.1818) + (414)(36.7143) + (1995)(48.2188)$$
$$+ (1698)(71.0526) + (859)(41.4667) + (731)(55.0000)$$
$$+ (424)(51.1429)] - 599486 = 18411.6$$

The sum of products for *methods* is negative, as we should expect from the fact that the initial mean is higher for A than for B, while the final mean is higher for B. In other words, the initial and final methods means are negatively correlated.

4. *Subtract the sum of products for M and for S from that for classes to secure the sum of products for $M \times S$.*

$$18411.6 - 18989.7 - (-1352.6) = 774.5$$

5. *Arrange the sum of squares and products for* M *and* M × S *in tabular form, and add the* M *and* M × S *terms in each column.*

	$\Sigma\, x^2$	$\Sigma\, xy$	$\Sigma\, y^2$
M	1319.5	− 1352.9	1382.5
M × S	904.7	774.5	2033.9
M + M × S	2224.2	− 578.4	3416.4

6. *Compute the adjusted sum of squares for* M × S.
   [According to (32), page 190.]

$$\Sigma\, y^2 - \frac{(\Sigma\, xy)^2}{\Sigma\, x^2} \quad \text{(for M × S)}$$

$$= 2033.9 - \frac{(774.5)^2}{904.7} = 1370.9$$

7. *Compute the adjusted sum of squares for* M + M × S.
   [According to (32), page 190.]

$$3416.4 - \frac{(-578.4)^2}{2224.2} = 3266.0$$

8. *Subtract the adjusted sum of squares for* M × S *from that for* M + M × S *to get the reduced sum of squares for* M.

$$3266.0 - 1370.9 = 1895.1$$

9. *Divide the reduced sum of squares for* M *by the d.f. for* M *to secure the reduced* METHODS *variance.*

$$1895.1 \div 1 = 1895.1$$

10. *Divide the adjusted sum of squares for* M × S *by its d.f. to secure the adjusted* M × S *(error) variance, noting that the d.f. for the adjusted* M × S *variance is one less than for the unadjusted* M × S *variance.* (One *d.f.* having been used in the computation of the regression coefficient from the $M × S$ terms.)

$$1370.9 \div 3 = 457.0$$

11. *Divide the reduced variance for* METHODS *by the adjusted* M × S *variance. The result is the* F *used to test the significance of the adjusted methods differences.*

$$F = \frac{1895.1}{457.0} = 4.15$$

For 1 and 3 *d.f.* an F of 10.13 is required for significance at the 5 per cent level.   Hence we cannot, in this case, reject the null hypothesis for the methods differences.

The foregoing test of significance would ordinarily conclude the analysis in an experiment of the type illustrated.   However, it may sometimes be desirable to test the hypothesis that there is no real interaction of methods and schools.   This hypothesis could be tested only if the pupils had been *randomly* assigned to the methods groups in each school, and then only on the assumption that the true regression of final on initial scores was the same, not only from group to group within the same school, but also from school to school.   It may be well to show then, in the case of our example, how to test the hypothesis that there is no real $M \times S$ interaction when the scores are adjusted for differences in initial ability.

Under this hypothesis, the scores would be adjusted on the basis of the regression *within classes*, just as was the case in the example on pages 191 ff.   Hence we would have to complete the analysis of initial and final scores begun in Step 4 preceding, so as to secure the sums of squares *within classes*.   We should also have to compute the sums of products for *within classes*, by computing first the sum of products for *classes* [see (21)] and for the total sample [see (20)] and subtracting the former from the latter.   For the example, the sums of squares and products for $M \times S$ and *within classes* are

	Σx^2	Σxy	Σy^2
$M \times S$	904.7	774.5	2033.9
Within Classes	39440.1	23915.4	32268.3
$M \times S +$ Within Classes	40344.8	24689.9	34302.2

We would then find the adjusted sums of squares for *within classes* and for $M \times S +$ *within classes* according to (31) and (32), and subtract the result for *within classes* to secure the "reduced" sum of squares for $M \times S$. In the example, the results are

Adjusted sum of squares for $M \times S + within\ classes$ = 19192.7
Adjusted sum of squares for *within classes* $\qquad$ = 17767.1
Reduced sum of squares for $M \times S$ $\qquad$ = 1425.6

The reduced variance for $M \times S$ is accordingly $1425.6 \div 4 = 356.4$, and the adjusted variance for within classes is $17767.1 \div (158 - 1)$ = 113.2. The ratio between these variances is $356.4/113.2 = 3.15$. Since, for 4 and 150 *d.f.*, the F required for significance at the 5 per cent level is 2.43, and at the 1 per cent level is 3.44, this F of 3.15 constitutes very convincing evidence that there is a real interaction effect. It was particularly appropriate, therefore, that we earlier used the interaction variance as the error term.

It is interesting to note, from the data in Step 4 preceding, that the $M \times S$ or *error* variance for the unadjusted final scores was $2033.9/4 = 508.5$, as compared to $1370.9/3 = 457.0$ for the adjusted scores. The increase in precision due to the use of analysis of covariance was in this case slight, amounting to only about a 10 per cent increase. It is significant, however, that the reduction in the sum of squares was more pronounced (from 2033.9 to 1370.9), but that this advantage was dissipated by the loss in *d.f.* (from 4 to 3). The loss of 1 *d.f.* was in this case very serious, since we had only 4 *d.f.* for $M \times S$ originally. In general, therefore, it would be best to use a sufficient number of schools so that the effect of the loss of 1 *d.f.* in computing the regression coefficient would be more nearly negligible.

It is difficult, for an experiment of this type, to predict the efficacy of the methods of analysis of covariance, even though one can anticipate accurately the correlation of initial and final scores. In a simple experiment of the type illustrated on pages 107 ff., the increase in precision due to the use of statistical controls depends only upon this correlation. (In that case the ratio of the adjusted error variance to the unadjusted error variance is very nearly equal to $(1 - r^2)$, r being the correlation *within classes* for the initial and final scores.) In the case of the present design, however, in which the interaction variance is used as the *error* term, the increase in precision depends upon the correlation of the interaction effects (upon class means) for initial and final scores. This correlation may be computed from the sums of squares and products for $M \times S$ by means of (24). In the case of the illustrative problem it is $774.5/\sqrt{904.7 \times 2033.9} = .57$. If there is no real interaction, this correlation will tend to be the same as the correlation *within* classes. If there is a real interaction, the effect may be either to decrease or increase the correlation of interaction effects. In the illustration, the correlation *within classes* is $23914.8/\sqrt{39440.1 \times 32268.3} = .66$. The difference between the correlations based on the $M \times S$ and *within classes* terms could be due to chance, but it is more probably due to the significant interaction effect. In general, the effect of the interaction would be to make the $M \times S$ correlation smaller than the correlation *within classes*, and hence would tend to make the use of analysis of covariance less profitable.

It is interesting that in the illustrative problem the variance ratio (F) for *methods* and $M \times S$ was 4.15 for the adjusted scores, but only 2.72 for the unadjusted scores. The change in the F's, then, was much larger than the change in the $M \times S$ (error) variances. It just happened in this case that there was an unusually large chance difference in initial means in favor of the A group, while the final difference favored the B group. The adjusted difference in final methods means was consequently larger than the unadjusted difference. In general, in experiments of this type, the difference in final means would tend to be in the same direction as the initial difference, hence more frequently the adjusted difference in final means would be smaller than the unadjusted difference, and the adjusted *methods* variance would be less than the unadjusted *methods* variance of final scores.

6. ANALYSIS OF COVARIANCE TO "HOLD CONSTANT" OTHER VARIABLES THAN INITIAL STATUS

In the preceding examples, the methods of analysis of covariance were employed primarily in order to increase the precision of the experiment, and not because the relationship of the initial to the criterion test scores was of any interest in itself. In such situations, the test to use as the initial test is that which is likely to show the highest correlation with the criterion, regardless of its other qualities. Usually, the test most likely to satisfy this requirement is one that measures initial status in the same trait that is measured by the criterion test — often exactly the same test may be used to secure both the initial and final measures.

The same methods of analysis may be employed with reference to any concomitant variable, whether or not it may be measured at the beginning of the experiment, in order to determine how the criterion means would have differed if this concomitant variable had been "held constant." For example, in an experiment concerned with certain methods, it may be suspected that one of the methods may motivate the pupils to spend more time in study out-of-class than the others, and it may be desired to know which method would have resulted in highest achievement had the pupils spent the same total time in study under each method. Suppose that a record was therefore kept during the experiment of the amount of study time for each pupil, and that from this record the total time for each pupil was determined. By the methods of analysis of covariance, the differences in mean scores on the criterion achievement test could then be "adjusted" so as to eliminate the effect of time differences. This would be done in exactly the same way as if the time measures represented scores on an initial test. One could thus determine whether or not the mean differences in achievement are significant both when time is "held constant" and when it is not, as well as whether or not the time differences themselves are significant. In other words, the adjustment would indicate what differences in achievement would have been found had all pupils spent the same amount of time in study (assuming linearity of regression, as well as constancy of regression from group to group). (If one also desired to allow for chance differences in initial status, one could do so by the methods suggested in the following section.)

7. STATISTICAL CONTROL OF MORE THAN ONE CONCOMITANT VARIABLE

If it is desired to eliminate the effect of more than one uncontrolled variable in an experiment of the type described in the preceding section, this may be done by an extension of the methods just considered. In this case the adjustment will be made in terms of the *multiple regression equation* (see Chapter VII) between the criterion and the uncontrolled variables. The regression coefficients can be computed as before from the error terms secured through analyses of the variances and covariances of the variables involved.

In the case where allowance is to be made for two initial measures (X and Z), the multiple regression equation will be

$$y' = b_1 x + b_2 z$$

To compute these regression coefficients, an analysis of variance must be carried through for each of the three variables and for the three possible covariances. Having found the *error* term (sum of squares or products) in each of these analyses, the results may be substituted in the following simultaneous equations, which may then be solved for b_1 and b_2.

$$\Sigma\, xy = b_1 \Sigma\, x^2 + b_2 \Sigma xz$$
$$\Sigma\, zy = b_1 \Sigma\, xz + b_2 \Sigma\, z^2$$

The formula for computing any adjusted score (Y_a) will then be

$$Y_a = Y - b_1 x - b_2 z$$

The total sum of squares for the adjusted scores will be (see page 190)

$$\Sigma(y - b_1 x - b_2 z)^2 =$$
$$\Sigma\, y^2 - 2\, b_1 \Sigma\, xy - 2\, b_2 \Sigma\, zy + b_1^2 \Sigma\, x^2 + 2\, b_1 b_2 \Sigma\, zx + b_2^2 \Sigma\, z^2$$

Each of the components of the total sum of squares of adjusted scores may be computed by the same formula from the corresponding components of the sums of squares and products for the three variables involved. The *error* variance for adjusted scores will then be computed as before, after having allowed for the *two* degrees of freedom utilized in computing the regression coefficients. The reduced variance for *methods* would then be computed in a manner similar to that already described, and the test of significance applied as before.

Similar methods could be employed to allow for still other initial measures, but obviously with a tremendous increase in the amount of labor involved. The computational task for two initial measures is not at all unmanageable, and may sometimes be worth while in educational experiments, considering the ease with which additional measures may be secured. The advantage gained depends upon the magnitude of the multiple correlation coefficient for the contemplated number of variables as compared to that for the best combination of a smaller number. Experience with educational tests has shown that in situations of this kind the multiple correlation of two initial measures with the criterion will seldom be very much higher than the higher of the two zero-order correlations, and that usually only a negligible increase in the multiple correlation is secured by adding a third dependent variable (assuming, of course, that the two already selected are the best two for the purpose). There would be very little point, therefore, to a discussion of the more complex procedures required for three or more initial measures.

For the case of two initial measures already considered, it may be worth pointing out that the multiple correlation $R_{y.xz}$ between the initial measures and the criterion may be computed from the formula

$$R^2_{y.xz} = \frac{b_1 \Sigma\, xy + b_2 \Sigma\, zy}{\Sigma\, y^2}$$

using either the total sums of products and squares or those for the error term secured from the analyses of variance and covariance, dependent upon whether the correlation is desired without or with the effects of schools and methods eliminated. How much the labor of allowing for both variables is worth while is then dependent upon how much $\sqrt{1 - R^2_{y \cdot xz}}$ is less than either $\sqrt{1 - r^2_{xy}}$ or $\sqrt{1 - r^2_{zy}}$.

CHAPTER VII

MISCELLANEOUS PROBLEMS IN CORRELATION ANALYSIS

1. INTRODUCTORY

THIS final chapter differs so much in character from those preceding that some introductory explanation seems demanded. As was explained in the Preface, this book has been written primarily in order to make more readily available and comprehensible to the research worker in education those relatively recent developments in statistical theory and practice which, although of apparently high promise in educational research, have thus far received no mention (or have been only very inadequately discussed) in the standard and widely used texts in educational statistics. Thus far in this book it has been possible to present a fairly comprehensive discussion of each general problem presented, without any consequential duplication of the content of other texts in this field; that is, each chapter has been fairly complete in itself. To attempt any comprehensive discussion here of the general problem of correlation analysis in educational research, however, would involve a great deal of duplication of what has already been well done elsewhere. Most of the major aspects and applications of correlation analysis have been adequately treated in many available texts. Indeed, methods of correlation analysis appear to have been more widely used and more critically studied in education and psychology than in any other field of research. This is true in part because in these fields we are naturally interested in the organization, i.e., in the *inter-relationships* of mental functions, and because correlation techniques are so well adapted to the objective study of those relationships. It is true also because the instruments available for measuring these traits are so much more fallible than the measuring instruments employed in most of the other fields of research. It is consequently of greater importance in this field that we know *how* fallible our measures are, or that we have objective estimates of the errors of measurement involved. Again, the methods of correlation analysis are peculiarly adapted to these purposes.

In accordance with the afore-mentioned purpose, then, this chapter will (with a few exceptions) deal only with those aspects of correlation theory that do not seem to have received adequate attention in current texts in this field. It may be noted in particular that, in spite of the frequency with which we have had occasion to use correlation methods in education, we appear to have given very little consideration to some of the assumptions underlying their use, and have consequently been guilty of many misapplications of them. One of the purposes of this chapter is to draw the student's attention to some of the more serious of these errors, and to point out the peculiar difficulties with which we are faced in correlation studies in educational research. Another purpose is to describe to the student certain special correlation techniques with which he may not have become acquainted in any introductory course in educational statistics.

In general, then, this chapter is intended only to *supplement* the general discussions of correlation theory elsewhere available, and is not intended to constitute a comprehensive and well balanced treatment of the subject. The content of this chapter is consequently miscellaneous and relatively lacking in unity, and the various sections may differ widely in their usefulness to students with highly specialized research interests. Unless this is clearly understood, there is some danger that the student may secure a false impression of the relative importance of some of the techniques here discussed. Before reading this chapter, therefore, the student is urged to review thoroughly the discussions of correlation methods in two or three available standard texts in educational statistics,[1] and thus prepare himself better to see in their proper perspective the specific problems which will here be considered.

[1] Recommended references are:

Statistics in Psychology and Education, H. E. Garrett, Longmans, Green and Company, 1937, Chapters IX–XIV.

Statistical Methods for Students in Education, Karl J. Holzinger, Ginn and Company, Chapters IX, X, XIV and XV.

A First Course in Statistics, E. F. Lindquist, Houghton Mifflin Company, Chapters X and XI.

2. THE SIGNIFICANCE OF A PRODUCT-MOMENT CORRELATION
COEFFICIENT

The customary procedure in educational research for determining whether or not an observed r is significant has been to compute the standard error of r, using formula (33) below, and to describe the coefficient as significant if it is more than 2.5 or 3 times the standard error. The formula used for σ_r is

$$\sigma_r = \frac{1 - r^2}{\sqrt{N}}, \tag{33}$$

in which the r in the right-hand term really represents the true r, but for which the obtained r is substituted to secure an estimate of σ_r.

There are two principal objections to this procedure. In the first place, it is inconsistent to use the obtained coefficient (r_o) as an estimate of the true r when testing the hypothesis that the true r is zero. Under this hypothesis, our estimate of the standard deviation of the sampling distribution of r_o should be $\frac{1 - 0^2}{\sqrt{N}} = \frac{1}{\sqrt{N}}$ rather than $\frac{1 - r_o^2}{\sqrt{N}}$. To avoid this inconsistency, we should describe an obtained correlation coefficient (r_o) as significant at the 1 per cent level if it exceeds $\frac{2.56}{\sqrt{N}}$, rather than if it exceeds $\frac{2.56(1 - r_o^2)}{\sqrt{N}}$. This, however, would assume that the sampling distribution is normal, and it is here that the second objection arises. When N is small (and the true r is zero) the sampling distribution of r_o differs slightly from the normal distribution. Hence, even though we avoided the first objection, we could not use the normal probability integral table to interpret the standard error exactly.

The appropriate procedure [1] for determining whether or not an r

---

[1] R. A. Fisher, *Statistical Methods for Research Workers*, 6th ed., p. 196.

obtained from a small random sample is significant is to compute the value of

$$t = \frac{r}{\sqrt{1 - r^2}} \cdot \sqrt{N - 2}, \qquad (34)$$

in which the r is that obtained from the sample. This t may be evaluated by means of Table 3, using $N - 2$ as the number of degrees of freedom.

For any given size sample, one can compute the minimum value of r that will be significant at any given level, by substituting in (34) the value of N and the value of t needed at that level, and solving for r. This has been done by the writer (at the 5 per cent and 1 per cent levels) for a selected number of values of N, and the results presented in Table 13. For example, in a sample of 60 cases r would have to exceed .254 to be significant at the 5 per cent level, or would have to exceed .330 to be significant at the 1 per cent level. Given this table, the student will have little occasion to use formula (34). If the size of the sample in question lies between two of the N's given in Table 13, it will be sufficiently accurate for most practical purposes to use the value of r for the nearest N given, or to interpolate linearly between the two nearest values given.

It may be well to show, in terms of a specific illustration, how misleading may be the procedure described at the beginning of this section. Suppose that we have obtained an r of .54 from a random sample of 16 cases. According to (33), the standard error of this r is .177. The observed r is more than 3 times this value. Hence, if we followed the procedure first described, we would conclude that the observed r is significant well beyond the 1 per cent level. From Table 13, however, we see that for a sample of 16 cases an r must exceed .623 to be significant at this level.

3. THE RELIABILITY OF A PRODUCT-MOMENT CORRELATION COEFFICIENT

The customary procedure for describing the reliability of a product-moment coefficient of correlation has been to compute its

TABLE 13

VALUES OF CORRELATION COEFFICIENT REQUIRED FOR SIGNIFICANCE
AT THE 5 PER CENT AND 1 PER CENT LEVELS FOR SAMPLES OF VARIOUS
SIZES (N)

N	5%	1%	N	5%	1%	N	5%	1%	N	5%	1%
10	.632	.765	21	.433	.549	34	.339	.436	65	.244	.317
11	.602	.735	22	.423	.537	36	.329	.424	70	.235	.306
12	.576	.708	23	.413	.526	38	.320	.413	75	.227	.296
13	.553	.684	24	.404	.515	40	.312	.403	80	.220	.287
14	.532	.661	25	.396	.505	42	.304	.393	100	.197	.256
15	.514	.641	26	.388	.496	44	.297	.384	125	.176	.230
16	.497	.623	27	.381	.487	46	.291	.376	150	.161	.210
17	.482	.606	28	.374	.479	48	.284	.368	200	.139	.182
18	.468	.590	29	.367	.471	50	.279	.361	400	.098	.128
19	.456	.575	30	.361	.463	55	.265	.345	1000	.062	.081
20	.444	.561	32	.349	.449	60	.254	.330			

standard error by (33), and to interpret the standard error by means of the normal probability integral table. This procedure is not valid for high values of r even though the sample is large. When the true correlation approaches ± 1.00, the sampling distribution of the r's obtained even from large samples will be markedly skewed, and any interpretations of the standard error based on the normal probability integral table may be very seriously misleading. However, Fisher has shown that for any value of r the function

$$z = \tfrac{1}{2} \log_e \frac{1 + r}{1 - r} \tag{35}$$

in which r is the observed correlation, is very nearly normally distributed, and has shown that the standard error of z is

$$\sigma_z = \frac{1}{\sqrt{N - 3}} \tag{36}$$

in which N is the number of cases in the sample.

This z-function may be used to test any exact hypothesis [1] con-

---

[1] The z-function may be used quite satisfactorily to test the null hypothesis that the true r is zero, but for such simple tests of significance the t-test of the preceding section is to be preferred as a slightly more exact and conservative test.

cerning the population value of r (given the r obtained from a random sample), or may be used to test the significance of a difference between two r's obtained from independent random samples.

In order that these uses of z may not require the student to deal with logarithms in transforming r to z by means of (35), the writer has prepared a table (Table 14) of values of z corresponding to various values of r. The manner in which this table may be used should be made clear by the following illustration.

Suppose that the r obtained from a random sample of 67 cases is .91. Is the hypothesis reasonable that the true r is .95? To test this hypothesis, we first find the value of z corresponding to the observed and hypothetical values, and then find the difference between these values of z. We then divide this difference by the standard error of the observed z, thus expressing the difference as a normal deviate which may be interpreted by means of the normal probability integral table. In this case, the z corresponding to the observed r of .91 is 1.528, while that corresponding to the hypothetical r or .95 is 1.832. The difference between these z's is .305. The standard error of z is $1/\sqrt{67-3} = .125$; hence the normal deviate equivalent of the difference is $.305/.125 = 2.44$. The probability that a measure selected at random from a normal distribution will deviate more than $2.44\,\sigma$ from the mean is less than 2 in 100. Hence, we could not very reasonably retain the hypothesis that the true r is as high as .95.

It will be instructive, for the same sample, to test the hypothesis that the true r is .87, since this value is as far below the observed r of .91 as the value first tested (.95) was above it. In this case, the value of z for the hypothetical r is 1.333; hence the difference between the observed and hypothetical z's is .195. The normal deviate equivalent of the difference is then $.195/.125 = 1.56$, which is not significant even at the 10 per cent level. Hence, we see that while it is quite reasonable to suppose that the true r is .04 below the observed value, it is not reasonable to suppose that it is an equal amount above. This illustration should give the student some appreciation of the degree of skewness in the sampling distribution of r for high correlations, and should indicate how misleading is the practice of appending "probable errors" to r's of large magnitude.

If desirable, this procedure may be extended to set up limiting values of the tenable hypotheses concerning the value of the true r. Suppose, for instance, that for the preceding example we wished to know within what limits we could be confident at the 1 per cent level that the true r lies. Since 99 per cent of the area under the normal curve lies within 2.576 σ of the mean, the normal deviate equivalent of the difference between observed and hypothetical z's must not exceed 2.576. In other words, in the limiting case

$$2.576 = \frac{z_H - z_o}{\sigma_z}.$$

Hence, the limiting values of z_H are

$z_o \pm 2.576\,\sigma_z = 1.528 \pm 2.576 \times .125,$ or 1.206 and 1.850.

The values of r corresponding to these values of z are .835 and .955, respectively. We may therefore be confident, at the 1 per cent level, that the true r lies somewhere within these limits. Again it is evident, from the fact that the lower limit deviates considerably farther from the observed r of .91 than does the upper limit, that the sampling distribution of r is markedly skewed for high values of the true r.

Let us contrast the result just obtained from that which would have been found had we followed the procedure described at the beginning of this section. According to (33), the estimated standard error of an r of .91 for a sample of 67 cases would be .021, from which we would have concluded that the limiting values of the true r (at the 1 per cent level) are .91 $\pm$ .021 $\times$ 2.576, or .856 and .964.

4. THE SIGNIFICANCE OF A DIFFERENCE BETWEEN r'S OBTAINED FROM INDEPENDENT RANDOM SAMPLES

The test of significance of a difference between two observed r's is similar in character to that just described, but requires that we find the standard error of the difference between the z's correspond-

TABLE 14
VALUES OF z FOR VARIOUS VALUES OF r

r	z	r	z	r	z	r	z	r	z
.000	.000000	.200	.202732	.400	.423648	.600	.693146	.800	1.098610
.005	.005000	.205	.207946	.405	.429615	.605	.700995	.805	1.112656
.010	.010000	.210	.213171	.410	.435610	.610	.708920	.810	1.127027
.015	.015001	.215	.218407	.415	.441635	.615	.716922	.815	1.141740
.020	.020003	.220	.223656	.420	.447691	.620	.725004	.820	1.156815
.025	.025005	.225	.228916	.425	.453778	.625	.733167	.825	1.172272
.030	.030009	.230	.234189	.430	.459896	.630	.741415	.830	1.188134
.035	.035014	.235	.239475	.435	.466046	.635	.749749	.835	1.204425
.040	.040021	.240	.244774	.440	.472230	.640	.758172	.840	1.221171
.045	.045030	.245	.250086	.445	.478447	.645	.766687	.845	1.238402
.050	.050042	.250	.255412	.450	.484699	.650	.775297	.850	1.256150
.055	.055056	.255	.260753	.455	.490987	.655	.784006	.855	1.274450
.060	.060072	.260	.266108	.460	.497310	.660	.792812	.860	1.293342
.065	.065092	.265	.271478	.465	.503671	.665	.801723	.865	1.312868
.070	.070115	.270	.276863	.470	.510069	.670	.810741	.870	1.333077
.075	.075141	.275	.282264	.475	.516506	.675	.819870	.875	1.354022
.080	.080171	.280	.287682	.480	.522983	.680	.829112	.880	1.375765
.085	.085205	.285	.293115	.485	.529501	.685	.838472	.885	1.398373
.090	.090244	.290	.298566	.490	.536059	.690	.847954	.890	1.421923
.095	.095287	.295	.304034	.495	.542660	.695	.857561	.895	1.446504
.100	.100335	.300	.309519	.500	.549305	.700	.867299	.900	1.472216
.105	.105388	.305	.315023	.505	.555994	.705	.877171	.905	1.499177
.110	.110447	.310	.320545	.510	.562728	.710	.887182	.910	1.527521
.115	.115511	.315	.326086	.515	.569510	.715	.897338	.915	1.557407
.120	.120581	.320	.331646	.520	.576339	.720	.907643	.920	1.589023
.125	.125657	.325	.337227	.525	.583216	.725	.918104	.925	1.622593
.130	.130740	.330	.342828	.530	.590144	.730	.928725	.930	1.658386
.135	.135829	.335	.348449	.535	.597123	.735	.939514	.935	1.696734
.140	.140925	.340	.354092	.540	.604154	.740	.950477	.940	1.738045
.145	.146029	.345	.359756	.545	.611240	.745	.961621	.945	1.782838
.150	.151140	.350	.365443	.550	.618380	.750	.972953	.950	1.831777
.155	.156259	.355	.371152	.555	.625577	.755	.984481	.955	1.885737
.160	.161386	.360	.376885	.560	.632832	.760	.996213	.960	1.945906
.165	.166522	.365	.382642	.565	.640146	.765	1.008158	.965	2.013945
.170	.171666	.370	.388422	.570	.647521	.770	1.020326	.970	2.092291
.175	.176820	.375	.394228	.575	.654959	.775	1.032725	.975	2.184719
.180	.181982	.380	.400059	.580	.662461	.780	1.045368	.980	2.297555
.185	.187155	.385	.405916	.585	.670029	.785	1.058265	.985	2.442657
.190	.192337	.390	.411799	.590	.677665	.790	1.071429	.990	2.646647
.195	.197529	.395	.417710	.595	.685370	.795	1.084873	.995	2.994474

ing to the observed r's. Suppose that the r between two variables for one sample of 35 cases is .82, and for another sample of 42 cases is .89. The corresponding values of z are 1.1568 and 1.4219, respectively. The difference between these z's is .2651. The standard error of the first z is $1/\sqrt{32}$, and of the second is $1/\sqrt{39}$.

Hence, the standard error of the difference is $\sqrt{\dfrac{1}{32}+\dfrac{1}{39}} = .238$.

Clearly the difference is not significant, being barely larger than its standard error. Since such differences are approximately normally distributed, the observed difference would have to be approximately 2.576 times its standard error to be significant at the 1 per cent level, or about 1.960 times its standard error to be significant at the 5 per cent level.

It should be noted that small differences in observed correlation coefficients will not be significant unless the samples employed are quite large. If, for example, the samples involved each contained 100 cases, the standard error of the difference in z's will be

$\sigma_{z_1 - z_2} = \sqrt{\dfrac{1}{97} + \dfrac{1}{97}} = .14.$ Hence, the difference in z's must be

at least $.14 \times 1.96 = .2744$ to be significant at the 5 per cent level, or at least $.14 \times 2.576 = .3606$ to be significant at the 1 per cent level. From Table 14 we see that a difference in z's of .274 would be found for r's of .10 and .36, or of .30 and .525, or of .50 and .675, or .70 and .815, or .80 and .88, or .90 and .94. It may be shown, similarly, that for samples of 100 cases each, differences between r's of .80 and .90, or .70 and .84, or .50 and .72, etc., would just fail to be significant at the 1 per cent level.

If, then, one is planning an experiment or investigation the purpose of which is to compare correlation coefficients derived from independent random samples, it will be well to determine in advance what size of sample will be needed to render significant any anticipated difference in the observed coefficients. Suppose, for example, that one anticipates that the observed correlations will be of the magnitude of .65 and .70 respectively. How large would the samples have to be if a difference in r's of this magnitude is to be significant at the 1 per cent level? The values of z corresponding to these r's are .7753 and .8673 respectively, with a difference of .0920. The standard error of the difference in z's must then not exceed $.0920/2.576 = .0361$. Hence, solving for N in

$$.0361 = \sqrt{\dfrac{1}{N-3} + \dfrac{1}{N-3}}$$

we get $N = 1640$, approximately. Unless the samples contained over 1500 cases each, then, one could not (at the 1 per cent level) regard observed r's of .65 and .70 as surely indicative of a real difference between the populations sampled. If the observed r's are high, the size of sample needed to render an observed difference of .05 significant at any given level will of course be less. For instance, a sample of 284 would be sufficient to render the difference between observed r's of .85 and .90 significant at the 1 per cent level, and the same difference would be significant at the 5 per cent level for a sample of 196.

It should be apparent, from the foregoing, that correlation studies in general require relatively large samples, and that many of the correlation studies which have been reported in the literature on educational research were doomed to inconclusiveness before they were conducted.

The student should note carefully that the procedure which has been described for determining the significance of a difference between correlation coefficients is valid only if the coefficients are obtained from *independent* random samples. If both are obtained from the same sample, and if there is any correlation between either of the variables involved in the first correlation and either involved in the second, the test just described would be invalid. In this case the coefficients obtained from a large number of similar samples would themselves show a positive correlation, and this relationship would result in a reduced standard error of the difference. Suppose, for example, that in a study of the relative validity of two tests, A and B, in relation to a criterion C, r_{AC} and r_{BC} were computed for the same sample. The difference in these "validity coefficients" could not be evaluated in the manner described in the preceding paragraphs; or, if this test were applied, the estimated standard error of the difference would be considerably larger than the true standard error. Similarly, the difference in the reliability coefficients of two tests, if computed for the same sample, might be really significant but fail to appear so by this test.

The mathematical statisticians have not yet devised a test of the significance of a difference between correlation coefficients for this situation.   This is particularly unfortunate from the point of view of the research student in education, since it is just in this situation (evaluation of test materials) that a test of significance is most needed.   However, there is available a formula for computing the correlation between r_{12} and r_{13} for a number of random samples (see Kelley, *Statistical Methods*, p. 179).   From this, and from formula (42), one can derive the following expression for the standard error of the difference between observed values of r_{12} and r_{13} for a random sample,

$$\sigma_{r_{12} - r_{13}} =$$

$$\sqrt{\frac{1}{N}\left[k_{12}^2 + k_{13}^2 - \frac{2\,k_{12}k_{13}r_{23} - r_{12}r_{13}(k_{23}^2 - r_{12}^2 - r_{13}^2 - 2\,r_{12}r_{13}r_{23})}{k_{12}k_{13}}\right]}$$

in which $k = \sqrt{1 - r^2}$.   The usefulness of this formula is impaired by the fact that the sampling distribution of $(r_{12} - r_{13})$ is not known, and hence one cannot use the above formula to test the significance of a difference except upon the unsupported assumption of normality.   Even so, the use of this formula seems decidedly preferable to the neglect of the correlation term which would be involved in the z-test suggested in the preceding paragraphs.

It may be well to emphasize again that the tests of significance described in this section are valid only for *random* samples.   If the sample is a stratified sample, or if it consists of several intact school groups which show systematic differences in the correlated variables, or which show systematic differences in the correlation between these variables, the procedures which have been described in this section will not yield valid estimates of error.   This problem will be considered in Section 6, following.

5. COMBINING CORRELATIONS FROM SEVERAL SAMPLES

The z-transformation described in the preceding section may be used to estimate the correlation for a population if the observed correlations are known for several samples independently drawn at random from that population (or from equally correlated popula-

tions).   The procedure is very simple, involving only the computation of the weighted average of the z's corresponding to the various r's, each z being weighted by $(N - 3)$.   The estimate required
is then the value of r corresponding to this average z.

Suppose, for example, that for samples of 80, 126, and 92 cases,
the values of the r between two given variables are .640, .720, and
.595 respectively.   What is the best estimate of the r for the population from which these samples were drawn?   The corresponding
values of z are .758172, .907643, and .685370 respectively.   The
weighted average of these z's is

$[(.758172)(77) + (.907643)(123) + (.685370)(89)] \div 289 = .799368.$
(The standard error of this z is $1/\sqrt{289}$ or .0588.)   The r corresponding to this weighted average is .665, which is the estimate
desired.

It should be emphasized that this method of combining r's should
not be employed unless the samples involved are known to be independent *random* samples from the *same* population (or from equally
correlated populations).[1]

6. THE EFFECT OF SCHOOL DIFFERENCES UPON CORRELATION
   COEFFICIENTS OBTAINED FROM HETEROGENEOUS SAMPLES
       CONSISTING OF INTACT SCHOOL GROUPS

The tests of significance described in the preceding sections of
this chapter are all designed for simple random samples.   However, as we have noted repeatedly throughout this text, samples
consisting of intact school groups may not be considered as random
samples of pupils.   Since most of the samples used in correlation
studies in educational research do consist of intact school groups,
it will be well to consider carefully the effect of school differences
upon the correlation coefficients obtained from such samples.

Let us consider first the effect of the larger-than-chance differences in school *means* which characterize the results obtained from

---

[1] See "Combinative Properties of Correlation Coefficients," Jack W. Dunlap,
Journal of Experimental Education, March, 1937 (Volume 5, page 286), for a general
method of combining correlations from different groups.

objective tests of school achievement.   Suppose, for example, that
we wish to determine the correlation between scores on a certain
arithmetic test and a certain reading test for seventh-grade pupils
in Iowa schools.   Suppose we decide to use a sample of 300 pupils,
and find that this number of cases may be most conveniently
secured by using all seventh-grade pupils in two school systems,
each of which can provide 150 pupils.   Now let us suppose that the
pupils in School A are doing outstandingly good work in arithmetic
and unusually poor work in reading, and that the reverse is true for
the pupils in School B.   If the scores for all 300 pupils were then
plotted on the same scattergram, the tally marks might be distributed as in diagram I below.   The tally marks for the pupils
in School A would lie at the lower (left) end of the reading scale,
and at the upper end of the arithmetic scale, or in the oval labeled
A.   The long narrow shape and orientation of the oval indicates
that the correlation between reading and arithmetic scores is positive and high.   The *B* oval in diagram I may be similarly interpreted.   If now we were to compute the correlation coefficient for
the entire scattergram, we would find a marked *negative* total
correlation between arithmetic and reading scores for the two
schools, even though the correlation within each school is positive
and high.

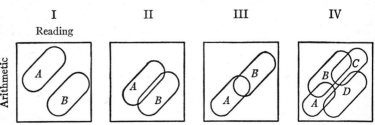

Diagram I of course represents a deliberate exaggeration, for the
sake of emphasis, over what one would be at all likely to find in an
actual situation of the type suggested.   Only very rarely would the
total correlation for two or more schools be negative at the same
time that the correlations within schools are positive and high.

It frequently happens, however, that the total correlation is markedly lower than within any individual school, as is suggested by diagram II.   More frequently, the total correlation would be higher than within any individual school, as is suggested by diagram III, and sometimes, but not often, the total correlation might be very nearly the same as within the individual schools, as could be true of diagram IV.

The manner in which this problem may be handled is directly suggested by the phraseology of the preceding discussion.   What we should compute, in situations of this kind, is the correlation *within schools*, rather than the *total* correlation, and the manner in which this may be done has already been described in Chapter VI. Our real interest, in the example cited, would be in the correlation between arithmetic and reading scores for pupils all of whom have had the *same* instruction in these subjects, and this is essentially what the correlation *within schools*, as computed by the methods of analysis of covariance, represents.   The computational procedure involves analyzing the sums of squares of the arithmetic and reading scores into their *between schools* and *within schools* components, computing the sum of products for *within schools*, and then computing the correlation *within schools* from the sums of squares and products *within schools*, using formula (24) on page 186.   This correlation could then be interpreted as the average of the correlations that would be found in the separate schools, or, with reference to diagram I, for instance, as that which would be found if the "A" and "B" ovals had been moved together, or superimposed, so that the school means coincided for each test. The correlation *within schools*, then, is unaffected by differences in school means, and hence may be considered as equivalent to that which would have been found had all pupils been taken from a single school.   Furthermore, if one may assume that in the population of *schools* involved the correlation within any one school is the same (except for chance) as in any other (the assumption of homogeneous correlation), a *within schools* correlation computed for a number of randomly selected schools may be treated as if it had been secured from a simple random sample of $N - m + 1$ cases (N represents total number of pupils and m represents the number of schools). For instance, the *within schools* correlation for a sample of 420 cases in 11 schools would be treated as a correlation coefficient obtained from a simple random sample of 410 cases, and any of the techniques described in the preceding sections could then be applied to this correlation. This would not be true, however, if the assumption of homogeneous correlation *within schools* is not satisfied, and this possibility will be more adequately considered later.

This effect of school differences in an actual instance may be illustrated by the data used in the example of Section 5 of Chapter VI (pages 196 to 203). These are actual data secured from five Iowa schools selected at random from over 250 available schools. We noted in this example (page 203) that the correlation *within schools* (between initial and final scores) was .66. The correlation for the total sample may be computed from the sums of squares and products for *total*, as follows:

$$r \text{ (total)} = \frac{\Sigma\, xy}{\sqrt{\Sigma\, x^2 \cdot \Sigma\, y^2}} \quad \text{(for total)}$$

$$= \frac{42327}{\sqrt{69495.0 \times 49999.1}} = .718$$

This correlation was reduced by the methods differences, as may be demonstrated by computing the correlation with methods differences (but not school differences) eliminated. The value of $\Sigma\, x^2$ for the total sample was 69495, and for *methods* alone was 1319.5, hence the value of $\Sigma\, x^2$ for *within methods* is $69495 - 1319.5 = 68175.5$. Similarly, the $\Sigma\, xy$ term for *within methods* is $42327 - (-1352.6) = 43679.6$, and the $\Sigma\, y^2$ term for *within methods* is $49999.1 - 1382.5 = 48616.6$. Accordingly, the correlation with methods differences (only) eliminated is

$$r = \frac{43679.6}{\sqrt{68175.5 \times 48616.6}} = .759.$$

The effect of the school differences alone, then, was to increase the correlation from .66 to .76 for this sample of five schools.

The effect of school differences in central tendency upon correlation coefficients computed from samples consisting of intact school groups is of particular concern in the evaluation of achievement tests intended for widespread use. When reliability coefficients or validity coefficients are computed for an objective test, they are usually obtained from heterogeneous samples containing pupils from several schools. The test user is of course primarily interested in the reliability or validity of the test for use within his own school, and therefore, aside from any other considerations, the reliability or validity coefficients *within schools* are those which logically should be used in describing the tests. Furthermore, *within schools* correlations computed for samples of this type are likely to be considerably more stable than the total correlations for the same samples. The writer would therefore strongly recommend the method of analysis of covariance as a standard procedure in computing the reliability and validity coefficients of standardized tests, in order that the more stable and more meaningful *within schools* correlations may be reported to the test user.

We have already noted that when a *within schools* correlation is computed for a sample of intact school groups, the reliability or significance of this correlation may be validly determined by the procedures of Sections 2 to 4 of this chapter only if the correlation within individual schools is fundamentally constant for the population of schools involved. The possibility that there may be real differences in correlation from school to school is therefore one to which we should give very careful consideration. If the true correlation between two variables differs markedly from school to school, then the *within schools* correlation computed for a number of schools becomes an "average" of dissimilar correlations, and will therefore be both relatively unstable and difficult to interpret, if, indeed, it may be considered as valid "average" at all.

This possibility that correlations between scores on the same tests may differ significantly from school to school was shown in a study, by G. V. Lannholm, of the relative reliability of several different types of tests of punctuation and capitalization ability for junior high school pupils.[1]   Among other things, Lannholm attempted to determine the relative validity of certain self-administering objective tests of capitalization by computing the correlation of scores on each test with the scores on a criterion test of the dictation type.   Six different types of capitalization tests, designated as types A to F, were evaluated.   Each of these tests, including the criterion test, was based on exactly the same content, and differed from the others only in form.   The whole study consisted of a number of independent experiments, in each of which the criterion test and two of the self-administering tests were administered to the pupils in several schools, different schools being involved in each experiment.   Test A, which consisted of uncapitalized printed sentences in which the pupil was to indicate the places where capitals were needed, was paired with one of the other tests in each of five experiments, so that five independent observations were made of the correlation of test A with the criterion, or of the "validity" coefficient of test A.   In all of these five experiments, both test A and the criterion were administered under the same very carefully controlled conditions.   The correlation computed for each experiment was the *within schools* correlation, so that the effect of differences in school *means* was eliminated.   The results of these five experiments were as follows:

Experiment Number	Number of Pupils	Number of Schools	*Within Schools* Correlation of Test A and Criterion Test	*Within Schools* Reliability of Test A
1	144	3	.35	.82
2	148	7	.57	.77
3	146	8	.66	.89
4	149	7	.48	.79
5	145	3	.67	.83
			Mean = .58	

[1] "The Measurement of Punctuation and Capitalization Ability," G. V. Lannholm, *Journal of Experimental Education*, September, 1939, vol. 8, no. 1, pp. 55–86.

It may be readily shown that the variation in these correlations is much greater than can be attributed to chance fluctuations in random sampling. In other words, the evidence is very convincing that the true "validity" of test A, as judged by the criterion employed, is considerably higher in some schools than in others. Larger-than-chance variations were also found in the reliability coefficients for test A, independently computed from the *within schools* correlation between equivalent forms of the test in each experiment, and these are given in the last column of the preceding table. Admitting that the procedure was questionable, Lannholm "averaged" these validity coefficients for the five experiments by the method of Section 5 of this chapter (see last line of table above), but wisely refrained from using the procedure of Section 3 to estimate the precision of this average correlation. Very obviously, this average coefficient is less stable and less meaningful than if it had been derived from individual coefficients that differed only as much as would coefficients obtained from random samples of the same number of cases.

In order to secure a more dependable and generalized description of the degree to which heterogeneity of correlation between scores on educational tests characterizes populations made up of intact school groups, the writer and J. H. Lyford analyzed certain data secured from the 1939 Iowa Every-Pupil Testing Program for Grades 6, 7, and 8. The data used were the scores made by seventh-grade pupils on the *1939 Iowa Every-Pupil Tests of Basic Skills.* *Test A* of this battery is a 67-minute objective test of silent reading comprehension. Part V of *Test A* is a 10-minute test of general vocabulary. *Test B* is a 78-minute test of work-study skills, including tests of ability to read maps, to read graphs and tables, to use an index, to use a dictionary, etc. *Test C* is a 70-minute test of basic language skills, including capitalization, punctuation, usage, and spelling. *Test D* is an 80-minute comprehensive test of achievement in arithmetic. All tests were administered under the same very carefully controlled conditions in all schools participating in the program. From each of 71 schools, 30 pupils were selected at random from all seventh-grade pupils in the school, and for each of these groups separately various inter-correlations were computed for total scores on the tests just described. The distributions of these correlation coefficients are given in Table 15. The heading of each column of frequencies identifies the tests involved. For example, the first distribution is that of r_{AD}, or of the correlations between total scores on the reading and arithmetic tests.

For each coefficient obtained the corresponding z was determined from Table 14 (page 215). The distributions of these z's for each distribution of r's is given in the lower part of Table 15. Had these z's been obtained from independent random samples of 30 cases each all drawn from the same population, the standard deviation of any of the z-distributions should approximate $1/\sqrt{N-3} = \dfrac{1}{\sqrt{27}} = .121$. The actual standard deviations, σ_z, are given at the bottom of Table 15. It will be noted that in each case the actual standard deviations are much larger than that expected on the hypothesis of random sampling. For example, the standard deviation of the z's corresponding to r_{AD} is .226, or almost twice that expected. These discrepancies are obviously larger than could be attributed to chance (as may be shown by applying exact tests).

If these studies are at all representative of the conditions that generally prevail in correlation studies in educational research, the problems of designing such studies and of interpreting the results are far more complex than we have heretofore supposed them to be. If, for example, the true reliability of a test fluctuates widely from school to school, then, in order to secure a meaningful and dependable generalized description of the test's reliability, we must determine its reliability coefficient separately for each school in a fairly large and representative sample of *schools*, and present the actual distribution of these reliability coefficients. The average or median of these reliability coefficients might then be taken as a generalized description of the reliability of the test, and the relia-

TABLE 15

DISTRIBUTIONS OF OBTAINED r'S AND z'S (EACH COMPUTED FOR A RANDOM SAMPLE OF 30 SEVENTH-GRADE PUPILS IN A SINGLE SCHOOL) FOR SCORES ON CERTAIN TESTS IN THE "1939 IOWA EVERY-PUPIL TESTS OF BASIC SKILLS" IN 71 IOWA SCHOOLS

Values of r (Lower Limits of Intervals)	Frequencies		
	For Tests A and D (r_{AD})	For Tests B and C (r_{BC})	For Tests A–V and C ($r_{A-V \cdot C}$)
.90	1		
.85		4	
.80	2	11	
.75	6	12	1
.70	8	16	5
.65	7	7	9
.60	11	5	6
.55	15	7	11
.50	6	1	9
.45	5	1	4
.40	2	1	9
.35	3	1	8
.30	2	1	2
.25		2	3
.20	1		1
.15		2	1
.10	1		1
.05			1
Values of z (Lower Limits of Intervals)	z_{AD}	z_{BC}	$z_{A-V \cdot C}$
1.40	1	3	
1.30			
1.20		5	
1.10	2	7	
1.00	3	10	
.90	7	17	4
.80	7	5	7
.70	13	8	8
.60	18	7	15
.50	10	2	11
.40	3	2	14
.30	5	1	5
.20		2	4
.10	2	2	2
.00			1
	$\sigma_z = .226$	$\sigma_z = .285$	$\sigma_z = .204$
	Expected $\sigma_z = .121$		

bility of this description would depend on the variance and number of the observed correlations for individual schools.   Clearly, under these conditions, a reliability coefficient computed for only a few schools, regardless of the number of pupils involved, would be relatively unstable, even though school differences in *means* have been eliminated by computing the *within schools* correlation.   A *total* coefficient of reliability computed for an entire sample involving only a few schools can obviously be only less meaningful and dependable, and it must be remembered that it is only this type of coefficient which has thus far been provided with most current standardized tests.   It is to be hoped, therefore, that further investigation will reveal a less pronounced heterogeneity of *within schools* intercorrelations and self-correlations for educational achievement tests in general than is suggested by Lannholm's and Lyford's data.

7. THE ESTIMATED VALIDITY OF A TEST n TIMES AS LONG AS A GIVEN TEST

In experimental comparisons of objective testing techniques, the standard procedure has been to construct several forms of a test using the same content but employing a different technique with each form, to administer all forms together with a criterion test to the same group or to equated groups of pupils, and then to evaluate the forms in terms of their correlations with the criterion and their reliabilities.   Suppose, for example, that we wish to compare the right-wrong type of spelling test, consisting of a printed list of words in which the pupil is to indicate which words are spelled correctly and which incorrectly, with the multiple-choice type in which each word is presented in, say, four spellings, and in which the pupil is to indicate which spelling is correct.

We might then prepare a list-dictation test (in which the words are dictated to the pupil) for use as a criterion (assuming *a priori* that this form is more valid than either of the experimental forms), and then build parallel forms of the right-wrong and multiple-choice types, each form being based on the same words as the criterion test, and then administer all three tests to the same group of pupils. Suppose that experience has shown that pupils require more time per item for the multiple-choice type than for the right-wrong, and that in the experiment the two forms are therefore administered under different time limits, arbitrarily determined. We might then find that the multiple-choice test, which required more time, yielded the higher correlation with the criterion. However, it is possible that had more words been included in the right-wrong form and the time increased proportionately, so that the administration time for both tests were the same, the right-wrong test might have shown the higher correlation with the criterion. If so, the right-wrong would be the better testing technique for the given amount of testing time, since the practical question is, "Given a certain amount of time, with which technique can the most valid score be obtained?" This, for instance, would be the problem faced by a constructor of a comprehensive achievement test who has a certain number of minutes to devote to the testing of achievement in spelling.

This being the case, we might wish to estimate, from the known validity and reliability of the original right-wrong test, how valid it would have been had it contained a sufficient number of words (of homogeneous quality and difficulty and administered at the same rate) to make the total administration time the same as for the multiple-choice test. This could be done, according to Kelley,[1] by means of the formula

$$r_{lc} = \frac{r_{sc}}{\sqrt{\dfrac{1 - r_{ss}}{n} + r_{ss}}} \tag{37}$$

in which r_{sc} is the correlation of the short form with the criterion, r_{ss} is the reliability coefficient of the short form, n is the ratio of the lengths of the short and long forms, and r_{lc} is the estimated correlation of the long form with the criterion. (If desired, the Spearman-Brown Prophecy formula could be similarly used to estimate the reliability of the long form.)

[1] *Statistical Method*, Truman L. Kelley, p. 200.

Suppose, for example, that our original right-wrong test, administered in 5 minutes, showed a correlation of .70 with the criterion and a reliability of .72, and that the multiple-choice test, administered in 18 minutes, showed a correlation of .75 with the criterion, and a reliability of .95. According to (37), then, a right-wrong test 3.6 times as long, and therefore administered in 18 minutes, would show a correlation with the criterion of

$$r_{lc} = \frac{.70}{\sqrt{\dfrac{.28}{3.6} + .72}} = .784.$$

According to this estimate, a right-wrong test 18 minutes in length (administered at the same rate in words per minute as the experimental test) is more valid than a multiple-choice test 18 minutes in length (also homogeneous with and administered at the same rate as the experimental test). It is significant, however, that if we estimate the validity coefficient of a 5-minute multiple-choice test by the same formula, we get a value of .706, as compared to a validity coefficient of .70 for a right-wrong test of the same length. In other words, which of these two forms is superior depends upon the length of test we wish to build.

(*Note: The data used in the preceding example are fictitious, and are in no sense indicative of the relative merits of the right-wrong and multiple-choice types of spelling test.*)

Formula (37) is appropriate if there is available only one form of the test, and if r_{ss} is estimated from the correlation between scores on chance halves by means of the Spearman-Brown formula. If two equivalent forms of the short test have been administered, it would be better to define s in (37) as the *sum* of the scores on the short forms, in which case r_{ss} would be the reliability of this total score estimated by the Spearman-Brown formula from the correlation between scores on the short forms. In this case, of course, the n in (37) would represent the number of times the long form (whose correlation with the criterion is being estimated) is longer than the combined short forms.

Formula (37) is important, not so much because of its possible applications in research, as because its careful study should add considerably to the student's insight into the problem of test evaluation. So far as the *technique* of testing involved is concerned, the important characteristic of the technique is the *validity which it will yield per unit of time*, but the validity per unit of time depends, among many other things, upon the length of the test and the *relation of the reliability to the validity* for any given length. If a test has a very high reliability and a low validity for a given length, then it is of relatively little avail to attempt to lengthen the test to secure a higher validity (assuming the material added is homogeneous with the original), but neither will the validity be lowered seriously if the test is shortened in length. On the other hand, if the reliability coefficient is only slightly higher than the "validity" coefficient for a given length of the test, then an increase in length will raise the validity coefficient almost as rapidly as it raises the reliability coefficient. Hence, one technique may be better than another if a short test is desired, but worse than another if a long test is desired. Strictly, therefore, experimental comparisons [1] of testing techniques should be designed to answer the question, "Which technique will yield the highest validity in a given time period?" rather than the insolvable question, "Which technique is in general the most valid for measuring a certain outcome?"

It is important to note, in the preceding example, that since the experimental administration times were arbitrarily determined, there is a possibility that more time than necessary was allotted to the multiple-choice form, and that the latter form was therefore unfairly penalized in the comparison. This factor could be controlled experimentally if the purpose of the experiment were to determine which form of test yields the more valid score for a given time limit. One could then build several right-wrong tests containing different amounts of homogeneous material, administer all

[1] See "Experimental Procedures in Test Evaluation," Lindquist, E. F., and Cook, Walter W., *Journal of Experimental Education*, March, 1933 (Vol. I, p 163).

tests under the given time limit, find which correlates most highly with the criterion, and thus determine empirically the *optimum* amount of material for the given time limit and the given technique. If the same were done for the multiple-choice test, one could then fairly compare the validity coefficients for the given time limit, both techniques having been applied to the optimum amount of material for that time limit.

It should be apparent, from formula (37), that while the correlation of a test with a certain criterion may be increased by increasing the length of the test there is an upper limit to the correlation which may thus be secured, and this limit is set by the reliability of the original test. If we let n in (37) approach infinity, r_{lc} approaches the limit (see also the last paragraph on page 230).

$$r_{\infty c} = \frac{r_{sc}}{\sqrt{r_{ss}}} \qquad (38)$$

In our example, for instance, the limiting value of the correlation with the criterion for a lengthened test of the right-wrong type would be estimated as

$$r_{\infty c} = \frac{.70}{\sqrt{.72}} = .82$$

while that for a lengthened multiple-choice test would be .77. In other words, the estimated correlations between obtained scores on the criterion test and *true* [1] scores on the experimental tests are .82 and .77 respectively.

Formula (38) can of course be used also to estimate the correlation between a fallible test and an infallible criterion, by interchanging s and c in the formula. That is, one would divide the correlation r_{sc} by the square root of the reliability of the *criterion*, rather than of the fallible test. This form of (38) is of much greater practical interest than the form given above, since it provides a measure of the validity of the test which corrects for errors in the

---

[1] *True* scores are perfectly reliable measures of whatever a test happens to be measuring. The *true* score of an individual on a given test may be defined as his mean score on an infinite number of equivalent forms of the test.

criterion and at the same time takes into consideration the errors which would characterize the test in actual use.

A means of estimating the correlation between *true* scores on both the criterion and the experimental test will be presented in the following section.

8. CORRELATION COEFFICIENTS CORRECTED FOR ATTENUATION

Correlations between scores on educational and psychological tests are systematically lowered (attenuated) as the result of errors of measurement. That is, the correlation between obtained scores on any two fallible tests will be lower than the correlation between *true* scores on the same tests, due to the fact that the obtained scores are in part the result of chance (and hence uncorrelated) errors of measurement. Spearman [1] has shown that the correlation between true scores on two tests for any group may be estimated by means of the formula

$$r_{\infty_1 \infty_2} = \frac{r_{12}}{\sqrt{r_{1I} r_{2II}}} \tag{39}$$

in which r_{12} is the estimated correlation between tests 1 and 2, whose reliability coefficients for the given group are r_{1I} and r_{2II} respectively.

Suppose, for example, that for a certain group of pupils the correlation between scores on two given spelling tests is .74, and that the reliability coefficients of these tests for the given group are .97 and .84, respectively. According to the "correction for attenuation" formula, the estimated correlation between *true* scores for this group is

$$r_{\infty_1 \infty_2} = \frac{.74}{\sqrt{.97 \times .84}} = .82.$$

This signifies that if we added homogeneous material to each of these tests to increase its reliability, we could not expect the correlation between the scores to exceed .82, no matter how long we made the tests. In other words, a correlation of .82 would pre-

[1] Spearman, C., "Demonstration of Formulae for True Measurement of Correlation," *American Journal of Psychology*, Volume 18 (1907), p. 161.

sumably be found between scores on infinitely long and hence perfectly reliable tests of these types.   This of course implies that
whatever is being measured by one of these tests is not exactly the
same as that being measured by the other.   If they were measuring the same thing the corrected coefficient should be 1.00, since
the correlation between perfectly reliable measures of the same
thing must obviously be unity.   If, then, the scores on the first of
these tests were considered as *criterion* measures of spelling ability,
the "corrected" coefficient of .82 would mean that the second type
of spelling test is in part measuring irrelevant factors, and could
not possibly be highly valid, no matter how long the test were
made.   However, even though the criterion is beyond question,
this should not be taken as evidence that this *particular* test (i.e., in
its original length) is not a "good" measure of spelling ability for
a test of its length, or that it is necessarily inferior to another particular test whose "corrected" validity coefficient is above .82 (see
next to last paragraph of the preceding section).   Suppose, for instance, that the scores on a third spelling test showed a correlation
of .65 with the criterion scores for the same pupils, and that this
correlation when corrected for attenuation was raised to .88.   This
would signify that if both tests were made infinitely long, the second type of test would be inferior in validity, but if the original
tests were to be used as found, the second type of test would nevertheless be the more valid.

*The mistake has frequently been made of interpreting a correlation
coefficient corrected for attenuation as the "true" correlation between
the traits which the tests are supposed to measure, rather than as the
estimated correlation between perfectly reliable measures of whatever
the tests actually do measure.*   This is but one of the many instances
of the so-called "jingle fallacy" in interpreting test results, that is,
the fallacy of dealing with test scores as if the tests were really
measuring what their names or titles imply that they are measuring.   It should be noted, therefore, that the "errors of measurement" whose effects upon correlations are presumably eliminated
by the correction for attenuation are only those which are due to the

lack of perfect *reliability*. If the tests are measuring the wrong things, a correction for attenuation will only indicate the correlation between true measures of these "wrong" things.

It should be noted also that the correction-for-attenuation formula is based upon an assumption that in some instances may be quite doubtful. This is the assumption that the errors of measurement in the two tests are unrelated. Furthermore, the "corrected" coefficient is subject to whatever sampling errors [1] are present in the obtained correlation and reliability coefficients. (As a result of these errors, and of errors due to the way in which the reliability coefficients are estimated, the corrected coefficient may sometimes exceed 1.00.) Correlations corrected for attenuation should therefore always be considered as only approximate in character, but if so considered may nevertheless prove highly useful.

9. TEST FOR LINEARITY OF REGRESSION

Sometimes, after having constructed a correlation diagram to compute the coefficient of correlation between two variables, we may note an apparent tendency for the means of the columns (or rows) to fall along a *curved* rather than a straight line. In other words, the distribution of tally marks may suggest that the relationship is non-linear. If it is, then of course the product-moment correlation coefficient will underestimate the degree of relationship actually present, and estimates based on the linear regression equation may be seriously biased. Before using these latter techniques on the hypothesis of linearity, we should, in cases of doubt, satisfy ourselves that this hypothesis is tenable. That is, we should demonstrate that the observed deviations of the column (or row) means from a straight line pattern could reasonably be considered as due only to chance fluctuation in random sampling.

The hypothesis of linear regression may be readily tested by the

---

[1] See Cureton, E., "On Certain Estimated Correlation Functions and Their Standard Errors," *Journal of Experimental Education*, Vol. 4 (March, 1936), pp. 252–263, formula (23).

methods of analysis of variance and covariance. Suppose that the scales on our correlation chart are labeled the X and Y scales in the customary fashion, that y represents the deviation of any Y-measure from the mean of all the Y's, and that x has a similar meaning. Let us first consider the possibility that the column means deviate significantly from a straight line pattern.

The first step in the procedure would be to analyze the total "sum of squares" ($ss_t = \Sigma\, y^2$) for the Y-distribution into its *between columns* (ss_c) and *within columns* (ss_{wc}) components. This would be done by the methods of Section 2 of Chapter V, viewing the correlation table just as we viewed Table 6 on page 93. Accordingly,

$$ss_{wc} = ss_t - ss_c = \Sigma\, y^2 - ss_c$$

The next step would be to compute the total "sums of products," $\Sigma\, xy$, by the method described on page 185. We may now note that the sum of the squared deviations of the Y-measures in the individual columns from the regression line ($y = bx$) is given by (see page 190)

$$\Sigma(y - bx)^2 = \Sigma\, y^2 - \frac{(\Sigma\, xy)^2}{\Sigma\, x^2}$$

in which $\Sigma\, x^2$ is of course the *total* sum of squares for the X-distribution. Now, if the observed means had fallen exactly on the straight regression line, then the sum of squared deviations from the regression line would be the same as the sum of squares *within columns*. That is, ss_{wc} would equal $\Sigma(y - bx)^2$. If this were true, then by the two equations above, ss_c would have to equal $\frac{(\Sigma\, xy)^2}{\Sigma\, x^2}$.

Since all column means do not fall on the regression line, ss_c will be larger than $\frac{(\Sigma\, xy)^2}{\Sigma\, x^2}$, and the difference between these terms will be indicative of the amount of departure from linearity. We may think, then, of the sum of squares *between columns* as consisting of two components, one of which, $\frac{(\Sigma\, xy)^2}{\Sigma\, x^2}$, is due to linear regression, and the other of which, $ss_c - \dfrac{(\Sigma\,xy)^2}{\Sigma\,x^2}$, is due to departure from linearity. The component due to linear regression has one degree of freedom, that due to departure from linear regression therefore has one less degree of freedom than the sum of squares *between columns*. If the departure from linearity is due only to chance, then the variance estimated from the sum of squares due to departure from linearity should be the same as the variance *within columns*. If the *F*-test shows a significant difference between these variances, we may take this as evidence that the regression is non-linear.

Suppose, for example, that we have a correlation chart in which 15 columns contain frequencies, and that 500 cases are involved. Suppose the analysis of the Y-distribution is

	d.f.	Sum of Squares	Variance
Between columns	14	14235.22	
Within columns	485	5126.30	10.57
Total	499	19361.52	

Suppose also that $\dfrac{(\Sigma\,xy)^2}{\Sigma\,x^2} = 13{,}782.72$. The variance *between columns* could then be analyzed as follows:

	d.f.		Sum of Squares	Variance
Total (between columns)	14		14,235.22	
Due to linear regression	1	(subtract)	13,782.72	
Due to departure from linearity	13		452.50	34.81

The ratio between these variances is

$$F = \frac{34.81}{10.57} = 3.29.$$

For 13 and 485 *d.f.*, an *F* need only exceed about 2.17 to be significant at the 1 per cent level, hence in this case we may confidently reject the hypothesis of linear regression in the population sampled. However, if we wish to show, not that the hypothesis of linear regression is tenable or otherwise, but rather that curvilinear regression is more *probable* than linear, we would be interested in an *F* at a much lower level of significance.

The test for linearity as applied to the row means would of course be exactly like that just described.

It should be evident that with a small sample a greater absolute divergence from linearity is necessary for significance than with a large sample. That is, the "significance" of the departure from linearity is not a measure of the *degree* of curvilinearity.

10. TEST FOR SIGNIFICANCE OF A NON-LINEAR RELATIONSHIP

We noted in Section 2 of this chapter that the test of significance there described assumed that the relationship, if any, is linear, and that we may have even a marked degree of non-linear relationship although the observed product-moment *r* proved not to be significant. In such instances, if there is any reason to suspect a curvilinear relationship, we might wish to apply a more inclusive test of independence. This test may be very simply described in terms of analysis of variance. It consists only of analyzing the variance of the total Y (or X) distribution into its *between columns* (or rows) and *within columns* (or rows) components. If the variance for *between columns* (or rows) differs significantly (by the *F*-test) from the variance for *within columns* (or *within rows*), we have evidence that there is *some* relationship between X and Y, or have disproved the hypothesis of independence. This test is superior to that of Section 2, in that it provides for the possibilities either of linear or non-linear regression.

It should be noted that a significant departure from linearity does not necessarily mean that the relationship follows any simple curve. It may be that, even though this test indicated a marked departure from linearity, a straight line would still be the best to use in predicting one variable from the other (Fisher gives an instance of this in § 44 of his *Statistical Methods*). The problem of fitting curved regression lines is beyond the scope of this book, but it may be worth observing that correlations computed from such regression lines may frequently prove worth while in educational research. The student interested in this problem should read F. C. Mills, *Statistical Methods*, pp. 432–441.

11. THE CORRELATION RATIO

If, in a study of the relationship between two variables, we have shown that the relationship is curvilinear, we may wish to have some index of the degree of relationship present. The measure used for this purpose is known as the correlation ratio, and is represented by the Greek letter η (eta). The nature of this ratio may perhaps best be shown in terms of its relationship to the product moment r.

The standard error of estimating one variable from known values of a linearly related variable by means of the linear regression equation is given by

$$\sigma_{y \cdot x} = \sigma_y \sqrt{1 - r_{xy}^2}.$$

If we solve for r in this formula, we have

$$r_{xy} = \sqrt{\frac{1 - \sigma_{y \cdot x}^2}{\sigma_y^2}}$$

We thus see that the value of r_{xy} is dependent upon the ratio of $\sigma_{y \cdot x}^2$, which is the variance about the regression line within the columns of the correlation diagram, and σ_y^2, which is the variance of the total Y-distribution. This suggests a similar measure of relationship when the regression is non-linear. We can define η_{yx} as

$$\eta_{yx} = \sqrt{1 - \frac{\sigma_{yx}^2}{\sigma_y^2}} = \sqrt{\frac{\sigma_y^2 - \sigma_{yx}^2}{\sigma_y^2}} \tag{40}$$

in which σ_{yx}^2 now represents the variance *within columns* about the *means* of the columns, rather than about the straight regression line. A similar ratio may be used to measure the relative concentration of the measures in the *rows* about the row means.   This is

$$\eta_{xy} = \sqrt{1 - \frac{\sigma_{xy}^2}{\sigma_x^2}} = \sqrt{\frac{\sigma_x^2 - \sigma_{xy}^2}{\sigma_x^2}} \qquad (41)$$

These ratios may be readily defined in terms of analysis of variance. The square of the ratio η_{yx} is simply the ratio (for large samples) of the "sum of squares" *between columns* (ss_c) and the total sum of squares (ss_y) for the Y-distribution.   That is,

$$\eta_{yx} = \sqrt{\frac{ss_c}{ss_y}}$$

and similarly,

$$\eta_{xy} = \sqrt{\frac{ss_r}{ss_x}}$$

in which ss_y represents the sum of squares *between rows* and ss_x the *total* sum of squares for the X-distribution.   These sums of squares may be computed by the method of Section 2 of Chapter V. The final step in the computation of a correlation ratio may be illustrated with the data in the example on page 237.   In this example, $ss_c = 14235.22$, and $ss_y = 19361.52$, hence,

$$\eta_{yx} = \sqrt{\frac{14235.22}{19361.52}} = \sqrt{.7352} = .86$$

It should be clear from (40) that if there is no relationship, then σ_{yx}^2 will equal σ_y^2, and η_{yx} will be zero.   If the relationship is perfect, σ_{yx}^2 will equal zero, and η_{yx} will equal unity.   Thus η_{yx} (or η_{xy}) may have any value from o to 1.00, but cannot take negative values, as does r.   It should be observed that the sum of squares *between columns* is somewhat dependent upon the number of columns, which is arbitrarily determined.   If so small an interval is used that no column contains more than one measure, then the sum of squares *between* columns will be the same as the *total* sum of squares, and η_{yx} will equal 1.00, regardless of the degree of relationship.   It is best, therefore, to use a relatively coarse grouping in computing correlation ratios, so that the column (or row) means will become relatively stable.

Since the variance of the measures in the columns about a

straight regression line can never be less than their variance about the observed means of the columns, it follows that η_{yx} (or η_{xy}) can never be smaller than r_{xy}. It is for this reason that we have said that r_{xy} underestimates the degree of relationship when the regression is non-linear.

12. BISERIAL CORRELATION

There are frequent occasions, in educational research, to compute a coefficient of correlation between a continuous variable and one which can be considered as *dichotomous*, that is, one which can be classed in only two categories. For example, in evaluating the individual items in an objective examination, one might wish to compute the correlation between the scores on a criterion test and the responses (right or wrong) to a single test item. Again, one might wish to measure the relationship between scores on an intelligence test and the responses (yes or no) to a questionnaire item. In such instances, the dichotomous variable may sometimes be considered as essentially continuous, and as capable of being classed in finer intervals if other methods of measurement were employed. For example, one might reason that in a given group of pupils there are many degrees of understanding of the same test item, and that the right-wrong method of scoring merely represents an arbitrary imposition of a dichotomy upon a continuous distribution of degrees of understanding. That is, the practice of classing the responses as either right or wrong may be considered as analogous to describing performances on a test as either "passing" or "failing" instead of in terms of scores. If the dichotomous variable is of this character one may, on the assumption that continuous measures of this variable would be *normally* distributed, validly compute the correlation by the *biserial* method.

The biserial correlation coefficient (r_{bis}) may be defined in terms of either of the following formulas:

$$r_{bis} = \frac{M_p - M_q}{\sigma} \cdot \frac{pq}{z} \tag{42}$$

$$r_{bis} = \frac{M_p - M_T}{\sigma} \cdot \frac{p}{z} \tag{43}$$

In these formulae, M_p represents the mean score (on the continuous variable) for the individuals in the first category (of the dichotomous variable), M_q represents the mean score for the individuals in the second category, M_T the mean score for the entire group, σ the standard deviation of scores for the entire group, p the proportion of the entire group in the first category, q the proportion in the second category ($p + q = 1$), and z the height of the ordinate at the point on the normal curve (of unit area and unit standard deviation) which divides the area under the curve into the proportions p and q. Formula (43) is the more convenient to use when a number of biserial coefficients are to be computed against the same continuous variable, as when the correlation with a single criterion is to be computed for the responses to each item in a test.

To illustrate the computational procedure, suppose that the mean and standard deviation of scores on a criterion test are 56.0 and 12.8 respectively for a given group of 200 pupils, and that 64 of these pupils have responded correctly and 136 incorrectly to a certain test item. The problem is to compute r_{bis} between the criterion scores and the responses to this item. To compute this correlation by means of (43), we must know what mean score on the criterion test was made by the 64 pupils that answered the item correctly. Suppose that this mean score is $M_p = 66.4$. In this case $p = .32$, and we must therefore find the height (z) of the normal curve at the point above (or below) which 32 per cent of the area lies, after which we must find p/z. The values of p/z for various values of p are given in Table 16. From this table we find that for $p = .32$, $p/z = .8948$. Hence for our example

$$r_{bis} = \frac{66.4 - 56.0}{12.8} \times .8948 = .726.$$

The biserial correlation coefficient has been quite widely used in educational research as an "index of validity" or "index of discrimination" of individual test items. There are, however, a number of other indices of discriminating power of a test item that may

TABLE 16

VALUES OF p/z FOR VARIOUS VALUES OF p (NORMAL CURVE OF UNIT AREA AND UNIT S.D.)

p	p/z	p	p/z	p	p/z	p	p/z	p	p/z
.01	.3752	.21	.7287	.41	1.0547	.61	1.5899	.81	2.9849
.02	.4131	.22	.7430	.42	1.0745	.62	1.6283	.82	3.1250
.03	.4409	.23	.7575	.43	1.0948	.63	1.6686	.83	3.2799
.04	.4642	.24	.7720	.44	1.1156	.64	1.7107	.84	3.4524
.05	.4848	.25	.7867	.45	1.1369	.65	1.7549	.85	3.6456
.06	.5037	.26	.8016	.46	1.1589	.66	1.8013	.86	3.8638
.07	.5213	.27	.8166	.47	1.1815	.67	1.8501	.87	4.1126
.08	.5382	.28	.8318	.48	1.2047	.68	1.9015	.88	4.3991
.09	.5542	.29	.8472	.49	1.2286	.69	1.9558	.89	4.7331
.10	.5698	.30	.8628	.50	1.2533	.70	2.0133	.90	5.1283
.11	.5850	.31	.8787	.51	1.2788	.71	2.0742	.91	5.6038
.12	.5999	.32	.8948	.52	1.3051	.72	2.1389	.92	6.1884
.13	.6145	.33	.9112	.53	1.3323	.73	2.2078	.93	6.9264
.14	.6290	.34	.9279	.54	1.3604	.74	2.2814	.94	7.8910
.15	.6433	.35	.9449	.55	1.3896	.75	2.3601	.95	9.2111
.16	.6576	.36	.9623	.56	1.4198	.76	2.4447	.96	11.1403
.17	.6718	.37	.9800	.57	1.4512	.77	2.5358	.97	14.2559
.18	.6860	.38	.9980	.58	1.4838	.78	2.6343	.98	20.2404
.19	.7002	.39	1.0165	.59	1.5177	.79	2.7411	.99	37.1454
.20	.7144	.40	1.0353	.60	1.5530	.80	2.8575		

(Values of p/z for values of p not given may be found by linear interpolation; more complete tables are available elsewhere, as in *Workbook in Statistical Method*, Jack W. Dunlap, p. 140.)

be much more readily computed and that may prove quite adequate for most practical purposes.

The standard error of biserial r is given approximately by

$$\sigma_{r_{bis}} = \frac{\sqrt{\frac{pq}{z^2} - r^2}}{\sqrt{N}}.$$

This formula is limited in usefulness by the fact that the form of the sampling distribution is not known, and that it is decidedly inaccurate for low values of p or q.

13. TETRACHORIC CORRELATION

When both of the variables to be correlated are dichotomous, as when one wishes to compute the correlation between responses (right or wrong) to two test items, the *tetrachoric* method may be employed. This method involves assumptions similar to that made in computing a biserial r. That is, it is assumed that both variables are essentially continuous, and that each would be normally distributed for the population involved if measured in sufficiently fine intervals.

The correlation table for two dichotomous variables is a 2 × 2 contingency table, as illustrated in the example of the following paragraphs. We shall let a represent the observed frequency in the upper left-hand cell, b that in the upper right-hand cell, c that in the lower left-hand and d that in the lower right-hand cell. (The table is usually so arranged that the right-hand column represents the "superior" category of one variable and the upper row the "superior" category of the other.) The total number of cases is represented by N, and p and q represent the proportions of the entire group in the "superior" and "inferior" categories, respectively, of one variable, such that $p = \dfrac{a+b}{N}$ and $q = \dfrac{c+d}{N}$. The height of the ordinate which divides the area under the normal curve (of unit area and S.D.) into the proportions p and q is then represented by z, while x represents the distance (in σ units) of this ordinate from the mean (x is negative if $p > .5$ and positive if $p < .5$). For the second variable, p', q', z', and x' have similar meanings $\left(p' = \dfrac{b+d}{N} \text{ and } q' = \dfrac{a+c}{N}\right)$. A close approximation to the tetrachoric correlation coefficient may then be computed by solving for r_{tet} in the equation [1]

$$\frac{bc - ad}{N^2 zz'} = r_{tet} + \left(\frac{xx'}{2}\right)r^2_{tet}. \tag{44}$$

Upon substitution of the known values in this equation, the result

---

[1] The complete formula for computing r_{tet} involves an infinite series in the right-hand side of the equation, but a fairly close approximation may be secured by dropping all but the first two terms of this series, as has been done in (44). See Pearson, Karl, "On the Correlation of Characters Not Quantitatively Measurable," *Philosophical Transactions*, Royal Society of London, Series A, 1900, 195, pp. 1–47.

A formula for the standard error of r_{tet} may be found in Kelley, T. L., *Statistical Methods*, p. 257.

may be simplified and expressed in the standard form of the quadratic equation. This standard form is $ax^2 + bx + c = 0$ [the symbols in this standard form do not have the same meaning as those used in (44)] and the roots of this equation may be computed from

$$x = \frac{-b \pm \sqrt{b^2 - 4ac}}{2a}.$$

To illustrate the computation of a tetrachoric-r by the direct method, let us suppose that for a group of 150 pupils, the contingency table representing the relationship between responses (right or wrong) on two test items is as follows:

Item # 1

		W	R
	R	24 (a)	56 (b)
Item # 2:	W	36 (c)	34 (d)

For this contingency table, $a = 24$, $b = 56$, $c = 36$, and $d = 34$. Hence $p = .5333$, $q = .4667$, $p' = .60$, and $q' = .40$. The values of z, z', and x and x' may be read from the table on pages 14 ff. in *The Kelley Statistical Tables* (Macmillan Co., 1938) for the given values of p and p'. According to this table, $z = .3976$, $x = -.0828$, $z' = .3863$, and $x' = -.2533$. Hence the equation for computing r_{tet} becomes

$$\frac{(56)(36) - (24)(34)}{150^2(.3976)(.3863)} = r_{tet} + \frac{(-.0828)(-.2533)}{2} r_{tet}^2$$

which, in the standard form, is

$$.010487\, r_{tet}^2 + r - .3472 = 0.$$

Hence

$$r_{tet} = \frac{-(+1) \pm \sqrt{(+1)^2 - 4(.010487)(-.3472)}}{(2)(.010487)}$$

One root of the quadratic equation is .35, the other has a negative value larger than − 1.00, and hence is impossible. The tetrachoric correlation coefficient between responses to these items is thus .35.

This direct method of computing r_{tet} is so complex and time-consuming that, if no easier method of computation were available, r_{tet} would perhaps be very rarely used. However, the computation of r_{tet} has been made extremely easy by the computing diagrams [1] prepared by L. L. Thurstone and others. The way in which these diagrams may be used is fully explained in the preface of the volume in which they are presented. In terms of the notation here used, one need only compute p and q', together with the relative frequency in one cell of the contingency table. The appropriate diagram is entered with these three values, and the value of r_{tet} is then read directly from the diagram.

When Thurstone's computing diagrams are used, r_{tet} is perhaps the easiest to compute of all correlation coefficients. For this reason, it has sometimes been used instead of the product-moment r when both variables are continuous, by arbitrarily imposing dichotomies on both distributions. For example, one might characterize a test performance as "above" or "below" the median, or as "above" or "below" any selected point on the scale, instead of in terms of a score. This procedure is not recommended except when only approximate values of r are desired (and when both distributions are approximately normal in form and the relationship is linear). Obviously, r_{tet} may similarly be used in place of r_{bis} as a convenient way of computing indices of discrimination for individual test items. In general, r_{tet} is not a satisfactory measure of relationship for small samples, or for contingency tables in which any of the values p, q, p', or q' are less than .05.

14. THE RANK CORRELATION COEFFICIENT

Sometimes it is possible to describe an individual's status in a group only in terms of rank position. For example, one might

[1] Chesire, L., Saffir, M., Thurstone, L. L., *Computing Diagrams for the Tetrachoric Correlation Coefficient*, University of Chicago Bookstore, 1933.

subjectively arrange the pupils in a given group in order of their "honesty," or in order of their "social adaptability," or in order of their "leadership qualities," etc.   If a quantitative measure of relationship is desired for qualities thus described, the *rank correlation* method may be employed.

The rank correlation coefficient (ρ) is based on the difference (D) in the two ranks for each individual.   The formula for ρ is

$$\rho = 1 - \frac{6\,\Sigma\,D^2}{N(N^2 - 1)} = 1 - \frac{6\,\Sigma\,D^2}{(N - 1)N(N + 1)} \qquad (45)$$

It should be noted that in every set of three consecutive numbers one is always divisible by 3 and one by 2, so that the 6 in the numerator of the last term may *always* be cancelled in the computation.   To illustrate the computation of the rank correlation coefficient, suppose that the pupils in a group of 20 are ranked in two traits in the order indicated in the following table.

Pupil	Trait 1	Trait 2	Ranks Difference (D) in Ranks	D^2
1	9	5	4	16
2	3	7	4	16
3	6	2	4	16
4	1	8	7	49
5	13	4	9	81
6	16	11	5	25
7	12	17	5	25
8	2	9	7	49
9	18	14	4	16
10	7	13	6	36
11	17	19	2	4
12	4	1	3	9
13	8	15	7	49
14	19	20	1	1
15	11	3	8	64
16	20	18	2	4
17	5	12	7	49
18	15	6	9	81
19	10	16	6	36
20	14	10	4	16
				642

From this table,

$$\rho = 1 - \frac{6 \Sigma D^2}{(N-1)N(N+1)} = 1 - \frac{6 \times 642}{19 \times \underset{10}{20} \times \underset{7}{21}} = 1 - \frac{642}{1330} = .52$$

The rank correlation coefficient should not be considered as equivalent to a product-moment r, although if quantitative measures of the traits ranked are normally distributed, ρ and r are very nearly equal in value for large samples.   In general, ρ should be considered as only an approximate measure of relationship which should be employed only when rank-position is the only available means of describing individual status.   A *rough* test of the significance of the observed ρ may be secured by comparing it with its standard error as given by the formula

$$\sigma_\rho = \frac{1.05(1 - \rho^2)}{\sqrt{N}}. \tag{46}$$

A good deal of work on the sampling distribution of ρ has been done recently, and the student interested in more exact tests of significance should see the article by Hotelling and Pabst in the January, 1936, number of *Annuals of Mathematical Statistics* and that by M. G. Kendall *et al.* in *Biometrika*, 1939, pp. 251 ff.

It is well worth noting here that data scored in ranks can be satisfactorily treated for many purposes by transforming them into equivalent normal deviates.   Fisher has provided a table for facilitating these transformations (Tables XX and XXI in Fisher and Yates, *Statistical Tables*) and notes that analysis of variance, correlations. etc., can be carried out with these transformed measures.

15. PARTIAL CORRELATION

The correlation between two variables for a given sample is very frequently influenced by the presence of a third variable, or of a number of other variables.   For example, if we were to take a large sample of public school children of all ages from 6 to 16, we would find a significant positive correlation between measures of height and spelling ability for this sample.   This of course would not mean that the taller pupils are better spellers *because* they are taller, nor that they are taller because they are better spellers. Rather, the observed correlation may be readily explained by the fact that both height and spelling ability increase with age, and hence the older pupils are both taller than the younger pupils and better spellers than the younger pupils. The fact that there is little or no intrinsic relationship between height and spelling ability may be readily demonstrated by computing the correlation between measures of these traits for a group of pupils all of whom are of the same age, in which case no significant correlation would be found (unless due to still other unspecified extraneous variables).

When the relationship between two variables for a given group is influenced by the presence of a third variable, a measure of the relationship with this influence removed may (if the relationships are linear) be computed by the technique of *partial correlation*. The partial correlation between variables 1 and 2, with variable 3 "taken out," is given by the formula

$$r_{12\cdot3} = \frac{r_{12} - r_{13}\,r_{23}}{\sqrt{(1 - r_{13}^2)(1 - r_{23}^2)}} \tag{47}$$

This coefficient $r_{12\cdot3}$ (read "r sub one two point three") is a partial correlation coefficient of the first order. The coefficients r_{12}, r_{13}, and r_{23} are zero order coefficients. Similar formulas may be written for $r_{13\cdot2}$ and $r_{23\cdot1}$. For example, suppose that for a given sample of 85 school pupils, variable 1 is a measure of chronological age, variable 2 a measure of height, and 3 a measure of spelling ability. Suppose also that $r_{12} = .85$, $r_{13} = .60$, and $r_{23} = .45$ (these are fictitious data). For this group

$$\begin{aligned} r_{23\cdot1} &= \frac{r_{23} - r_{12}\,r_{13}}{\sqrt{(1 - r_{12}^2)(1 - r_{13}^2)}} \\ &= \frac{.45 - (.85)(.60)}{\sqrt{(1 - .85^2)(1 - .60^2)}} = \frac{-.06}{.4214} = -.142. \end{aligned}$$

The significance of this partial correlation may be tested in the same manner as a zero order coefficient, except that the effective size of the sample is considered as one less than the actual size. Hence we would test this partial r for a sample of 85 as if it were a zero order r for a sample of 84. From Table 13, page 212, we see that for a sample of 84 an r of .142 is not significant even at the 5 per cent level, whereas for a sample of 85 an r of .45 is highly significant. These data, then, are quite consistent with the hypothesis that there is no intrinsic relationship between height and spelling ability for the population involved.

We have already observed that the partial correlation between height and spelling ability, with the effect of age eliminated, may be experimentally determined by selecting a number of pupils of the same age from the population and computing the correlation for these pupils alone. The partial correlation computed from the original age-variable sample by (47) may be considered as an average of such zero order r's. Suppose we had a very large sample of pupils varying in ages 6 to 16, and that we split this sample into all possible age groups such that all pupils in each group were within one-half year of the same age. That is, we would have one group of six-year-olds, another of seven-year-olds, etc., up to a group of sixteen-year-olds. We could then compute the correlation between height and spelling ability for each of these age groups. The average of these correlation coefficients would then be essentially the same as the partial correlation between height and spelling ability with age held constant, computed by (47) from the entire sample (ages having been expressed in years at the nearest birthday).

In a manner similar to that already explained, it is possible to compute partial correlations with more than one variable held constant. The general formula for a partial correlation coefficient is

$$r_{12\cdot34\ldots n} = \frac{r_{12\cdot34\ldots(n-1)} - [r_{1n\cdot34\ldots(n-1)}]\,[r_{2n\cdot34\ldots(n-1)}]}{\sqrt{[1 - r^2_{1n\cdot34\ldots(n-1)}]\,[1 - r^2_{2n\cdot34\ldots(n-1)}]}} \tag{48}$$

In the case where two variables are held constant, this formula becomes

$$r_{12\cdot34} = \frac{r_{12\cdot3} - r_{14\cdot3}\,r_{24\cdot3}}{\sqrt{(1 - r^2_{14\cdot3})(1 - r^2_{24\cdot3})}}.$$

When three variables are held constant it becomes

$$r_{12 \cdot 345} = \frac{r_{12 \cdot 34} - r_{15 \cdot 34}\, r_{25 \cdot 34}}{\sqrt{(1 - r^2_{15 \cdot 34})(1 - r^2_{25 \cdot 34})}}$$

and so forth. (See page 257 for references on computational procedures.)

In general, the *order* of a partial correlation coefficient is the number of variables held constant. The significance of any partial r from a random sample may be tested by means of Table 17 by considering the effective size of the sample as reduced by one for each variable held constant.

The interpretation of partial correlation coefficients has caused considerable difficulty in educational research. It should be recalled particularly that a correlation coefficient tells nothing whatever about the nature of the cause-and-effect connections between variables. The fact that $r_{AB} \neq 0$ may mean that A is in part caused by B, or that B is in part caused by A, or that each is in part caused by the other, or that both are in part caused by other and unspecified variables. The correlation coefficient in itself provides no clue whatever as to which of these is the correct explanation. The same is true of partial correlation coefficients. The partial correlation $r_{AB \cdot C}$ is essentially a zero order r_{AB} for a group in which those factors which would otherwise give rise to variations in C are inoperative, but even if it is possible to identify these factors, the problem of interpreting the remaining correlation is of the same nature as before.

The interpretation of partial r's in educational research is complicated further by the prevalence of the so-called "jingle fallacy," to which reference has been made earlier (page 234). Partial r's computed for the scores on educational or psychological tests are always highly ambiguous, and in most instances it is practically impossible to arrive at a clear-cut interpretation of them. Suppose, for example, that we compute $r_{AB \cdot C}$ for a group in which A represents the score on a reading test, B that on an arithmetic test, and C that on a general intelligence test. In the first place, we must recognize that the factor which is held constant is only the *score* on the intelligence test. Because of the unreliability of that test, there is still considerable uncontrolled variability in whatever the test measures. In the second place, none of the scores is a *pure* or perfectly valid measure, even aside from chance errors in measurement, of the ability implied in the title of the test, but is partly a measure of many irrelevant factors which may or may not influence the scores on the other tests as well. In the third place, a good measure of general intelligence is in part a measure of arithmetic ability and of some of the factors involved in reading. In "holding constant" intelligence we may therefore be holding constant more than we should. In the fourth place, we are rarely able to provide a very meaningful and exact description of what each test is *intended* to measure, to say nothing of what it actually *does* measure. In the fifth place, the observed $r_{AB \cdot C}$ is subject to sampling errors, and may be very markedly influenced by chance fluctuations in the zero order r's (see page 211). In fact, partial r's cannot possibly be very meaningful unless computed from much larger samples than have usually been employed for this purpose in educational research. Finally, there are many other factors, in addition to those measured by a general intelligence test, which might in part account for the correlation between the scores on the arithmetic and reading tests, and which have not been held constant in this analysis. Under all of these conditions, it would be foolhardy indeed to attempt to say much, on the basis of partial correlations, about the cause-and-effect relationships between the traits implied in the test titles. Unfortunately, however, many such attempts have been made in educational research, with results often obviously inconsistent with common-sense considerations.

The foregoing is by no means intended as an adequate discussion of the use and interpretation of partial correlation techniques in educational research. Before attempting to make any use of these techniques, the student should familiarize himself with the contents of more exhaustive discussions of these techniques which are readily available in the literature of educational research. Among the best of these discussions are those in Chapter XIV of *Statistics in Psychology and Education*, by Henry E. Garrett, in Chapter XI of *The Scientific Study of Educational Problems*, by W. S. Monroe and M. D. Engelhart, and in an article "On the Analysis of Causation," by Jack W. Dunlap and E. E. Cureton, *Journal of Educational Psychology*, December, 1930 (Volume XXI).

16. MULTIPLE CORRELATION AND REGRESSION

The student will recall, from his study of simple correlation theory, that whenever a linear relationship exists between two variables, the regression equations for these variables may be used to estimate or predict values of one variable from known values of the other variable. The precision of this prediction depends upon the correlation between the variables, and is measured by the standard error of estimate.

For example, suppose that for a sample of college freshmen, X represents the grade-point average of a student, X_2 his score on an entrance examination, M_1 the mean of the X_1's, M_2 the mean of the X_2's, σ_1 and σ_2 the corresponding standard deviations, and that $x_1 = X_1 - M_1$ and $x_2 = X_2 - M_2$. If r_{12} is known, we can then predict the grade-point average of any student from his entrance examination score by means of the following regression equation. In deviation form, this equation is

$$x_1' = r_{12} \frac{\sigma_1}{\sigma_2} x_2 \tag{49}$$

and in raw score form

$$X_1' = r_{12} \frac{\sigma_1}{\sigma_2} X_2 + \left(M_1 - r_{12} \frac{\sigma_1}{\sigma_2} M_2 \right). \tag{50}$$

In these equations x_1' and X_1' are the *estimated* values of x_1 and X_1, respectively. If such estimates were made for all students, then $r_{x_1'x_1}$ or $r_{x_1'x_1}$ would be the same as r_{12}. The standard error [1] of these

[1] Strictly, this standard error is valid only for estimates based upon values of X_2 near the mean, because of sampling errors in the regression coefficient. For a discussion of this problem, see "The Application of the Theory of Error to the Interpretation of Trends," H. Working and H. Hotelling, *Journal of American Statistical Asso-*

estimates would be given by

$$\sigma_{1\cdot2} = \sigma_1\sqrt{1 - r_{12}^2}.\tag{51}$$

If several entrance examinations had been given these students, one could of course predict the first year grades in this fashion from the scores on any one of the examinations, although the examination to use would obviously be that for which the scores correlate most highly with grades. However, by computing a *composite* of the scores on all examinations for each student, and finding the regression equation for estimating grades from these composites, one might secure better estimates of grades than could be secured from the scores on any one examination alone. Obviously, there is an unlimited number of ways in which the scores on such examinations may be combined. The simplest composite would be the sum of the scores on the various examinations. In most instances, however, a better composite could be secured by giving certain scores more weight than others. The problem then is to find what system of weights will produce a composite which will correlate more highly with grades than will any other composite. An approximate solution to this problem could be found empirically by trying out each of a large number of arbitrary systems of weights, actually computing a composite for each student according to each system for a large number of students, and finding which composite correlated most highly with grades. Fortunately, this problem may be more conveniently and satisfactorily solved by the methods of *multiple correlation*. By these methods, it is possible to compute directly the equation which gives the *best possible* linear combination of a number of (independent) variables for the purpose of predicting another (dependent) variable. This equation is known as the multiple regression equation. The first order multiple regression equation (for two independent variables) is expressed in deviation form as

$$x_1' = r_{12\cdot3}\frac{\sigma_{1\cdot3}}{\sigma_{2\cdot3}}x_2 + r_{13\cdot2}\frac{\sigma_{1\cdot2}}{\sigma_{3\cdot2}}x_3\tag{52}$$

ciation (1929), Volume XXIV, pp. 73–85. This article also has important implications for the use of the formula for the standard error of measurement as applied to scores on educational tests.

in which $r_{12\cdot3}$ and $r_{13\cdot2}$ are the partial correlation coefficients computed as in (47), in which $\sigma_{1\cdot3}$, $\sigma_{2\cdot3}$, and $\sigma_{3\cdot2}$ are the partial σ's computed as in (51), x_1' is the estimated x_1, and x_2 and x_3 are the known deviations of the values of the dependent variables from their respective means.

The correlation ($R_{1\cdot23}$) between these estimates (x_1') and the actual values of x_1 is known as the multiple correlation coefficient, that is, $R_{1\cdot23} = r_{x_1'x_1}$. This multiple correlation coefficient may be computed [1] from the zero order r's or first order partial r's by

$$R_{1\cdot23} = \sqrt{\frac{r_{12}^2 + r_{13}^2 - 2\,r_{12}r_{13}r_{23}}{1 - r_{23}}} \tag{53}$$

or

$$R_{1\cdot23} = \sqrt{1 - (1 - r_{12}^2)(1 - r_{13\cdot2}^2)}. \tag{54}$$

The standard error [2] of estimates based on a first order multiple regression equation is given by

$$\sigma_{1\cdot23} = \sigma_1\sqrt{1 - r_{12}^2}\,\sqrt{1 - r_{13\cdot2}^2} \tag{55}$$

The raw score form of the first order multiple regression equation is

$$X_1' = r_{12\cdot3}\frac{\sigma_{1\cdot3}}{\sigma_{2\cdot3}}X_2 + r_{13\cdot2}\frac{\sigma_{1\cdot2}}{\sigma_{3\cdot2}}X_3$$

$$+ \left(M_1 - r_{12\cdot3}\frac{\sigma_{1\cdot3}}{\sigma_{2\cdot3}}M_2 - r_{13\cdot2}\frac{\sigma_{1\cdot2}}{\sigma_{3\cdot2}}M_3\right) \tag{56}$$

To illustrate the use of these first order equations in the prediction-of-grades situation previously referred to, suppose that variable 1 represents grade-point averages, that variables 2 and 3 are scores on two entrance examinations (which we will call Test 2 and Test 3), and that for a given sample of freshmen

$M_1 = 2.10$	$\sigma_1 = 1.16$	$r_{12} = .650$
$M_2 = 48.70$	$\sigma_2 = 11.15$	$r_{13} = .524$
$M_3 = 62.05$	$\sigma_3 = 15.25$	$r_{23} = .475$

[1] When only two dependent variables are involved, and only $R_{1\cdot23}$ and the multiple regression equation are needed (that is, when the partial r's and σ's are not needed), a simpler method of computation is that suggested on pages 206 to 207.

[2] See footnote on page 253.

Then

$$r_{12\cdot3} = \frac{.650 - (.524)(.475)}{\sqrt{(1 - .524^2)(1 - .475^2)}} = .535$$

$$r_{13\cdot2} = \frac{.524 - (.650)(.475)}{\sqrt{(1 - .650^2)(1 - .475^2)}} = .322$$

and

$$\sigma_{1\cdot3} = \sigma_1\sqrt{1 - r_{13}^2} = 0.988$$

$$\sigma_{2\cdot3} = \sigma_2\sqrt{1 - r_{23}^2} = 9.812$$

$$\sigma_{1\cdot2} = \sigma_1\sqrt{1 - r_{12}^2} = 0.882$$

$$\sigma_{3\cdot2} = \sigma_3\sqrt{1 - r_{23}^2} = 13.420$$

from which the multiple regression equation in deviation form is

$$x_1' = .535\frac{0.988}{9.812}x_2 + .322\frac{0.882}{13.420}x_3$$

$$= 0.05387\,x_2 + 0.02116\,x_3$$

or, in raw score form, is

$$X_1' = 0.05387\,X_2 + 0.02116\,X_3 - 1.8365$$

The multiple correlation $R_{1\cdot23}$ in this case is

$$R_{1\cdot23} = \sqrt{1 - (1 - .650^2)(1 - .322^2)} = .6945$$

and the corresponding standard error of estimate is

$$\sigma_{1\cdot23} = 1.16\sqrt{1 - .650^2}\ \sqrt{1 - .322^2} = 0.8345$$

If, then, a certain student made a score of 50 on Test 2 and of 70 on Test 3, our estimate of his grade-point average ("Test 1") would be 2.77, with a standard error of 0.835. We might then be reasonably sure that his actual grade-point average will lie within two standard errors of the estimate, or between 1.10 and 4.44.

The general forms of the preceding equations, for any number (n) of variables, are

$$x_{1\cdot23\ldots n}' = r_{12\cdot34\ldots n}\frac{\sigma_{1\cdot34\ldots n}}{\sigma_{2\cdot34\ldots n}}x_2 + r_{13\cdot24\ldots n}\frac{\sigma_{1\cdot24\ldots n}}{\sigma_{3\cdot24\ldots n}}x_3$$

$$+ \cdots\cdots + r_{1\,n\cdot23\ldots(n-1)}\frac{\sigma_{1\cdot23\ldots(n-1)}}{\sigma_{n\cdot23\ldots(n-1)}}x_n \qquad (57)$$

$$\sigma_{1 \cdot 23 \ldots n} =$$
$$\sigma_1 \sqrt{1 - r_{12}^2} \ \sqrt{1 - r_{13 \cdot 2}^2} \ \sqrt{1 - r_{14 \cdot 23}^2} \cdots \sqrt{1 - r_{1 n \cdot 23 \ldots (n-1)}^2} \qquad (58)$$

$$R_{1 \cdot 234 \ldots n} =$$
$$\sqrt{1 - \left[(1 - r_{12}^2)(1 - r_{13 \cdot 2}^2)(1 - r_{14 \cdot 23}^2) \cdots (1 - r_{1 n \cdot 23 \ldots (n-1)}^2) \right]} \qquad (59)$$

The computational work involved in a multiple-correlation problem for more than three or four variables is obviously very laborious and time-consuming. Excellent outlines of preferred computational procedures are given on pages 120–124 of *Workbook in Statistical Method*, by Jack W. Dunlap (Prentice-Hall, Inc., 1939). The same reference also presents (page 127) an excellent bibliography on the methodology of multiple correlation. Other excellent discussions of the computational procedures in multiple correlation analysis are given in *Statistics in Psychology and Education*, Henry E. Garrett, pp. 409–460, and in *Statistical Methods for Students of Education*, Karl J. Holzinger, pp. 283–315.

No attempt is made here to present any adequate discussion of the use and interpretation of partial and multiple correlation techniques in educational research. The primary purpose of this book has been to make more readily available to students of education only those relatively recent developments in statistical theory which have not yet been adequately treated in educational texts in statistics or with specific reference to educational applications. The uses and interpretation of partial and multiple correlation techniques have been very adequately treated in the texts by Garrett and Holzinger, and in *The Scientific Study of Educational Problems*, by Monroe and Engelhart, pages 323–389. The student who is interested in these techniques or hopes to make any application of them is strongly urged to become familiar with these references.

APPENDIX

Table 17[1]

Absolute Deviations $\left(\dfrac{x}{\sigma}\right)$ from the Mean of a Normal Distribution Exceeded by Given Proportions of the Cases

(Deviations in terms of the standard deviation)

	.01	.02	.03	.04	.05	.06	.07	.08	.09	.10
.00	2.575829	2.326348	2.170090	2.053749	1.959964	1.880794	1.811911	1.750686	1.695398	1.644854
.10	1.598193	1.554774	1.514102	1.475791	1.439521	1.405072	1.372204	1.340755	1.310579	1.281552
.20	1.253565	1.226528	1.200359	1.174987	1.150349	1.126391	1.103063	1.080319	1.058122	1.036433
.30	1.015222	.994458	.974114	.954165	.934589	.915365	.896473	.877896	.859617	.841621
.40	.823894	.806421	.789192	.772193	.755415	.738847	.722479	.706303	.690309	.674490
.50	.658838	.643345	.628006	.612813	.597760	.582841	.568051	.553385	.538838	.524401
.60	.510073	.495850	.481727	.467699	.453762	.439913	.426148	.412463	.398855	.385320
.70	.371856	.358459	.345125	.331853	.318639	.305481	.292375	.279319	.266311	.253347
.80	.240426	.227545	.214702	.201893	.189118	.176374	.163658	.150969	.138304	.125661
.90	.113039	.100434	.087845	.075270	.062707	.050154	.037608	.025069	.012533	0

[1] This table is taken by consent from *Statistical Methods for Research Workers*, by R. A. Fisher, published at 15/ by Oliver and Boyd, Edinburgh. Attention is drawn to the larger collection in *Statistical Tables*, by R. A. Fisher and F. Yates, published at 12/6 by Oliver and Boyd, Edinburgh.

The value of P for each entry is found by adding the column heading to the value in the left-hand margin. The corresponding value of $\dfrac{x}{\sigma}$ is the deviation such that the probability of an observation falling outside the range from $-\dfrac{x}{\sigma}$ to $+\dfrac{x}{\sigma}$ is P. For example, $P = .23$ for $\dfrac{x}{\sigma} = 1.200359$; so that 23 per cent of normally distributed values will have positive or negative deviations exceeding the standard deviation in the ratio 1.200359.

Values of x/σ for Small Values of P

P	.001	.000,1	.000,01	.000,001	.000,000,1	.000,000,01	.000,000,001
x	3.29053	3.89059	4.41717	4.89164	5.32672	5.73073	6.10941

TABLE 18
TABLE OF RANDOM NUMBERS [1]

	1	2	3	4	5	6	7	8	9	10	11	12	13	14	15	16	17	18	19	20
1	03	47	43	73	86	36	96	47	36	61	46	98	63	71	62	33	26	16	80	45
2	97	74	24	67	62	42	81	14	57	20	42	53	32	37	32	27	07	36	07	51
3	16	76	62	27	66	56	50	26	71	07	32	90	79	78	53	13	55	38	58	59
4	12	56	85	99	26	96	96	68	27	31	05	03	72	93	15	57	12	10	14	21
5	55	59	56	35	64	38	54	82	46	21	31	62	43	90	90	06	18	44	32	53
6	16	22	77	94	39	49	54	43	54	82	17	37	93	23	78	87	35	20	96	43
7	84	42	17	53	31	57	24	55	06	88	77	04	74	47	67	21	76	33	50	25
8	63	01	63	78	59	16	95	55	57	19	98	10	50	71	75	12	86	73	58	07
9	33	21	12	34	29	78	64	56	07	82	52	42	07	44	38	15	51	00	13	42
10	57	60	86	32	44	09	47	27	96	54	49	17	46	09	62	90	52	84	77	27
11	18	18	07	92	46	44	17	16	58	09	79	83	86	19	62	06	76	50	03	10
12	26	62	38	97	75	84	16	07	44	99	83	11	46	32	24	20	14	85	88	45
13	23	42	40	64	74	82	97	77	77	81	07	45	32	14	08	32	98	94	07	72
14	52	36	28	19	95	50	92	26	11	97	00	56	76	31	38	80	22	02	53	53
15	37	85	94	35	12	83	39	50	08	30	42	34	07	96	88	54	42	06	87	98
16	70	29	17	12	13	40	33	20	38	26	13	89	51	03	74	17	76	37	13	04
17	56	62	18	37	35	96	83	50	87	75	97	12	25	93	47	70	33	24	03	54
18	99	49	57	22	77	88	42	95	45	72	16	64	36	16	00	04	43	18	66	79
19	16	08	15	04	72	33	27	14	34	09	45	59	34	68	49	12	72	07	34	45
20	31	16	93	32	43	50	27	89	87	19	20	15	37	00	49	52	85	66	60	44
21	68	34	30	13	70	55	74	30	77	40	44	22	78	84	26	04	33	36	09	52
22	74	57	25	65	76	59	29	97	68	60	71	91	38	67	54	13	58	18	25	27
23	27	42	37	86	53	48	55	90	65	72	96	57	69	36	10	96	46	92	42	45
24	00	39	68	29	61	66	37	32	20	30	77	84	57	03	29	10	45	65	04	26
25	29	94	98	94	24	68	49	69	10	82	53	75	91	93	30	34	25	20	57	27
26	16	90	82	66	59	83	62	64	11	12	67	19	00	71	74	60	47	21	29	68
27	11	27	94	75	06	06	09	19	74	66	02	94	37	34	02	76	70	90	30	86
28	35	24	10	16	20	33	32	51	26	38	79	78	45	04	91	16	92	53	56	16
29	38	23	16	86	38	42	38	97	01	50	87	75	66	81	41	40	01	74	91	62
30	31	96	25	91	47	96	44	33	49	13	34	86	82	53	91	00	52	43	48	85
31	66	67	40	67	14	64	05	71	95	86	11	05	65	09	68	76	83	20	37	90
32	14	90	84	45	11	75	73	88	05	90	52	27	41	14	86	22	98	12	22	08
33	68	05	51	18	00	33	96	02	74	19	07	60	62	93	55	59	33	82	43	90
34	20	46	78	73	90	97	51	40	14	02	04	02	33	31	08	39	54	16	49	36
35	64	19	58	97	79	15	06	15	93	20	01	90	10	75	06	40	78	78	89	62
36	05	26	93	70	60	22	35	85	15	13	92	03	51	59	77	59	56	78	06	83
37	07	97	10	88	23	09	98	42	99	64	61	71	62	99	06	51	29	16	93	15
38	68	71	86	85	85	54	87	66	47	54	73	32	98	11	12	44	95	92	63	16
39	14	65	52	68	74	87	37	78	22	41	26	78	63	06	55	13	08	27	01	50
40	17	53	77	58	71	71	59	36	50	72	12	41	94	96	26	44	95	27	36	99
41	90	26	59	21	19	23	41	61	33	12	96	93	02	18	39	07	02	18	36	07
42	41	23	52	55	99	31	52	23	69	96	10	47	48	45	88	13	41	43	89	20
43	26	99	61	65	53	58	04	49	80	70	42	10	50	67	42	32	17	55	85	74

[1] Taken by consent from Table 33, *Statistical Tables for Biological, Agricultural and Medical Research*, R. A. Fisher and F. Yates, by permission of Oliver and Boyd, Edinburgh.

Table 18 (continued)

	1	2	3	4	5	6	7	8	9	10	11	12	13	14	15	16	17	18	19	20
1	53	74	23	99	67	61	32	28	69	84	94	62	67	86	24	98	33	41	19	95
2	63	38	06	86	54	99	00	65	26	94	02	82	90	23	07	79	62	67	80	60
3	35	30	68	21	46	06	72	17	10	94	25	21	31	74	96	49	28	24	00	49
4	63	43	36	92	69	65	51	18	37	88	61	38	44	12	45	32	92	84	88	65
5	98	25	37	55	26	01	91	82	81	46	74	71	12	94	97	24	02	71	37	07
6	02	63	31	17	69	71	50	80	39	56	38	15	40	11	48	43	40	45	86	98
7	64	55	22	21	82	48	22	28	06	00	61	64	13	54	91	82	78	12	23	29
8	85	07	26	13	89	01	10	07	82	04	59	63	69	36	03	69	11	15	83	80
9	58	54	16	24	15	51	54	44	82	00	62	61	65	04	69	38	18	65	18	97
10	34	85	27	84	87	61	48	64	56	26	90	18	48	13	26	37	70	15	42	57
11	03	92	18	27	46	57	99	16	96	56	30	33	72	85	22	84	64	38	56	98
12	95	30	27	59	37	62	75	41	66	48	86	97	80	61	45	23	53	04	01	63
13	08	45	93	15	22	60	21	75	46	91	98	77	27	85	42	28	88	61	08	84
14	07	08	55	18	40	45	44	74	13	90	24	94	96	61	02·	57	55	66	83	15
15	01	85	89	95	66	51	10	19	34	88	15	84	97	19	75	12	76	39	43	78
16	72	84	71	14	35	19	11	58	49	26	50	11	17	17	76	86	31	57	20	18
17	88	78	28	16	84	13	52	53	94	53	75	45	69	30	96	73	89	65	70	31
18	45	17	75	65	57	28	40	19	72	12	25	12	74	75	67	60	40	60	81	19
19	96	76	28	12	54	22	01	11	94	25	71	96	16	16	88	68	64	36	74	45
20	43	31	67	72	30	24	02	94	08	63	38	32	36	66	02	69	36	38	25	39
21	50	44	66	44	21	66	06	58	04	62	68	15	54	35	02	42	36	48	96	32
22	22	66	22	15	86	26	63	74	41	99	58	42	36	62	24	58	37	52	18	51
23	96	24	40	14	51	23	22	30	88	57	95	67	47	29	83	94	69	40	06	07
24	31	73	91	61	19	60	20	72	93	48	98	57	07	23	69	65	95	39	69	58
25	78	60	73	99	84	43	89	94	36	34	56	69	47	07	41	90	22	91	07	12
26	84	37	90	61	56	70	10	23	98	05	85	11	34	76	60	76	48	45	34	60
27	36	67	10	08	23	98	93	35	08	86	99	29	76	29	81	33	34	91	58	93
28	07	28	59	07	48	89	64	58	89	75	83	85	62	27	89	30	14	78	56	27
29	10	15	83	87	60	79	24	31	66	56	21	48	24	06	93	91	98	94	05	49
30	55	19	68	97	65	03	73	52	16	56	00	53	55	90	27	33	42	29	38	87
31	53	81	29	13	39	35	01	20	71	34	62	33	74	82	14	53	73	19	09	03
32	51	86	32	68	92	33	98	74	66	99	40	14	71	94	58	35	94	19	38	81
33	35	91	70	29	13	80	03	54	07	27	96	94	78	32	66	50	95	52	74	33
34	37	71	67	95	13	20	02	77	95	94	64	85	04	05	72	01	32	90	76	14
35	93	66	13	83	27	92	79	64	64	72	28	54	96	53	84	48	14	52	98	94
36	02	96	08	45	64	13	05	00	41	84	93	07	54	72	59	21	45	57	09	77
37	49	83	43	48	36	92	88	33	69	96	72	36	04	19	76	47	45	15	18	60
38	84	60	71	62	46	40	80	81	30	37	34	39	23	04	38	25	15	35	71	30
39	18	17	30	88	71	44	91	14	88	47	89	23	30	63	15	56	34	20	47	89
40	79	69	10	61	78	71	32	76	95	62	87	00	22	58	40	92	54	01	75	25
41	75	93	36	47	83	56	20	14	82	11	74	21	97	90	65	96	42	68	63	96
42	38	30	92	29	03	06	28	81	39	38	62	25	06	84	63	61	29	08	93	67
43	51	29	50	10	34	31	57	75	95	80	51	97	02	74	77	76	15	58	49	44
44	21	31	38	86	24	37	79	81	53	74	73	24	16	10	33	52	83	90	94	76
45	29	01	23	87	88	58	02	39	37	67	42	10	14	20	92	16	55	23	42	45
46	95	33	95	22	00	18	74	92	00	18	38	79	58	69	32	81	76	80	26	92
47	90	84	60	79	80	24	36	59	87	38	82	07	53	89	35	96	35	23	79	18
48	46	40	62	98	82	54	97	20	45	95	15	74	80	08	32	16	46	70	50	80
49	20	31	89	03	43	38	36	92	68	72	32	14	82	99	70	80	60	47	18	97
50	71	59	73	05	50	08	22	23	71	77	91	01	93	20	49	82	96	59	26	94

TABLE 18 (*continued*)

	1	2	3	4	5	6	7	8	9	10	11	12	13	14	15	16	17	18	19	20
1	22	17	68	65	84	68	94	23	92	35	86	02	22	57	51	61	09	43	95	06
2	19	36	27	69	46	13	79	93	37	55	39	77	32	77	09	85	52	05	30	62
3	16	77	23	02	77	09	61	87	25	21	28	06	25	24	93	16	71	13	59	78
4	03	28	28	26	08	73	37	32	04	05	69	30	16	90	05	88	69	58	29	99
5	78	43	76	71	61	20	44	90	32	64	97	67	63	99	61	46	38	03	93	22
6	93	22	53	64	39	07	10	63	76	35	87	03	04	79	88	08	13	13	85	51
7	78	76	58	54	74	92	38	70	96	92	52	06	79	79	45	82	63	18	27	44
8	23	68	35	26	00	99	53	93	61	28	52	70	05	48	34	56	64	04	61	86
9	15	39	24	70	99	93	86	52	77	64	15	33	59	05	28	22	87	26	07	47
10	58	71	96	30	24	18	46	23	34	27	85	13	99	24	44	49	18	09	79	49
11	57	35	27	33	72	24	53	63	94	09	41	10	76	47	91	44	04	95	49	66
12	48	50	86	54	48	22	06	34	72	52	82	21	15	65	20	33	29	94	71	11
13	61	96	48	95	03	07	16	39	33	66	98	56	10	56	79	77	21	30	27	12
14	36	93	89	41	26	29	70	83	63	51	99	74	20	52	36	87	09	41	15	09
15	18	87	00	42	31	57	90	12	02	07	23	47	37	17	31	54	08	01	88	63
16	88	56	53	27	59	33	35	72	67	47	77	34	55	45	70	08	18	27	38	90
17	09	72	95	84	29	49	41	31	06	70	42	38	06	45	18	64	84	73	31	65
18	12	96	88	17	31	65	19	69	02	83	60	74	86	90	68	24	64	19	35	51
19	85	94	57	24	16	92	09	94	38	76	22	00	27	69	95	29	81	94	78	70
20	38	64	43	59	98	98	77	87	68	07	91	51	78	62	44	40	98	05	93	78
21	53	44	09	42	72	00	41	86	79	79	68	47	22	00	20	35	55	31	51	51
22	40	76	66	26	84	57	99	99	90	37	36	63	32	08	58	37	40	13	68	97
23	02	17	79	18	05	12	59	52	57	02	22	07	90	47	03	28	14	11	30	79
24	95	17	82	06	53	31	51	10	96	46	92	06	88	07	77	56	11	50	81	69
25	35	76	22	42	92	96	11	83	44	80	34	68	35	48	77	33	42	40	90	60
26	26	29	13	46	41	85	47	04	66	08	34	72	47	59	13	82	43	80	46	15
27	77	80	20	75	82	72	82	32	99	90	63	95	73	76	63	89	73	44	99	05
28	46	40	66	44	52	91	36	74	43	53	30	82	13	53	00	78	45	63	98	35
29	37	56	08	18	90	77	53	85	46	47	31	91	18	95	59	24	16	74	11	53
30	61	65	61	68	66	37	27	47	39	19	84	83	70	07	38	53	21	40	06	71
31	93	43	69	96	07	34	18	04	52	35	56	27	09	24	86	61	85	53	83	45
32	21	96	60	12	99	11	20	99	45	18	48	13	93	55	34	18	37	79	49	90
33	95	20	47	97	97	27	37	83	28	71	00	06	41	41	74	45	89	09	39	84
34	97	86	21	78	73	10	64	81	92	59	58	76	17	14	97	04	76	62	16	17
35	69	92	06	34	13	59	71	74	17	32	27	55	10	24	19	23	71	82	13	74
36	04	31	17	21	56	33	73	99	19	87	26	72	39	27	67	53	77	57	68	93
37	61	06	98	03	91	87	14	77	43	96	43	00	65	98	50	45	60	33	01	07
38	85	93	85	86	88	72	87	08	62	40	16	06	10	89	20	23	21	34	74	97
39	21	74	32	47	45	73	96	07	94	52	09	65	90	77	47	25	76	16	19	33
40	15	69	53	92	80	79	96	23	53	10	64	39	07	16	29	45	33	02	43	70
41	02	89	08	04	49	20	21	14	68	86	87	63	93	95	17	11	29	01	95	80
42	87	18	15	89	79	85	43	01	72	73	08	61	74	51	69	89	74	39	82	15
43	98	83	71	94	22	59	97	50	99	52	08	52	85	08	40	87	80	61	65	31
44	10	08	58	21	66	72	68	49	29	31	89	85	84	46	06	59	73	19	85	23
45	47	90	56	10	08	88	02	84	27	83	42	29	72	23	19	66	56	45	65	79
46	22	85	61	68	80	49	64	92	85	44	16	40	12	89	88	50	14	49	81	06
47	67	80	43	79	33	12	83	11	41	16	25	58	19	36	70	77	02	43	00	52
48	27	62	40	96	72	79	44	61	40	15	14	53	40	64	39	27	31	59	50	28
49	33	78	80	87	15	38	30	06	38	21	14	47	47	07	26	54	96	87	53	32
50	13	13	92	66	99	47	24	49	57	74	32	25	43	62	17	10	97	11	69	84

INDEX